Water Treatment

Grade 1

American Water Works Association

ABC
Association of
Boards of Certification

Disclaimer
Many of the photographs and illustrative drawings that appear in this book
have been furnished through the courtesy of various product distributors and
manufacturers. Any mention of trade names, commercial products, or services does
not constitute endorsement or recommendation for use by the American Water
Works Association or the US Environmental Protection Agency. In no event will
AWWA be liable for direct, indirect, special, incidental, or consequential damages
arising out of the use of information presented in this book. In particular, AWWA
will not be responsible for any costs, including, but not limited to, those incurred as
a result of lost revenue. In no event shall AWWA's liability exceed the amount paid
for the purchase of this book.

Library of Congress Cataloging-in-Publication Data
CIP data has been applied for.

ISBN: 9781625761231

000200010271962107

6666 West Quincy Avenue
Denver, CO 80235-3098
303.794.7711

Contents

Chapter 1
Basic Microbiology and Chemistry

Microbiological Contaminants

Overview

More than 2,500 years ago, Hippocrates, who is called the father of medicine, theorized that many diseases were caused by drinking water, but he was unable to explain why. Over the ages, great epidemics caused by contaminated drinking water periodically killed large segments of populations. It was not until the nineteenth century that the germ theory was developed by researchers, such as Friedrich Henle, Robert Koch, and Louis Pasteur.

Practically all pathogenic organisms that can be carried by water originate from the intestinal tracts of warm-blooded animals, particularly humans (via the fecal–oral route). Some waterborne diseases can be spread by "carriers"—individuals in whose bodies the disease is active but who show few or no symptoms. One famous carrier was Mary Mallon, a woman who became known as Typhoid Mary. In the 1930s, she infected perhaps as many as 1,000 people in the United States with typhoid fever but never showed severe symptoms of the deadly disease herself.

The disease-causing organisms that are considered the principal sources of potential waterborne diseases are listed in Table 1-1. Most of these diseases can also be transmitted by other means, such as through food (e.g., contaminated water used to wash or prepare the food) or body contact (e.g., improper washing of hands and surfaces after handling contaminated objects in day-care centers, hospitals, and so on). Many of the diseases that caused tremendous loss of life just 100 years ago have been virtually eradicated in most areas of the world through a combination of improved sanitation and the use of new medications.

In 1990, the **US Environmental Protection Agency's (USEPA's)** Science Advisory Board (SAB), an independent panel of experts established by Congress, cited drinking water contamination as one of the most important environmental risks and indicated that disease-causing microbial **contaminants** (i.e., bacteria, protozoa, and viruses) are probably the greatest remaining challenge that drinking water suppliers face in managing risks to public health. Information on the number of waterborne disease outbreaks from the US Centers for Disease Control and Prevention (CDC) underscores this concern. The CDC indicates that, between 1980 and 1996, 401 waterborne disease outbreaks were reported. Of the more than 750,000 associated cases of disease reported during this period, 403,000 were from the Milwaukee, Wisconsin, *Cryptosporidium* incident of 1993. During this period, a number of agents were implicated as the cause, including protozoa, viruses, and bacteria. In 2003 and 2004, 30 waterborne "mixed-agent" outbreaks were reported; approximately 2,700 persons became ill, and 4 people died.

US Environmental Protection Agency
A US government agency responsible for implementing federal laws designed to protect the environment.

contaminant
Anything found in water other than water itself.

Full glossary definitions can be found on pages 401–410.

Table 1-1 Waterborne diseases

Waterborne Illness	Causative Organism	Source of Organism in Water	Symptom/Outcome
Gastroenteritis	*Salmonella* (bacteria) *Campylobacter* (bacteria)	Animal or human feces	Acute diarrhea and vomiting
Typhoid	*Salmonella typhi* (bacteria)	Human feces	Inflamed intestine, enlarged spleen, high temperature—fatal
Dysentery	*Shigella*	Human feces	Diarrhea—rarely fatal
Cholera	*Vibrio cholerae* (bacteria)	Human feces	Vomiting, severe diarrhea, rapid dehydration, mineral loss—high mortality
Infectious hepatitis	Virus (Hepatitis A)	Human feces, shellfish grown in polluted waters	Yellowed skin, enlarged liver, abdominal pain; lasts as long as 4 months—low mortality
Amoebic dysentery	*Entamoeba histolytica* (protozoa)	Human feces, sewage	Mild diarrhea, chronic dysentery
Giardiasis	*Giardia lamblia* (protozoa)	Animal feces, sewage	Diarrhea, cramps, nausea, general weakness; lasts 1–30 weeks—not fatal
Cryptosporidiosis	*Cryptosporidium*	Human and animal feces	Diarrhea, abdominal pain, vomiting, low-grade fever

pathogen

A disease-causing organism.

microorganism

An organism too small to be seen by the naked eye and visible only with a microscope.

parasite

An organism that lives within, and may cause harm to, other organisms.

bacteria

A one-celled microscopic organism that has no chlorophyll. Usually has a spherical, rodlike, or curved shape.

Following the September 11, 2001, terrorist attacks and other security threats, the CDC has grown more concerned about the potential for multiple contaminants to interact and cause mixed-agent outbreaks. Thus, the CDC now keeps track of waterborne illnesses as "mixed causes" to include all sources of illness, including chemicals, microbial agents, and other sources such as radiological contaminants.

Waterborne diseases are usually described as acute, meaning the symptoms are sudden but in healthy people last only a short time. Most waterborne **pathogens** cause gastrointestinal illness with diarrhea, abdominal discomfort, nausea, vomiting, and other symptoms. Some waterborne pathogens can be associated with more serious disorders such as hepatitis, gastric cancer, peptic ulcers, myocarditis, swollen lymph glands, meningitis, encephalitis, and many other diseases.

Protozoa, bacteria, and viruses are microorganisms. **Microorganisms** are organisms too small to be seen by the naked eye and can be seen only with a microscope. **Parasites** are microorganisms that live within, and may cause harm to, other organisms—including humans. Note that the term pathogen is the broadest of these terms, referring to an agent that causes harm to its host organism.

The pathogens that are still of some concern as sources of waterborne disease are discussed in the following sections.

Bacteria

Bacteria are single-cell microorganisms that are smaller than parasites but larger and more complex than viruses. They multiply by binary fission—that is, by replicating their single strand of deoxyribonucleic acid (DNA) and dividing in half. The more common shapes are spheres, rods, spirals, and branching threads (described as *filamentous*). Bacteria range in diameter from 0.5 to 1 micrometer (μm) and in length from 2 to 4 μm. Some have flagella, a taillike structure for movement; others are nonmotile.

Pathogenic bacteria of interest in drinking water are *Salmonella*, pathogenic *Escherichia coli* (*E. coli*), *Shigella*, *Legionella*, and *Campylobacter*. *Salmonella typhi* causes typhoid fever, which has been virtually eradicated in the United States due to sanitation. Enteropathogenic *E. coli* causes gastroenteritis in humans, most notably diarrhea, but certain pathogens of the family such as *E. coli* O157:H7 can cause kidney failure and death in susceptible individuals. *Shigella* causes bacillary dysentery that is usually not life threatening. *Campylobacter* infections result in diarrhea and vomiting. *Legionella* causes pneumonialike symptoms; infection of susceptible hosts occurs through inhalation of the bacteria from aerosols. It is often found in cooling towers and colonizes plumbing systems. An example of the aerosol route *Legionella* takes when infecting humans is through the mist from showerheads.

Opportunistic pathogens are not normally a danger to persons in good health, but they can cause sickness or death in those who are in a weakened condition. Particularly at risk are newborns, the elderly, immunocompromised individuals, and individuals who already have a serious disease.

Included among the opportunistic bacteria are *Pseudomonas*, *Aeromonas hydrophila*, *Edwardsiella tarda*, *Flavobacterium*, *Klebsiella*, *Enterobacter*, *Serratia*, *Proteus*, *Providencia*, *Citrobacter*, and *Acinetobacter*. These organisms are prevalent in the environment, and with modern multibarrier treatment techniques—including improved coagulation control, improvements in the type and construction of filters including membranes, additional types and combinations of disinfection, and improved monitoring of the treatment process for particulate removal—the probability that they will be removed from the water supply is greatly increased.

Viruses

Viruses are complex molecules that typically contain a protein coat surrounding a DNA or ribonucleic acid (RNA) core of genetic material. Viruses have no independent metabolism and depend on living cells for reproduction. They range in diameter from 10 to 25 nanometers (nm), which is smaller than can be seen with an optical microscope.

Viruses can survive for varying periods of time in the environment outside of a human's or an animal's body, remaining alive in the presence of heat, drying, and chemical agents. Some viruses are much more resistant than bacteria to chlorine in water, and the adenoviruses are very resistant to ultraviolet (UV) light.

Some types of viruses have caused acute epidemics of gastroenteritis. The waterborne hepatitis A virus (HAV) is the source of some of the most serious health problems. HAV causes infectious hepatitis, which can result in serious liver damage or death. The CDC documented 23 outbreaks of disease caused by HAV between 1971 and 1985. Newly recognized viruses include noroviruses that cause rapid-onset diarrhea and vomiting; children are particularly susceptible to the viruses.

Protozoa

The protozoan parasites of concern in drinking water are *Giardia lamblia* and *Cryptosporidium*. Both parasites reproduce in the intestine of a susceptible host (humans or animals) and shed environmentally resistant cysts (*Giardia*) or oocysts (*Cryptosporidium*) in their feces. The cysts and oocysts can survive for long periods in the environment and are fairly resistant to disinfection. Chlorine inactivates

Escherichia coli (E. coli)
A bacterium of the coliform group used as a substitute for fecal coliforms in the regulations of the Total Coliform Rule.

filter
A porous layer of paper, glass fiber, or cellulose acetate used to remove particulate matter from water samples and other chemical solutions.

virus
The smallest and simplest form of life.

protozoa
Small single-celled animals including amoebae, ciliates, and flagellates.

Giardia cysts, and the contact times established in the Surface Water Treatment Rule are based on inactivation of this parasite. *Cryptosporidium* is resistant to some chemical disinfectants but is very susceptible to UV light, which has therefore become a widely accepted treatment for surface waters in the past decade.

Giardia lamblia

Giardia is a parasite that causes the most frequently diagnosed waterborne disease in the United States—giardiasis. Symptoms include skin rash, flulike problems, diarrhea, fatigue, and severe cramps. The symptoms may last anywhere from a few days to months. Sometimes there are periods of remission when there are no symptoms, and then the illness recurs. The protozoan attaches itself to the upper intestinal tract and produces cysts, which are shed in the feces. *Giardia* cysts are relatively large, ranging from 8 to 18 μm in length and from 5 to 15 μm in width.

One of the major reasons that giardiasis continues to be a problem is that the cysts survive well under adverse conditions. They are highly resistant to chlorine and can live in cold water for months. Three of the major hosts for *Giardia* cysts are humans, beavers, and muskrats. Although water can be a major means of transmitting the disease, the largest percentage of recorded cases is attributed to person-to-person contact.

 WATCH THE VIDEO
Microorganisms (www.awwa.org/wsovideoclips)

Cryptosporidium

Cryptosporidium is a parasite that has caused several outbreaks of cryptosporidiosis and poses serious health risks. Sixteen species are currently recognized. *Cryptosporidium parvum* is found in humans and animals, while *C. hominis* is found only in humans.

In healthy individuals, cryptosporidiosis is an infection that usually causes 7 to 14 days of diarrhea with possibly a low-grade fever, nausea, and abdominal cramps. The effects on immunocompromised individuals can be life threatening. No antibiotic treatment currently exists for cryptosporidiosis.

Oocysts averaging about 4–6 μm in size may be found in all types of water, including untreated surface water and filtered swimming-pool water. Outbreaks can be caused by contamination of food and of water in swimming pools and sprinklers. The 1993 outbreak in Milwaukee resulted in the deaths of 50 individuals, most of whom died of other diseases related to their immunocompromised conditions or who were already suffering from an underlying illness. An estimated 403,000 illnesses were attributed to this event—about two-thirds of the population served by the water system (Milwaukee's population at the time was about 617,000).

Cryptosporidium infections are contracted by the ingestion of oocysts, and therefore effective control measures must aim to reduce or prevent oocyst transmission. *Cryptosporidium* oocysts are resistant to the disinfectants used in most water treatment plants. Conventional water treatment is effective at oocyst removal through coagulation and filtration. Currently, UV light is the most effective treatment for inactivating oocysts.

Giardia
A protozoan that can survive in water and that causes human disease.

 WATCH THE VIDEO
The 1993 Milwaukee *Cryptosporidium* Outbreak (www.awwa.org/wsovideoclips)

Indicator Organisms

The tests required to detect specific pathogens are still considered time intensive and expensive, so it is impractical for water systems to routinely test for specific pathogens. A more practical approach is to examine the water for indicator organisms specifically associated with contamination. An indicator organism essentially provides evidence of fecal contamination from humans or warm-blooded animals. The criteria for an ideal indicator organism are that it should

- always be present in contaminated water,
- always be absent when fecal contamination is not present,
- generally survive longer in water than pathogens, and
- be easy to identify.

The coliform group of bacteria has been used for 100 years as an indicator of drinking water quality. These bacteria are generally not pathogenic, yet they may be present when pathogens are present.

Coliform bacteria are easily detected in the laboratory. As a rule, where coliforms are found in water, it is assumed that pathogens may also be present, making the water bacteriologically unsafe to drink. If coliform bacteria are absent, the water is assumed safe.

Many methods exist for determining the presence of coliform bacteria in a water sample, including the **multiple-tube fermentation (MTF) method**, the **presence–absence (P–A) method**, the **MMO–MUG method**, and the **membrane filter (MF) method**. Detailed descriptions of the analytical procedures for these tests can be found in the latest edition of *Standard Methods for the Examination of Water and Wastewater*.

Coliform Analysis

The detection of coliform bacteria in a water sample by any of the four analytical techniques is a warning of possible contamination. One positive test does not conclusively prove contamination, however, and additional tests must be conducted. Samples are often contaminated by improper sampling technique, improperly sterilized bottles, and laboratory error. Regulatory agencies recognize this fact, and drinking water regulations require further checking or repeat sampling after findings that show a positive test for coliform in a sample. Drinking water regulations and maximum contaminant levels for coliform bacteria are discussed in Chapter 3.

Sampling   Sterile containers must be used for all samples collected for bacteriological analysis. The same sampling procedures should be used for coliform analysis and heterotrophic plate count analysis. See Table 1-2.

WATCH THE VIDEO
Coliform Sampling 1 (www.awwa.org/wsovideoclips)

Test Methods

The MTF and P–A Methods   The MTF and P–A tests are designed on the principle that coliform bacteria produce gas from the fermentation of lactose within 24 to 48 hours when incubated at 35°C (95°F). Although the bacteria themselves cannot be seen, their presence is signified by the gas that is formed and trapped in an inverted vial in the fermentation tube.

coliform bacteria
A group of bacteria predominantly inhabiting the intestines of humans or animals but also occasionally found elsewhere.

multiple-tube fermentation (MTF) method
A laboratory method used for coliform testing that uses a nutrient broth placed in culture tubes.

MMO–MUG method
An approved bacteriological procedure for detecting the presence or absence of total coliforms and *E. coli*.

presence–absence (P–A) method
An approved bacteriological procedure for the detection of total coliforms.

membrane filter (MF) method
A laboratory method used to detect bacteria by capturing them on a membrane filter.

Table 1-2 Total coliform sampling requirements, according to population served

Population Served	Minimum Number of Routine Samples per Month*	Population Served	Minimum Number of Routine Samples per Month*
15 to 1,000†	1‡	59,001 to 70,000	70
1,001 to 2,500	2	70,001 to 83,000	80
2,501 to 3,300	3	83,001 to 96,000	90
3,301 to 4,100	4	96,001 to 130,000	100
4,101 to 4,900	5	130,001 to 220,000	120
4,901 to 5,800	6	220,001 to 320,000	150
5,801 to 6,700	7	320,001 to 450,000	180
6,701 to 7,600	8	450,001 to 600,000	210
7,601 to 8,500	9	600,001 to 780,000	240
8,501 to 12,900	10	780,001 to 970,000	270
12,901 to 17,200	15	970,001 to 1,230,000	300
17,201 to 21,500	20	1,230,001 to 1,520,000	330
21,501 to 25,000	25	1,520,001 to 1,850,000	360
25,001 to 33,000	30	1,850,001 to 2,270,000	390
33,001 to 41,000	40	2,270,001 to 3,020,000	420
41,001 to 50,000	50	3,020,001 to 3,960,000	450
50,001 to 59,000	60	3,960,001 or more	480

Source: *Water Quality and Treatment.* 1999.

*In lieu of the frequency specified in this table, a noncommunity water system using groundwater and serving 1,000 persons or fewer may monitor at a lesser frequency specified by the state until a sanitary survey is conducted and the state reviews the results. Thereafter, noncommunity water systems using groundwater and serving 1,000 persons or fewer must monitor in each calendar quarter during which the system provides water to the public, unless the state determines that some other frequency is more appropriate and notifies the system in writing. Five years after promulgation of the Total Coliform Rule (TCR), noncommunity water systems using groundwater and serving 1,000 persons or fewer must monitor at least once per year.

†Includes public water systems that have at least 15 service connections but serve fewer than 25 persons.

‡For a community water system serving 25 to 1,000 persons, the state may reduce this sampling frequency if a sanitary survey conducted in the last 5 years indicates that the water system is supplied solely by a protected groundwater source and is free of sanitary defects. However, in no case may the state reduce the sampling frequency to less than once per quarter.

The MTF test (Figure 1-1) progresses through three distinct steps:

1. Presumptive test
2. Confirmed test
3. Completed test

The P–A test is a simple modification of the MTF method. It is intended for use on routine samples collected from a distribution system or water treatment plant. A 100-mL portion of the sample is inoculated into a 250-mL milk dilution bottle containing special P–A media and a small inverted tube. The sample is then incubated at 35°C (95°F) for 24 and 48 hours.

The presence of total coliforms is indicated by the purple P–A medium turning yellow (indicating acid production) and by the formation of gas in the medium. All yellow and gas-producing samples from this presumptive stage must then be confirmed as described for the MTF-confirmed step using brilliant green bile (BGB) tubes. Gas production indicates the presence of total coliforms and must be reported as a positive sample (presence) in the monthly report to the primacy agency.

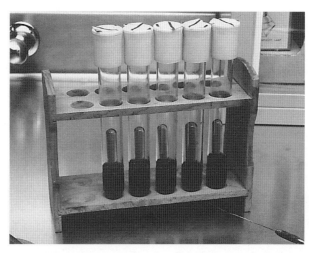

Figure 1-1 Typical multiple-tube fermentation setup
Source: Opflow.

Samples confirmed for total coliforms must also be analyzed for either fecal coliforms or *E. coli*. A check or repeat sample must also be collected and analyzed. A positive finding in the check/repeat sample can result in an acute violation of the **Total Coliform Rule (TCR)** and must be reported to the primacy agency within 24 hours after results become known.

When testing for fecal coliform, if the MTF or P–A method is being used, then as the presumptive positive samples are being inoculated into the BGB broth, 0.1 mL of the presumptive broth is also transferred into an EC broth tube. (The actual name of the broth is EC, as it tests for *E. coli*.)

The MMO–MUG Method   The MMO–MUG method was approved by USEPA shortly after promulgation of the TCR. MMO and MUG are acronyms for the constituents in the medium used in the tests. MMO represents minimal media with ONPG (ONPG stands for *ortho*-nitrophenyl-beta-D-galactopyranoside). *E. coli* produces a specific enzyme that reacts with ONPG to give a yellow color. MUG stands for 4-methylumbelliferyl-beta-D-glucuronide. Only *E. coli* produces an enzyme that reacts with MUG. Therefore, a medium containing MMO and MUG can be used to identify both total coliforms and *E. coli* in a single-sample inoculation.

Two procedures may be used. In the *10-tube procedure*, 10 tubes are purchased with the medium already in them. A 10-mL portion of sample is transferred into each tube and incubated at 35°C (95°F) for 24 hours. In the *P–A procedure*, the medium is purchased in vials. The medium is transferred into a bottle containing 100 mL of sample, is mixed, and is incubated as in the 10-tube procedure. If total coliforms are present in either procedure, the medium will turn yellow. If *E. coli* bacteria are present, the medium will also fluoresce blue under a UV light.

The presence of *E. coli* can be determined using the MUG test. A 0.l-mL portion of the presumptive media or a swab is used to transfer a sample from a membrane filter into an EC–MUG tube. A tube that fluoresces under a long-wave UV light is confirmation for *E. coli*.

The MF Method   The MF method of coliform testing begins with the filtering of 100 mL of sample under a vacuum through a membrane filter. The filter is then placed in a sterile container or petri dish (Figure 1-2) and incubated in contact with a selective culture medium.

A coliform bacteria colony will develop at each point on the filter where a viable coliform bacterium was left during filtration. After a 24-hour incubation period, the number of colonies is counted (Figure 1-3).

Total Coliform Rule (TCR)

A regulation that became effective December 31, 1990, doing away with the previous maximum contaminant level relating to the density of organisms and relating only to the presence or absence of the organisms in water.

Figure 1-2 Placement of membrane on a pad soaked with culture medium

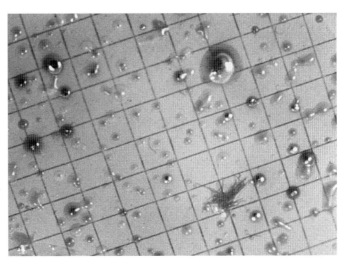

Figure 1-3 Membrane filter after incubation with positive growth colonies

A typical coliform colony on M-Endo media is pink to dark red with a distinctive green metallic surface sheen. All organisms producing such colonies within 24 hours are considered presumptive coliforms. For confirmation, representative colonies are inoculated into lauryl tryptose and BGB broth.

When testing for fecal coliform, if the MF method is used, bacterial growth is transferred into an EC tube. This tube is then incubated for 24 hours in a water bath at 44.5°C (112°F). The presence of gas in the tube confirms the presence of fecal coliforms.

USEPA is revising the TCR, and the proposed new rule will use *E. coli* as the indicator for fecal contamination. Total coliform will be used as an indicator that there may be a problem in the system and will trigger a system investigation.

Alternate Methods   Other methods for coliform and *E. coli* detection are being developed using a combination of enzymes, ß-glucuronidase, and ß-galactosidase in combination with ONPG and MUG. In tests that are positive for coliform, a yellow substance is produced that fluoresces at 366 nm UV light after an incubation period of 24 ± 2 hours at 35.0°C ± 0.5°C (94.5–95.5°F). There are various methods of determination, from just adding the water sample to a test bottle containing the media and incubating, to pouring the water sample into a tray containing the detection media with volumetric cells for counting, similar to the most probable number (MPN) method. The method has been approved for use by USEPA but may need to be confirmed with the drinking water primacy agency for the given area.

Heterotrophic Plate Count Procedure

heterotropic plate count (HPC)
A laboratory method used to estimate the bacteria population present in the water (by culturing them on a specific agar).

The heterotropic plate count (HPC) procedure is a way to estimate the population of bacteria in water. The test determines the total number of bacteria in a sample that grows under specific conditions in a selected medium.

Uses of the HPC Procedure   No single food supply, incubation temperature, and moisture condition suits every type of bacterium being tested for, so a standardized procedure must be used to obtain consistent and comparable results. The procedure therefore generally permits only a fraction of the total population to be cultured. Often the number of HPC colonies is orders of magnitude lower than the total population present.

Plate-count tests are sensitive to changes in raw-water quality and are useful for judging the efficiency of various treatment processes in removing bacteria. For example, if a plate count is higher after filtration than before filtration, there may be bacterial growth on or in the filters. The problem would probably not show up during routine coliform analysis.

It is also common for water leaving a treatment plant to have a low bacterial population but for the population to have greatly increased by the time the water reaches the consumer. This occurrence is caused by bacterial aftergrowth (regrowth)—bacteria reproducing in the distribution system. Standard plate-count determinations may indicate whether this problem exists. Bacterial aftergrowth can generally result from water becoming stagnant in the dead ends in the system, inadequate chlorination, or recontamination of the water after chlorination.

Performing the HPC Procedure   The HPC is performed by placing diluted water samples on plate-count agar. The samples are incubated for 48–72 hours. Bacteria occur singly, in pairs, in chains, and in clusters. The bacteria colonies that grow on the agar are counted using colony-counting equipment. Properly treated water should have an HPC of less than 500 colonies per milliliter. Higher counts indicate an operational problem that should be investigated.

Water Chemistry

The Structure of Matter

If you could take a sample of an element and divide it into smaller and smaller pieces, you would eventually come down to a tiny particle that, if subdivided any more, would no longer show the characteristics of the original element. The smallest particle that retains the characteristics of the element is called an **atom**, from the Greek word *atomos*, meaning "uncut" or "indivisible."

Although an atom is the smallest particle that retains the characteristics of the element from which it is taken, and is so small that it cannot be seen even with today's most powerful microscopes, the atom itself can be broken down into even smaller particles called *subatomic particles*. The different number and arrangement of subatomic particles distinguish the atoms of one element from those of another and give each element specific qualities. A general understanding of the structure of atoms is fundamental to an understanding of chemical reactions and equations.

Atomic Structure

A great many subatomic particles have been identified, many of which exist for only a fraction of a second. In the study of chemistry and chemical reactions, however, the structure of the atom is adequately explained on the basis of three fundamental particles: the **proton**, the **neutron**, and the **electron**.

As shown in Figure 1-4, the center of the atom, called the **nucleus** (plural: *nuclei*), is made up of positively charged particles called protons and uncharged particles called neutrons. Negatively charged particles called electrons occupy the space surrounding the nucleus and make up most of the atom's volume. The electrons are said to occupy the space around the nucleus in "shells."

The basic defining characteristic of the atoms of any one element is the number of protons in the nucleus. An atom of carbon, for example, always has six

atom
The smallest particle of an element that still retains the characteristics of that element.

proton
One of the three elementary particles of an atom (along with neutrons and electrons). A positively charged particle located in the nucleus of an atom.

neutron
An uncharged elementary particle that has a mass approximately equal to that of the proton. Neutrons are present in all known atomic nuclei except the lightest hydrogen nucleus.

electron
One of the three elementary particles of an atom (along with protons and neutrons). A tiny, negatively charged particle that orbits around the nucleus of an atom.

nucleus
The center of an atom, made up of positively charged particles called protons and uncharged particles called neutrons.

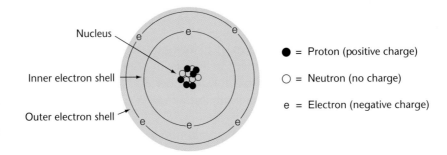

Figure 1-4 Model of an atom of carbon, C

protons in the nucleus; and any atom with exactly six protons in the nucleus must be a carbon atom. Boron atoms have five protons in the nucleus, whereas nitrogen atoms have seven. The number of protons in the nucleus of an atom is called the **atomic number**. Therefore, the atomic number of carbon is six; boron, five; and nitrogen, seven.

The nucleus is extremely small in comparison with the total size of the atom. If the atom were the size of a football stadium, the nucleus would be no larger than a small insect flying in the middle. Nonetheless, because neutrons and protons (which have nearly identical weights) are much heavier than electrons, the nucleus contains most of the mass (weight) of the atom. The **atomic weight** of an atom is defined as the sum of the number of protons and the number of neutrons in the nucleus. In the nucleus of a carbon atom, there are six protons and six neutrons; therefore, the atomic weight of the atom is 12.

Atomic weights are not "weights" in the usual sense of the word. They do not indicate the number of pounds or grams an atom weighs, but merely how the weight of one atom *compares* with the weight of another. For example, the atomic weight of hydrogen is 1 (the hydrogen nucleus has one proton and no neutrons), and the atomic weight of carbon is 12. Therefore, an atom of carbon weighs 12 times as much as an atom of hydrogen.

Isotopes All atoms of a given element have the same number of protons in the nucleus, but the number of neutrons may vary. Atoms that are of the same element but contain varying numbers of neutrons in the nucleus are called **isotopes** of that element. The atoms of each element that have the most common numbers of neutrons are called the *principal isotopes* of the element.

The atomic weight of an element is generally given in tables as a whole number with decimals, the result of averaging together the atomic weights of the principal (most common) isotopes. The average also takes into account how often each isotope occurs. The element chlorine, for example, has a listed atomic weight of 35.45—an average of its principal isotopes. (About 75 percent of all chlorine atoms have atomic weight 35, and about 25 percent have atomic weight 37.)

Ions As shown in Figure 1-4, there are the same number of electrons (negative charges) surrounding the carbon atom as there are protons (positive charges) in the nucleus. The atom is said to be electrically stable.

Now consider the effect on the atom's charge if an electron is removed from the outer electron shell or if an electron is added to the outer shell (Figure 1-5). In either case, the charges on the atom are no longer balanced. With one electron removed from the outer shell, there are six protons (positive charges) counterbalanced by only five electrons (negative charges), resulting in a net charge on the atom of plus 1. In contrast, with one electron added to the outer shell, there

atomic number

The number of protons in the nucleus of an atom.

atomic weight

The sum of the number of protons and the number of neutrons in the nucleus of an atom

isotope

An atom of the same element, but containing varying numbers of neutrons in the nucleus.

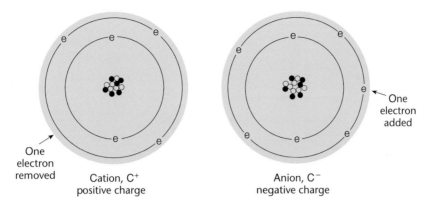

One electron removed

Cation, C⁺
positive charge

One electron added

Anion, C⁻
negative charge

Figure 1-5 Models of ionized carbon atoms

are six protons (positive charges) counterbalanced by seven electrons (negative charges), resulting in a net charge on the atom of minus 1.

When the charges on the atom are *not* balanced, the atom is no longer stable (i.e., it has a plus or minus charge). In this unstable condition, the atom is called an **ion**. When the net charge on an atom is positive (more protons than electrons), the ion is called a **cation**. When the net charge on an atom is negative (more electrons than protons), the ion is called an **anion**.

Of the three fundamental particles—protons, neutrons, and electrons—the electron is the most important particle in understanding basic chemistry. During chemical reactions, the nucleus of an atom remains unchanged; only the electrons of atoms interact, and only those in the outermost shell.

The Periodic Table

The elements can be arranged according to the number of electron shells they have and according to similarities of chemical properties. When so arranged, a table is formed called the **periodic table** (see Appendix B for the complete periodic table). In the periodic table, the horizontal rows are called *periods*, and the vertical columns are called *groups*. Elements of the same period have the same number of electron shells; elements in the same group have similar chemical properties.

As an example of members of the same period, hydrogen and helium are members of the first horizontal row (period) in the periodic table. Each element has only one electron shell. Lithium, beryllium, boron, carbon, nitrogen, oxygen, fluorine, and neon are members of the second period, and all have two electron shells.

The vertical columns (groups) are important because the elements within groups tend to have similar chemical properties. For example, notice that the two elements chlorine and iodine, both of which can be used for disinfecting water, are in the same chemical group.

Although the individual boxes of a large periodic table may contain as many as nine or more kinds of information about each element (including element name, symbol, electron structure, atomic number and weight, oxidation states, boiling points, melting points, and density), the four basic kinds of information included in almost all periodic tables are (1) atomic weight, (2) element symbol, (3) element name, and (4) atomic number. Consider the carbon atom model again, this time as it appears in the periodic table (Figure 1-6).

The number at the top of the box is the atomic weight of the element. As discussed before, this number represents the average weight of the common isotopes of the element. The letter in the box is the standard abbreviation, or **chemical symbol**, that has been assigned to the element. Often, two letters are used because a single letter has already been assigned to a specific element. For example, *H* stands for hydrogen; *Hg* for mercury. The bottom number in the box is the

ion

An atom that is electrically unstable because it has more or fewer electrons than protons.

cation

A positive ion.

anion

A negative ion.

periodic table

A chart showing all elements arranged according to similarities of chemical properties.

chemical symbol

The standard abbreviation, either one or two letters, for an element.

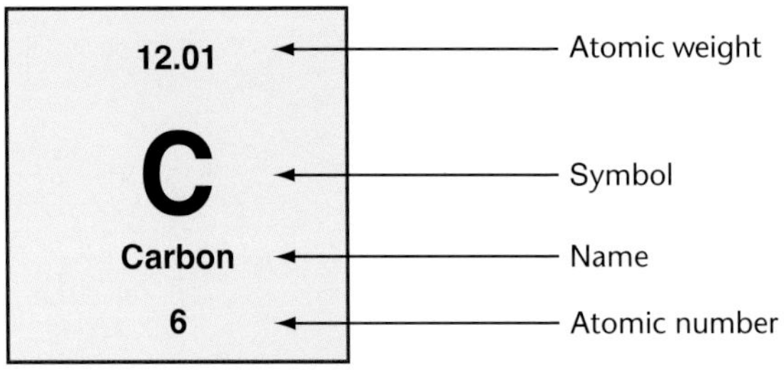

Figure 1-6 Carbon as it appears in the periodic table

atomic number—the number of protons in the nucleus of an atom of that element. (It also indicates the number of electrons in a stable atom of the element, because the number of protons is the same as the number of electrons in a stable atom.)

The Classification of Matter

Matter is anything that occupies space and has weight (mass). Matter includes subatomic particles—protons and electrons—as well as the atoms that such particles form. Matter also includes everything formed by atoms—nearly everything you encounter in the world.

Matter exists in three forms: (1) solids, (2) liquids, and (3) gases. Solids, liquids, and gases may exist in pure form, may combine chemically with other elements to form compounds, or may be mixed together without chemically combining to form mixtures.

Pure Elements

As discussed previously, elements are matter constructed of subatomic particles, with properties determined by the element's nucleus (protons and neutrons) and electron shells. All of the atoms of an element have the same number of protons in their nuclei. Elements do not break down into simpler elements. There are more than 100 known elements; 92 occur naturally, and others have been produced in the laboratory. Elements important in water chemistry are listed in Table 1-3.

A few elements exist in pure form. Carbon is an example. A diamond is pure carbon in a particular arrangement. Oxygen in the air is another example of an element in its pure form. However, most elements are unstable and are usually found combined with other elements in the form of compounds.

Compounds

Compounds are two or more elements that are "stuck" (bonded) together by a chemical reaction. A compound can be broken down into its original elements only by a reversal of the chemical reaction that formed it. The weight of the atoms of any one element in a compound is always a definite fraction (or proportion) of the weight of the entire compound. For example, in water, the compound's weight is 18, which is derived by adding two atoms of hydrogen (each with an atomic weight of 1) plus one atom of oxygen (which has an atomic weight of 16). Thus, in any given weight of water, 2/18 of the weight comes from atoms of hydrogen.

When two or more atoms are joined together, the resulting particle is called a molecule. A molecule may be only two atoms of one or more elements bonded together; or it may be dozens of atoms bonded together and may consist of several elements. For example, when two atoms of hydrogen and one of oxygen combine, a molecule of water is formed. When one atom of carbon and two of

matter
Anything that occupies space and has weight (mass).

compound
Two or more elements bonded together by a chemical reaction.

molecule
Two or more atoms joined together by a chemical bond.

Table 1-3 Elements important in water treatment

Element	Symbol	Element	Symbol
Aluminum	Al	Lead*	Pb
Antimony*	Sb	Magnesium	Mg
Arsenic*	As	Manganese	Mn
Barium*	Ba	Mercury*	Hg
Beryllium*	Be	Nickel*	Ni
Boron	B	Nitrogen	N
Bromine	Br	Oxygen	O
Cadmium*	Cd	Phosphorus	P
Calcium	Ca	Potassium	K
Carbon	C	Radium*	Ra
Chlorine	Cl	Selenium*	Se
Chromium*	Cr	Silicon	Si
Copper*	Cu	Silver	Ag
Fluorine†	F	Sodium	Na
Hydrogen	H	Strontium	Sr
Iodine	I	Sulfur	S
Iron	Fe	Thallium*	Tl

*This element must be monitored according to the requirements of the Safe Drinking Water Act.
†Fluoride, an anion of the element fluorine, must be monitored according to the requirements of the Safe Drinking Water Act.

oxygen combine, a molecule of carbon dioxide is formed. When two atoms of oxygen combine, a molecule of oxygen is formed.

Other examples of compounds include the following:

- Salt (sodium and chlorine)
- Sulfuric acid (hydrogen, sulfur, and oxygen)
- Ammonia (nitrogen and hydrogen)
- Rust (iron and oxygen)
- Lime (calcium, oxygen, and hydrogen)
- Sand (silicon and oxygen)

The number of compounds that can be formed by chemical reaction between elements is enormous. Well over two million compounds have been identified by chemists, and the number is still increasing.

Mixtures

When two or more elements, compounds, or both, are mixed together and no chemical reaction (bonding between individual particles) occurs, the result is a **mixture**. No new compounds are formed, and the elements or compounds may be mixed in any proportion. Any mixture can be separated into its original elements or compounds by "physical" means, such as filtering, settling, or distillation. For example, a mixture of saltwater can be separated into its compounds, salt and water, by the process of distillation. Heating the mixture causes the water to evaporate, leaving the salt behind.

mixture

Two or more elements, compounds, or both, mixed together with no chemical reaction (bonding) occurring.

Neon is an element. Each particle is a single atom of neon.

Water is a compound. Each particle is a molecule consisting of one oxygen atom and two hydrogen atoms.

Brass is a mixture. Each particle is either an atom of copper or an atom of zinc. The copper and zinc are not bonded together into molecules.

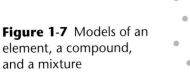

Figure 1-7 Models of an element, a compound, and a mixture

The following are other examples of mixtures:

- Air (mostly oxygen, carbon dioxide, and nitrogen)
- Glass (sand, various metals, and borax)
- Steel (primarily iron and carbon)

It is helpful to think of the differences between elements, compounds, and mixtures by considering Figure 1-7.

Valence, Chemical Formulas, and Chemical Equations

As we have discussed, atoms of elements can combine to form molecules of compounds. Experience has shown that only certain combinations of atoms will react (bond) together. For example, two atoms of iron will bond to three atoms of oxygen to form a molecule of ferric oxide (rust), but atoms of iron will not bond to atoms of magnesium. Iron and magnesium can be blended into a mixture—an alloy—but not combined into a compound.

It has also been found through experiments that the number of atoms of each element in a molecule is very definite. A water molecule is formed of two hydrogen atoms and one oxygen atom; no other combination of hydrogen and oxygen makes water, and other compounds of hydrogen and oxygen can be formed only under special circumstances. Similarly, exactly one atom of hydrogen is required to combine with one atom of chlorine to form a molecule of hydrogen chloride.

To explain why only certain molecules occur, chemists have defined characteristics of an atom that determine which chemical combinations the atom can enter into. These characteristics are briefly described in the following discussion.

Valence

In nature, atoms of elements tend to form molecules whenever the molecule is more chemically stable than the individual element. The number of electrons on the very outside of each atom (in the outermost shell) is the most important factor in determining which atoms will combine with other atoms to achieve greater stability. The electrons in the outermost shell are called the **valence electrons**.

Based on experience, chemists have assigned to every element in the periodic table one or more numbers, indicating the ability of the element to react with other elements. The numbers, which depend on the number of valence electrons, are called the *valences* of the element.

In the formation of chemical compounds from the elements, the valence electrons are transferred from the outer shell of one atom to the outer shell of another atom, or they are shared among the outer shells of the combining atoms. When electrons are transferred, the process is called *ionic bonding*. If electrons are shared, it is called *covalent bonding*. This rearrangement of electrons produces *chemical*

valence electron
An electron in an outermost electron shell.

bonds. The actual number of electrons that an atom gains, loses, or shares in bonding with one or more other atoms is the valence of the atom. For example, an atom that gives away one electron in a reaction has a valence of +1. Similarly, an atom that must gain one electron to complete a reaction has a valence of –1.

The following example of ionic bonding (transfer of electrons) shows how valence works. A diagram of the sodium and chlorine atoms and how they react to form sodium chloride (NaCl) is shown in Figure 1-8. Sodium has an atomic number of 11, indicating that it has 11 protons in a nucleus surrounded by 11 electrons. As illustrated, there is only one electron in the outermost shell, or ring. Chlorine, with an atomic number of 17, has 17 protons in the nucleus, surrounded by 17 electrons; 7 of the chlorine electrons are in the outermost shell. As the diagram indicates, to form a molecule of sodium chloride, the sodium atom transfers one electron to the chlorine atom. The molecule has greater chemical stability than the separate elements, so when sodium and chlorine are mixed together (under conditions that make the electron transfer possible), sodium chloride molecules will form. *Note that mixing pure sodium with chlorine will cause a violent explosion.*

Covalent bonding is a process similar to ionic bonding, but the electrons are shared rather than transferred, as illustrated for hydrogen chloride in Figure 1-9. Since electrons are not lost or gained, the valence of an atom involved in a covalent bond is expressed without a + or – sign. In the example, the valence of both hydrogen and chlorine is 1, since the bond is formed by sharing a single electron.

Many elements (iron and copper, for example) have more than one valence. The number of electrons involved in a reaction—the valence number—depends on several factors, such as the conditions under which the reaction occurs and the other elements involved. Iron has a valence of +2 when it forms $FeSO_4$, ferrous sulfate, but it has a valence of +3 when it forms Fe_2O_3, common red rust.

Some groups of elements bond together and act like single atoms or ions in forming compounds. Such groups of elements are called **polyatomic ions**. For example, the sulfate ion (SO_4^{-2}) and the nitrate ion (NO_3^{-1}) are important ions in drinking water quality. The valences of some common elements and ions are listed in Tables 1-4 and 1-5.

Chemical Formulas and Equations

As discussed, a group of chemically bonded atoms forms a particle called a molecule. The simplest molecules contain only one type of atom, such as when two atoms of oxygen combine (O_2) or when two atoms of chlorine combine (Cl_2). Molecules of compounds are made up of the atoms of at least two different elements;

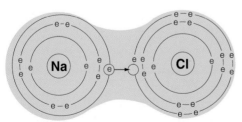

Sodium atom becomes   Chlorine atom becomes
a positive ion, Na⁺   a negative ion, Cl⁻

Figure 1-8 Ionic bonding, illustrated by sodium chloride (NaCl)

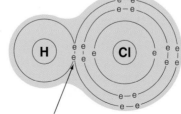

Electron is shared by
hydrogen and chlorine

Figure 1-9 Covalent bonding, illustrated by hydrogen chloride (HCl)

polyatomic ion
A group of elements chemically bonded together and acting like single atoms or ions in their ability to form other compounds.

Table 1-4 Oxidation numbers of various elements

Element	Common Valences	Element	Common Valences
Aluminum (Al)	+3	Lead (Pb)	+2, +4
Arsenic (As)	+3, +5	Magnesium (Mg)	+2
Barium (Ba)	+2	Manganese (Mn)	+2, +4
Boron (B)	+3	Mercury (Hg)	+1, +2
Bromine (Br)	−1	Nitrogen (N)	+3, −3, +5
Cadmium (Cd)	+2	Oxygen (O)	−2
Calcium (Ca)	+2	Phosphorus (P)	−3
Carbon (C)	+4, −4	Potassium (K)	+1
Chlorine (Cl)	−1	Radium (Ra)	+2
Chromium (Cr)	+3	Selenium (Se)	−2, +4
Copper (Cu)	+1, +2	Silicon (Si)	+4
Fluorine (F)	−1	Silver (Ag)	+1
Hydrogen (H)	+1	Sodium (Na)	+1
Iodine (I)	−1	Strontium (Sr)	+2
Iron (Fe)	+2, +3	Sulfur (S)	−2, +4, +6

Table 1-5 Charges of common polyatomic ions

Ion	Charge	Ion	Charge
Ammonium (NH_4)	+1	Carbonate (CO_3)	−2
Bicarbonate (HCO_3)	−1	Sulfate (SO_4)	−2
Hydroxide (OH)	−1	Sulfite (SO_3)	−2
Nitrate (NO_3)	−1	Phosphate (PO_4)	−3
Nitrite (NO_2)	−1		

for example, one oxygen atom and two hydrogen atoms form a molecule of the compound water (H_2O). "H_2O" is called the **chemical formula** of water. The formula is a shorthand way of writing *what* elements are present in a molecule of a compound, and *how many* atoms of each element are present in each molecule.

Reading Chemical Formulas The following example describes a chemical formula.

chemical formula

Using the chemical symbols for each element, a shorthand way of writing what elements and how many elements of each are present in a molecule.

Example 1

The chemical formula for calcium carbonate is $CaCO_3$. According to the formula, what is the chemical makeup of the compound?

First, the letter symbols given in the formula indicate the three elements that make up the calcium carbonate compound:

Ca = calcium

C = carbon

O = oxygen

Second, subscripts (small numerals at the base of a symbol) indicate how many atoms of each element are present in a single molecule of the compound. There is no number just to the right of the Ca or C symbols; this indicates that only one atom of each is present in the molecule. The subscript 3 to the right of the O symbol indicates that there are three oxygen atoms in each molecule.

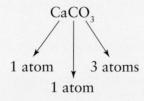

$$CaCO_3$$

1 atom   3 atoms
1 atom

Determining Percent by Weight of Elements in a Compound   If 100 lb of sodium chloride (NaCl) were separated into the elements that make up the compound, there would be 39.3 lb of pure sodium (Na) and 60.7 lb of pure chlorine (Cl). We say that sodium chloride is 39.3 *percent* sodium *by weight* and that it is 60.7 *percent* chlorine *by weight*. The **percent by weight** of each element in a compound can be calculated using the compound's chemical formula and atomic weights from the periodic table.

The first step in calculating percent by weight of an element in a compound is to determine the **molecular weight** (sometimes called *formula weight*) of the compound. The molecular weight of a compound is defined as the sum of the atomic weights of all the atoms in the compound.

For example, to determine the molecular weight of sodium chloride, first count how many atoms of each element a single molecule contains:

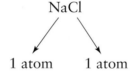

NaCl

1 atom   1 atom

Next, find the atomic weight of each atom, using the periodic table:

atomic weight of Na = 22.99
atomic weight of Cl = 35.45

Finally, multiply each atomic weight by the number of atoms of that element in the molecule, and total the weights:

	Number of Atoms		Atomic Weight		Total Weight
sodium (Na)	1	×	22.99	=	22.99
chlorine (Cl)	1	×	35.45	=	35.45
molecular weight of NaCl				=	58.44

Once the molecular weight of a compound is determined, the percent by weight of each element in the compound can be found with the following formula:

$$\text{percent element by weight} = \frac{\text{weight of element in compound}}{\text{molecular weight of compound}} \times 100$$

percent by weight
The proportion, calculated as a percentage, of each element in a compound.

molecular weight
The sum of the atomic weights of all the atoms in the compound.

Using the formula, first calculate the percent by weight of sodium in the compound:

$$\text{percent Na by weight} = \frac{\text{weight of Na in compound}}{\text{molecular weight of compound}} \times 100$$

$$= \frac{22.99}{58.44} \times 100$$

$$= 0.393 \times 100$$

$$= 39.3\% \text{ sodium by weight}$$

Then, calculate percent by weight of chlorine in the compound:

$$\text{percent Cl by weight} = \frac{\text{weight of Cl in compound}}{\text{molecular weight of compound}} \times 100$$

$$= \frac{35.45}{58.44} \times 100$$

$$= 0.607 \times 100$$

$$= 60.7\% \text{ chlorine by weight}$$

To check the calculations, add the percentages. The total should be 100:

$$
\begin{array}{rl}
39.3\% & \text{Na} \\
+ \ 60.7\% & \text{Cl} \\
\hline
100.0\% & \text{NaCl}
\end{array}
$$

Chemical Equations   A **chemical equation** is a shorthand way, through the use of chemical formulas, to write the reaction that takes place when certain chemicals are brought together. As shown in the following example, the left side of the equation indicates the *reactants*, or chemicals that will be brought together; the arrow indicates which direction the reaction occurs; and the right side of the equation indicates the *products*, or results, of the chemical reaction.

calcium bicarbonate	plus	calcium hydroxide	react to form	calcium carbonate	plus	water
$Ca(HCO_3)_2$	$+$	$Ca(OH)_2$	$\longrightarrow$	$2CaCO_3$	$+$	$2H_2O$
Reactants				Products		

chemical equation
A shorthand way, using chemical formulas, of writing the reaction that takes place when chemicals are brought together, with reactants on the left and products on the right of an arrow indicating the direction of the reaction.

The 2 in front of $CaCO_3$ is called a *coefficient*. A coefficient indicates the relative number of molecules of the compound that are involved in the chemical reaction. If no coefficient is shown, then only one molecule of the compound is involved. For example, in the above equation, one molecule of calcium bicarbonate reacts with one molecule of calcium hydroxide to form two molecules of calcium carbonate and two molecules of water. Without the coefficients, the equation could be written

$$Ca(HCO_3)_2 + Ca(OH)_2 \longrightarrow CaCO_3 + CaCO_3 + H_2O + H_2O$$

If you count the atoms of calcium (Ca) on the left side of the equation and then count the ones on the right side, you will find that the numbers are the same. In fact, for each element in the equation, as many atoms are shown on the left side as on the right. An equation such as this, in which each side is equal, is said to be *balanced*. A balanced equation accurately represents what really happens in a chemical reaction: because matter is neither created nor destroyed, the number of atoms of each element going into the reaction must be the same as the number coming out. Coefficients allow balanced equations to be written compactly.

Coefficients and subscripts can be used to calculate the molecular weight of each term in an equation, as illustrated in the following example.

Example 2

Calculate the molecular weights for each of the four terms in the following equation:

$$Ca(HCO_3)_2 + Ca(OH)_2 \longrightarrow 2CaCO_3 + 2H_2O$$

First, calculate the molecular weight of $Ca(HCO_3)_2$:

	Number of Atoms		Atomic Weight		Total Weight
calcium (Ca)	1	×	40.08	=	40.08
hydrogen (H)	2	×	1.01	=	2.02
carbon (C)	2	×	12.01	=	24.02
oxygen (O)	6	×	16.00	=	96.00
molecular weight of $Ca(HCO_3)_2$				=	162.12

The molecular weight for $Ca(OH)_2$ is determined as follows:

	Number of Atoms		Atomic Weight		Total Weight
calcium (Ca)	1	×	40.08	=	40.08
oxygen (O)	2	×	16.00	=	32.00
hydrogen (H)	2	×	1.01	=	2.02
molecular weight of $Ca(OH)_2$				=	74.10

The coefficient 2 in front of the next term of the equation ($2CaCO_3$) indicates that two molecules of $CaCO_3$ are involved in the reaction. First find the weight of *one molecule*, then double that weight to determine the weight of *two molecules*:

	Number of Atoms		Atomic Weight		Total Weight
calcium (Ca)	1	×	40.08	=	40.08
carbon (C)	1	×	12.01	=	12.01
oxygen (O)	3	×	16.00	=	48.00
weight of one molecule of $CaCO_3$				=	100.09
weight of two molecules of $CaCO_3$				=	2 × 100.09
				=	200.18

The coefficient 2 in front of the fourth term in the equation ($2H_2O$) again indicates that two molecules are involved in the reaction. As in the last calculation, first determine the weight of one molecule of H_2O, then the weight of two molecules:

	Number of Atoms		Atomic Weight		Total Weight
hydrogen (H)	2	×	1.01	=	2.02
oxygen (O)	1	×	16.00	=	16.00
weight of one molecule of H_2O				=	18.02
weight of two molecules of H_2O				=	2 × 18.02
				=	36.04

In summary, the weights that correspond to each term of the equation are

$$Ca(HCO_3)_2 + Ca(OH)_2 \longrightarrow 2CaCO_3 + 2H_2O$$

$$162.12 \qquad 74.10 \qquad 200.18 \quad 36.04$$

Notice that the total weight on the left side of the equation (236.22) is equal to the total weight on the right side of the equation (236.22), meaning the equation is balanced.

The practical importance of the weight of each term of the equation is that the chemicals shown in the equation will always react in the proportions indicated by their weights. For example, from the calculation above, you know that $Ca(HCO_3)_2$ reacts with $Ca(OH)_2$ in the ratio 162.12:74.10. This means that, given 162.12 lb of $Ca(OH)_2$, you must add 74.10 lb of $Ca(HCO_3)_2$ for a complete reaction. Given twice the amount of $Ca(HCO_3)_2$ (i.e., 324.24 lb), you must add twice the amount of $Ca(OH)_2$ (equal to 148.20 lb) to achieve a complete reaction. The next example illustrates a more complicated calculation using the same principle.

Example 3

If 25 g of $Ca(OH)_2$ were added to some $Ca(HCO_3)_2$, how many grams of $Ca(HCO_3)_2$ would react with the $Ca(OH)_2$?

Remember, the molecular weights indicate the weight ratio in which the two compounds will react. The molecular weight of $Ca(HCO_3)_2$ is 162.12, and the molecular weight of $Ca(OH)_2$ is 74.10. Use this information to set up a proportion in order to determine how many grams of $Ca(HCO_3)_2$ will react with the $Ca(OH)_2$:

$$\underset{\text{known ratio}}{\frac{74.10 \text{ g } Ca(OH)_2}{162.12 \text{ g } Ca(HCO_3)_2}} = \underset{\text{desired ratio}}{\frac{25 \text{ g } Ca(OH)_2}{x \text{ g } Ca(HCO_3)_2}}$$

Next, solve for the unknown value:[†]

$$\frac{74.10}{162.12} = \frac{25}{x}$$

$$\frac{(x)(74.10)}{162.12} = 25$$

$$x = \frac{(25)(162.12)}{74.10}$$

$$x = 54.7 \text{ g Ca(HCO}_3)_2$$

Given the molecular weights and the chemical equation indicating the ratio by which the two chemicals would combine, we were able to calculate that 54.7 g of $Ca(HCO_3)_2$ would react with 25 g of $Ca(OH)_2$.

Solutions

A **solution** consists of two parts: a **solvent** and a **solute**. These parts are completely and evenly mixed, forming what is referred to as a *homogeneous* mixture. The solute part of the solution is dissolved in the solvent (Figure 1-10).

In a true solution, the solute will remain dissolved and will not settle out. Saltwater is a true solution; salt is the solute and water is the solvent. In contrast, sand mixed into water does not form a solution; the sand will settle out when the water is left undisturbed.

In water treatment, the most common solvent is water. Before it is dissolved, the solute may be solid (such as dry alum), liquid (such as sulfuric acid), or gaseous (such as chlorine).

The **concentration** of a solution is a measure of the amount of solute dissolved in a given amount of solvent. In a *concentrated* (strong) solution, a relatively large amount of solute is dissolved in the solvent. In a *dilute* (weak) solution, a relatively small amount of solute is dissolved in the solvent.

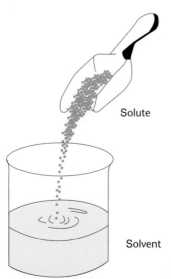

Solute

Solvent

Figure 1-10 Solution, composed of a solute and a solvent

solution
A liquid containing a dissolved substance.

solvent
The liquid used to dissolve a substance.

solute
The substance dissolved in a solution.

concentration
In chemistry, a measurement of how much solute is contained in a given amount of solution, commonly measured in milligrams per liter (mg/L).

There are many ways of expressing the concentration of a solution, including the following:

- Milligrams per liter
- Grains per gallon
- Percent strength
- Molarity
- Normality

Milligrams per Liter and Grains per Gallon

The measurements milligrams per liter (mg/L) and grains per gallon (gpg) each express the *weight* of solute dissolved in a given *volume* of solution. The mathematics needed to deal with grains per gallon and milligrams per liter are covered in Chapter 2.

Percent Strength

The percent strength of a solution can be expressed as percent by weight or percent by volume. The percent-by-weight calculation is used more often in water treatment.

Percent Strength by Weight

The equation used to calculate percent by weight is as follows:

$$\text{percent strength (by weight)} = \frac{\text{weight of solute}}{\text{weight of solution}} \times 100$$

where

weight of solutions = weight of solute + weight of solvents

Use of the equation is illustrated in the following examples.

Example 4

If 25 lb of chemical is added to 400 lb of water, what is the percent strength of the solution by weight?

Recall the formula:

$$\text{percent strength (by weight)} = \frac{\text{weight of solute}}{\text{weight of solution}} \times 100$$

The weight of the solute is given as 25 lb of chemical, but the weight of the solution is not given. Instead, the weight of the solvent (400 lb of water) is given. To determine the weight of the solution, combine the weights of the solute and the solvent:

weight of solution = weight of solute + weight of solvent

$$= 25 \text{ lb} + 400 \text{ lb}$$

$$= 425 \text{ lb}$$

Using this information, calculate the percent concentration:

$$\text{percent strength (by weight)} = \frac{\text{weight of solute}}{\text{weight of solution}} \times 100$$

$$= \frac{25 \text{ lb chemical}}{425 \text{ lb solution}} \times 100$$

$$= 0.059 \times 100$$

$$= 5.9\% \text{ strength}$$

Example 5

If 40 lb of chemical is added to 120 gal of water, what is the percent strength of the solution by weight?

First, calculate the weight of the solution. The weight of the solution is equal to the weight of the solute plus the weight of solvent. To calculate this, first convert gallons of water to pounds of water using the following formula:

volume of water (in gallons) × 8.34 = weight of water (in pounds)

Therefore:

$$(120 \text{ gal})(8.34 \text{ lb/gal}) = 1,001 \text{ lb water}$$

Then calculate the weight of solution:

weight of solution = weight of solute + weight of solvent
$$= 40 \text{ lb} + 1,001 \text{ lb}$$
$$= 1,041 \text{ lb}$$

Now calculate the percent strength of the solution:

$$\text{percent strength (by weight)} = \frac{\text{weight of solute}}{\text{weight of solution}} \times 100$$

$$= \frac{40 \text{ lb chemical}}{1,041 \text{ lb solution}} \times 100$$

$$= 0.038 \times 100$$

$$= 3.8\% \text{ strength}$$

Inorganic Compounds: Acids, Bases, and Salts

Inorganic compounds (compounds generally not containing carbon) can be classified into three main groups: (1) acids, (2) bases, and (3) salts. These three terms are commonly used throughout chemistry, and it is important that you understand the basic features that distinguish them. The following definitions are

inorganic compound
A chemical substance of mineral origin not having carbon in its molecular structure.

adequate for most water treatment chemistry; however, somewhat different definitions may be used in advanced work.

Acids

An **acid** is any substance that releases hydrogen ions (H^+) when it is mixed into water. For example, shortly after sulfuric acid (H_2SO_4) is mixed into water, many of the H_2SO_4 molecules *dissociate* (come apart), forming H^+ and SO_4^- ions. The release of H^+ ions indicates that H_2SO_4 is an acid.

Acids that dissociate readily are known as *strong acids*. Most of the molecules of a strong acid dissociate when mixed into water, releasing a large concentration of hydrogen ions. Examples of strong acids are sulfuric (H_2SO_4), hydrochloric (HCl), and nitric (HNO_3).

Acids that dissociate poorly are known as *weak acids*. They release very few hydrogen ions in water. Examples include carbonic acid (H_2CO_3), which is the acid found in soft drinks, and hydrogen sulfide (H_2S), the compound responsible for the rotten-egg odor found naturally in some groundwaters and certain deep surface waters. The following four equations are examples of how acids dissociate when mixed into water:

$$HCl \xrightarrow{H_2O} H^+ + Cl^-$$

(a strong acid: generally, more than 99% of the molecules dissociate in water)

$$H_2SO_4 \xrightarrow{H_2O} 2H^+ + SO_4^{-2}$$

(a strong acid: generally, more than 99% of the molecules dissociate in water)

$$H_2S \xrightarrow{H_2O} 2H^+ + SO^{-2}$$

(a weak acid: generally, less than 0.1% of the molecules dissociate in water)

$$H_2CO_3 \xrightarrow{H_2O} 2H^+ + CO_3^{-2}$$

(a weak acid: generally, less than 0.1% of the molecules dissociate in water)

Solutions that contain significant numbers of H+ ions are called *acidic*. Three other features that distinguish acids from bases and salts include the following:

1. Acids change the color of chemical color indicators.
   - Acids turn litmus paper red.
   - Acids turn phenolphthalein colorless.
   - Acids turn methyl orange to red.
2. Acids neutralize bases, resulting in the formation of a salt and water.
3. Acids found naturally in foods give the foods a sour taste. The sour flavor of citrus fruits is caused by citric acid. *It is vital to note that tasting the acids found in laboratories and water treatment plants can be dangerous, even fatal.*

Bases

A **base** is any substance that produces hydroxyl ions (OH^-) when it dissociates in water. Lime [$Ca(OH)_2$], caustic soda (sodium hydroxide, or $NaOH$), and common household ammonia (NH_4OH) are familiar examples of bases. *Strong bases* are those that dissociate readily, releasing a large concentration of hydroxyl ions. $NaOH$ is an example of a very strong, caustic base. (*Caustic* refers to a substance's ability to eat through or corrode a material.) *Weak bases*, such as $Ca(OH)_2$ and NH_4OH, dissociate poorly, releasing few OH^- ions.

acid

Any substance that releases hydrogen ions (H^+) when it is mixed into water.

base

Any substance that produced hydroxide ions when it dissociates in water.

The following equations are examples of how bases dissociate when mixed into water:

$$NaOH \longrightarrow Na^+ + OH^-$$ (a strong base: generally, more than 99% of the molecules dissociate in water)

$$KOH \longrightarrow K^+ + OH^-$$ (a strong base: generally, more than 99% of the molecules dissociate in water)

$$Ca(OH)_2 \longrightarrow Ca^{+2} + 2OH^-$$ (a relatively weak base: generally, less than 15% of the molecules dissociate in water)

$$NH_4OH \longrightarrow NH_4^+ + OH^-$$ (a weak base: generally, less than 0.5% of the molecules dissociate in water)

Solutions that contain significant numbers of OH^- ions are called *basic solutions* or *alkaline solutions*. The term *alkaline* should not be confused with the term *alkalinity*, which has a special meaning in water treatment.

Three other features that distinguish bases from acids and salts include the following:

1. Bases change the color of chemical color indicators.
   - Bases turn litmus paper blue.
   - Bases turn phenolphthalein red.
   - Bases turn methyl orange to yellow.
2. Bases neutralize acids, resulting in the formation of a salt and water.
3. Bases found naturally in foods give the foods a bitter taste. Baking soda and milk of magnesium both taste bitter because they contain basic compounds. *It is vital to note that tasting the bases found in laboratories and water treatment plants can be dangerous, even fatal.*

Salts

Salts are compounds resulting from an acid–base mixture. The process of mixing an acid with a base to form a salt is called *neutralization*. Calcium sulfate ($CaSO_4$), for example, is a salt formed by the following acid–base neutralization:

$$H_2SO_4 + Ca(OH)_2 \longrightarrow CaSO_4 + H_2O$$

Another example is sodium chloride (NaCl):

$$HCl + NaOH \longrightarrow NaCl + H_2O$$

Notice that each acid–base reaction results in a salt plus water. Salts generally have no effect on color indicators. When occurring naturally in foods, salts taste salty; however, like all chemicals found in the laboratory or water treatment plants, *salts may be poisonous, and tasting them could be dangerous or fatal.*

pH

Solutions range from very acidic (having a high concentration of H^+ ions) to very basic (having a high concentration of OH^- ions). When there are exactly as many OH^- ions as H^+ ions, the solution is *neutral*—neither acidic nor basic—and each OH^- can combine with an H^+ to form a molecule of H_2O. Pure water is neutral, and most salt solutions are neutral or very nearly so.

The **pH** of a solution is a measurement of how acidic or basic the solution is (Figure 1-11). The pH scale runs from 0 (most acidic) to 14 (most basic).

pH
A measurement of how acidic or basic a substance is, from 0 (most acidic) to 14 (most basic). A pH of 7 indicates the substance is neutral.

High concentration
of H⁺ Ions

H⁺ and OH⁻
ions in balance

High concentration
of OH⁻ Ions

0 — 1 — 2 — 3 — 4 — 5 — 6 — 7 — 8 — 9 — 10 — 11 — 12 — 13 — 14

Pure acid   Neutral   Pure base

Figure 1-11 The pH scale

The scale is logarithmic, which means that each pH measurement is 10 times greater than the preceding value. For example, if OH⁻ at pH 7 equals 10, at pH 8, OH⁻ equals 100, and at pH 9, OH⁻ equals 1,000. The same system is employed for H⁺ in acidic solutions, moving from pH 7 to pH 1. Pure water has a pH of 7, the center of the range, neither acidic nor basic.

For each treatment process, there is a pH at which the operation is most effective. If the pH of the water is too low (the water is too acidic) for an operation to be effective, then the pH can be increased by the addition of a base, such as lime [$Ca(OH)_2$]. The OH⁻ ions released by the base will combine with some of the H⁺ ions of the acidic water, forming H_2O molecules and lowering the concentration of H⁺ ions.

Similarly, if the pH of water is too high (the water is too basic), then the pH can be lowered by the addition of an acid. In water treatment, pH is often lowered by bubbling carbon dioxide (CO_2) gas through the water. The CO_2 reacts with water to form carbonic acid (H_2CO_3), and the acid dissociates into $2H^+ + CO_3^{-2}$. The H⁺ ions then combine with some of the OH⁻ ions of the basic water, forming H_2O molecules and lowering the concentrations of OH⁻ ions.

Alkalinity

When acid is added to water that has a high concentration of OH⁻ ions (basic water, high in pH), the H⁺ ions released by the acid combine with the OH⁻ ions in the water to form H_2O. As long as the water contains OH⁻ ions, those ions will *neutralize* the added acid and the water will remain basic. In natural waters, **alkalinity** is measured by bicarbonate (HCO_3^-) concentration. Bicarbonate maintains pH by taking on H⁺:

$$HCO_3^- + H^+ \longrightarrow H_2CO_3$$

or by giving H⁺:

$$HCO_3^- \longrightarrow H^+ + CO_3^{-2}$$

These reactions maintain the pH of natural water at around pH 7. After enough acid has been added to combine with all the OH⁻ ions, addition of more acid will give the water a high concentration of H⁺ ions, meaning the water will become acidic.

However, if acid is added to water containing carbonate (CO_3^{-2}) ions in addition to OH⁻ ions, then some of the H⁺ ions released by the acid will combine with the OH⁻ to form H_2O, and some will combine with the CO_3^{-2} ions to form HCO_3^- (bicarbonate). As more acid is added, the H⁺ ions released will combine with the ions to form H_2CO_3 (carbonic acid). A concentration of H⁺ ions will begin to accumulate (the water will become acidic) only after enough acid has been added to convert all the OH⁺ to H_2O and to convert all the CO_3^{-2} to HCO_3^- and then to H_2CO_3.

The CO_3^{-2} and HCO_3^- ions in the water increase the capacity of the water to neutralize (or *buffer*) an acid. Alkalinity is a measurement of a water's capacity

alkalinity

A measurement of water's capacity to neutralize an acid.

to neutralize an acid, whether the neutralization is the result of OH⁻, CO_3^{-2}, HCO_3^-, or other negative ions.

In water treatment, OH⁻, CO_3^{-2}, and HCO_3^- are the ions causing most of the alkalinity. Alkalinity caused by OH⁻ is called *hydroxyl alkalinity*; if caused by CO_3^{-2}, it is called *carbonate alkalinity*; and if caused by HCO_3^-, it is called *bicarbonate alkalinity*. The combined effect of all three types is reported by a lab as the *total alkalinity*.

The experiment illustrated in Figure 1-12 demonstrates the relationship between alkalinity and pH. In step 1, equal volumes of two solutions are prepared. Solution 1 is made up by mixing a base [lime, $Ca(OH)_2$] into water. The pH of solution 1 is 11, and the only alkalinity is provided by the hydroxyl ions (OH⁻) released by the base. Solution 2 is made up by mixing the same base [$Ca(OH)_2$] and calcium carbonate ($CaCO_3$) into water. The pH of solution 2 is also 11; that is, solution 1 and solution 2 have the same concentration of OH⁻ ions. However, solution 2 has a higher alkalinity than solution 1, because the alkalinity of

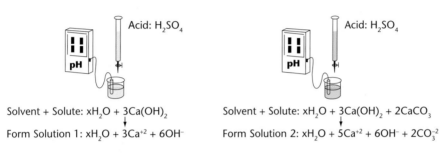

Step 1

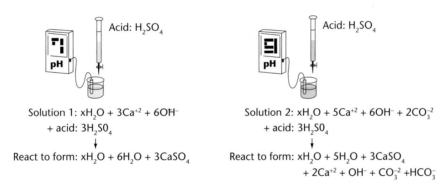

Step 2

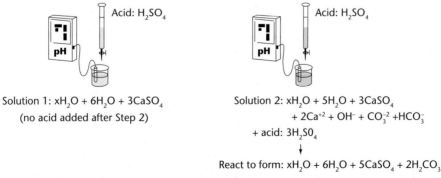

Step 3

Figure 1-12 Alkalinity compared with pH

solution 2 includes carbonate ions (CO_3^{-2} released by the calcium carbonate) in addition to the hydroxyl ions (OH^- released by the lime).

In step 2, sulfuric acid (H_2SO_4) is slowly added to solution 1 until the pH drops to 7, as indicated by the pH meter. The pH of 7 means that enough H^+ ions have been added (released by the acid) to combine with all the OH^- ions originally in the basic solution. The same volume of acid is added to solution 2, but the pH meter still indicates a basic solution: pH greater than 7. The carbonate ions (CO_3^{-2}) in solution 2 have combined with some of the H^+ ions released by the acid; as a result, there are not yet enough H^+ ions in solution 2 to balance the original concentration of OH^- ions.

To complete the experiment in step 3, more acid is added to solution 2 until the pH drops to a neutral 7. The solutions had the same pH at the beginning of the experiment, and they have the same pH at the end. But solution 2, which had the higher alkalinity, was capable of neutralizing a greater volume of acid than solution 1. (Note that the pH meter readings and equations in Figure 1-12 indicate a slightly simpler behavior of the chemicals than actually would occur in a laboratory.)

 WATCH THE VIDEOS
Chemistry 1 and Chemistry 2 (www.awwa.org/wsovideoclips)

Organic Contaminants

All organic compounds or contaminants contain carbon in combination with one or more elements. Organic compounds comprising the group called *hydrocarbons* contain only carbon and hydrogen (Figures 1-13 and 1-14). Many organics contain carbon, hydrogen, and oxygen. Naturally occurring organic compounds often contain low concentrations of nitrogen, phosphorus, and sulfur. Synthetic organic chemicals may contain halogens—for example, chlorine or fluorine—and inorganic metals.

Natural Organic Substances

Organic compounds differ from inorganic metallic and nonmetallic compounds. In general, the following characteristics describe organic compounds, but these may not be applicable in all cases:

- Combustible
- Have lower melting and boiling points
- Are only slightly soluble in water
- Exhibit isomerism, in which more than one compound may exist for a chemical formula
- Have very high molecular weights
- Serve as substrate or food for bacteria
- Have slower reaction rates

Organic compounds find their way into water from three sources. The first source is humic materials from plants and algae, microorganisms and their secretions, and hydrocarbons. A few of the aromatic hydrocarbons may cause adverse health effects. Humic materials are precursors in the formation of trihalomethanes (THMs). The second source is domestic and commercial activities and effluent from wastewater treatment plants and industries into surface waters such

organic compound
A chemical substance of animal or vegetable origin having carbon in its molecular structure.

trihalomethanes (THMs)
Disinfection by-product compounds formed by the reaction of organic material in water with chlorine or other disinfectants, consisting of chloroform, dichlorobromomethane, bromodichloromethane, and bromoform.

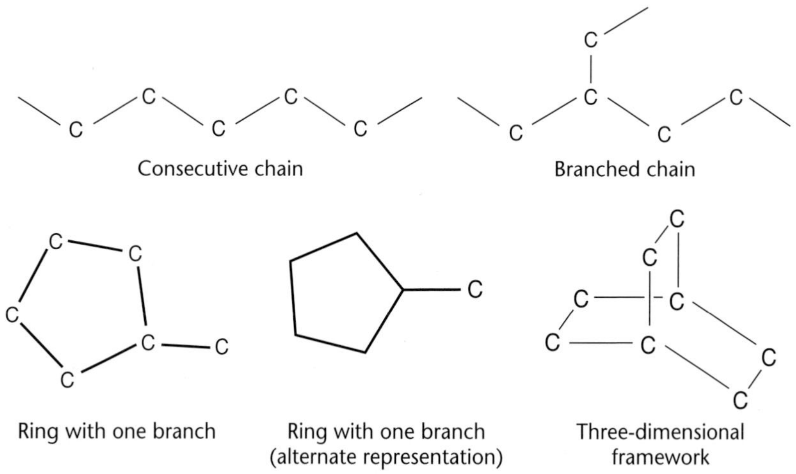

Figure 1-13 Typical arrangement of carbon atoms

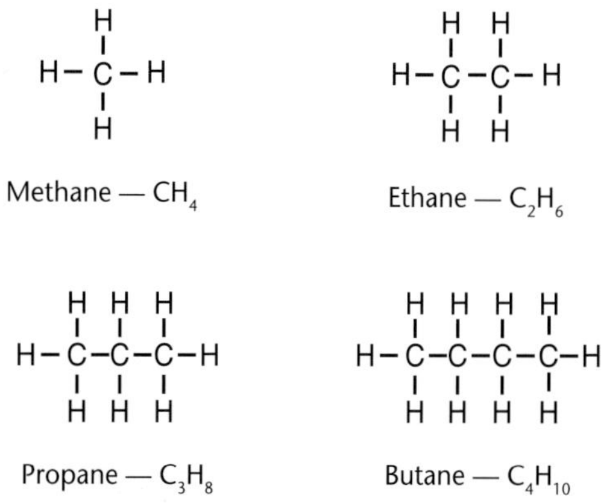

Consecutive chain

Branched chain

Ring with one branch

Ring with one branch (alternate representation)

Three-dimensional framework

Figure 1-14 Typical hydrocarbons in chain configuration

Methane — CH_4

Ethane — C_2H_6

Propane — C_3H_8

Butane — C_4H_{10}

as rivers. The third source is reactions that occur during water treatment and transmission.

Groundwater

It is rare for groundwater sources to contain elevated levels of natural organic compounds, but one situation in which such levels can occur is in a relatively shallow well overlain by an existing or previously swampy area. If the taste, odor, and/or color are excessive, treatment may have to be provided to make the water palatable in the same manner as for a surface water source. It is not likely that such naturally occurring contaminants alone will create a serious health hazard. In such cases, if the amount of organic matter in the groundwater is relatively modest, it may not adversely affect taste, odor, or color. However, it might create excessive levels of disinfection by-products (DBPs) when the water is chlorinated.

Groundwater is also occasionally contaminated by naturally occurring hydrocarbons. In areas where natural gas and oil come in contact with aquifers, the water may be slightly contaminated but still usable, with treatment, as a drinking water source. If the water is heavily contaminated, it will probably not be a suitable source of drinking water.

Recent studies have shown that groundwater can be contaminated with synthetic organic chemicals created for use by industries (electronics, metals) and the military (explosives, rocket fuels) and in the production and use of fossil fuels, such as oxygen-enhancing compounds. Some of these compounds have been found to attach themselves to water molecules and move through the soil layers to become part of the groundwater makeup.

Surface Water

In general, surface waters are more prone to contamination by natural organic compounds than are groundwaters. The various types of vegetation growing in the watershed are one source of contamination. Many water systems regularly experience operational problems caused by decaying leaves and plants that have been washed from farms and forests during heavy rains in the spring and fall. This organic matter is generally decomposed by biological action and breaks down eventually into carbon dioxide and water. However, some organic compounds are quite complex and persist in the water environment for some time. For example, humic acid, derived from the decomposition of plant matter, is found in most surface waters and does not readily biodegrade (break down).

Microorganisms are another source of organic compounds in water. In addition to cellular matter, many plants and microorganisms release organic matter into a water source through their metabolic processes.

Various types of algae and vegetation flourishing in a lake or reservoir can also be the source of objectionable organic compounds in water. If the concentration of this vegetation is low, it usually has no adverse effect on drinking water quality. However, a sudden die-off of the vegetation can cause deterioration in water quality. Some adverse health effects of large quantities of certain blue-green and red algae may also occur.

Serious taste and odor problems can also be caused when a reservoir becomes stratified and matter near the bottom that has decomposed anaerobically (in the absence of free oxygen) is brought into the water system. Excessive amounts of algae in source water can also cause water treatment problems such as taste and odor, filter clogging, and formation of slime in the treatment plant.

DBPs form when water containing organic substances is disinfected. In most cases, the organic substances are naturally occurring, such as humic and fulvic acids resulting from decaying vegetation. A group of chlorinated organic compounds called THMs was one of the first products of the reaction of chlorine with humic substances to be recognized. The principal THMs of concern are chloroform, bromodichloromethane, chlorodibromomethane, and bromoform. At one time, chloroform was widely used in cough medicine and other medications, but its use was discontinued when research suggested that chloroform may be carcinogenic (capable of causing cancer). The other THMs are also suspected of being carcinogens or have been demonstrated to have other adverse health effects, such as possible birth defects. These issues are being studied to determine the validity of these concerns. Thus, the various THMs are regulated as a group, with a **maximum contaminant level (MCL)** established for total THMs (TTHM).

As more knowledge about DBPs develops, additional regulations limiting their concentration in finished water are expected. The next DBPs being considered for regulation are a group of five **haloacetic acids (HAA5)**. DBPs are discussed in more detail in Chapter 3.

Domestic and commercial activities contribute synthetic organic chemicals to wastewater discharges, agricultural runoff, urban runoff, and leachate from contaminated soils. Most of the organic contaminants identified in water supplies as having adverse health concerns are part of this group. They include pesticides (such as atrazine and aldicarb), solvents and metal degreasers (such as trichlorobenzene, tetrachloroethylene, trichloroethylene, and trichloroethane), and a family of compounds formerly in wide use, the polychlorinated biphenyls.

Organic contaminants formed during water disinfection include by-products such as THMs (e.g., chloroform) and HAAs (e.g., di- and trichloroacetic acids). Other compounds, such as acrylamide or epichlorohydrin, are components of coagulants (e.g., polyacrylamide) that can leach out during treatment. During finished-water transmission, undesirable components of pipes, coatings, linings, and joint adhesives, such as polynuclear aromatic hydrocarbons (PAHs), epichlorohydrin, and solvents, have been shown to leach into water. This small amount of leaching decreases as the pipe ages.

maximum contaminant level (MCL)
The maximum permissible level of a contaminant in water as specified in the regulations of the Safe Drinking Water Act.

haloacetic acids (HAA5)
Chemicals formed as a reaction of disinfectants with contaminants in water, consisting of monochloroacetic acid, dichloroacetic acid, trichloroacetic acid, monobromoacetic acid, and dibromoacetic acid.

Synthetic Organic Substances

The category of synthetic organic chemicals (SOCs) has become a regulatory rather than a chemical description. It has evolved to distinguish a group of mostly volatile organic chemicals (VOCs), regulated first under the 1986 amendments of the federal Safe Drinking Water Act, from "SOCs" regulated under Phase 2 and later regulations. However, some of those SOCs are also VOCs (e.g., ethylbenzene, styrene, toluene, and xylenes, and the fumigant pesticides). The bulk of SOCs are pesticides but also include the PAHs, the polychlorinated biphenyls, and two water treatment polymers.

Health Effects of Organic Chemicals

USEPA has designated three categories to describe the health effects of organic chemicals:

- Category I—It is known, or there is strong evidence, that the chemical is a carcinogen.
- Category II—There is limited but not positive evidence that the chemical is a carcinogen, and there are other known adverse health effects.
- Category III—There is no firm evidence that the chemical is a carcinogen, but there are other known adverse health effects.

Noncarcinogens

To the water system operator, the principal significance of a chemical's carcinogenic status is the way the maximum contaminant level goal (MCLG) is established. For noncarcinogens, the MCLG is a number indicating the level of the contaminant that health-effects experts consider acceptable in drinking water. The MCL is then set at the same level as the MCLG, or as close to it as is considered technically achievable. The MCLG for these contaminants will be changed only if new information on their toxicity to humans becomes available.

The noncarcinogenic effects of organic chemicals on humans vary. Damage to the liver, kidneys, cardiovascular system, and central nervous system are the principal effects.

Carcinogens

For carcinogens, USEPA policy is that the MCLG must be zero. In other words, it is presently assumed that any exposure to the chemical could cause cancer, so ideally none of the chemical would be present in drinking water.

In the real world, though, there are two restrictions in controlling carcinogens: (1) the ability to detect the chemical by reasonable and reliable laboratory technique and (2) the technology to remove the chemical from water if it is found to be present. These factors are considered when the MCLs are established, and the MCLs are set as close to the MCLGs as experts consider to be realistically achievable.

From time to time, then, USEPA must review all MCLs for carcinogens, and if the factors considered in setting the MCL have changed, the MCL will be changed. In short, the intention is to continually edge the MCL for carcinogens closer to zero, so the allowable level is likely to be changed periodically. Changes may occur as the methods of testing improve or as further data are reviewed and proven to be of merit. So far the only contaminants that have had a change in status are nickel (delisted) and arsenic (MCL reduced from a level of 50 µg/L to 10 µg/L).

synthetic organic chemical (SOC)

A chemical produced by humans that can contaminate water.

maximum contaminant level goal (MCLG)

Nonenforceable health-based goals published along with the promulgation of an MCL.

Radiological Contaminants

One of the more significant public health concerns regarding drinking water is the relatively high level of natural **radioactivity** found in some water sources. Most radioactivity in water occurs naturally, but there is also a threat of radionuclide contamination from various industrial and medical processes.

The harmful effects to a living organism of consuming water containing radioactivity are caused by the energy absorbed by the cells and tissues of the organism. This absorbed energy (or dose) produces chemical decomposition of the molecules present in the living cells. Each of the forms of radiation reacts somewhat differently within the human body.

Radioactive Materials

A radioactive atom (Figure 1-15) emits alpha particles, beta particles, and gamma rays.

Alpha Particles (Radiation)

Alpha particles are the most prevalent naturally occurring radionuclide present in drinking water and are therefore of the greatest concern. Alpha particles are the heaviest particles.

Alpha radiation is not true electromagnetic radiation like light and X-rays. It consists of particles of matter. Alpha particles are doubly charged ions of helium. Although they are propelled from the nucleus of atoms at approximately 10 percent of the speed of light, they do not travel much more than 10 cm in air at room temperature. They are stopped by an ordinary sheet of paper. The alpha particles emitted by a particular element are all released at the same velocity. The velocity varies, however, from element to element. Alpha particles have extremely high ionizing action within their range.

Beta Radiation

Beta radiation consists of negatively charged particles—electrons—that move at speeds ranging from 30 to 99 percent of the speed of light. The penetrating power

radioactivity
Behavior of a material that has an unstable atomic nucleus, which spontaneously decays or disintegrates, producing radiation.

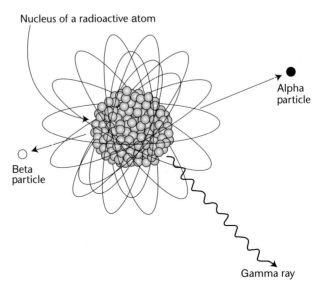

Nucleus of a radioactive atom

Alpha particle

Beta particle

Gamma ray

Figure 1-15 Emissions from the nucleus of a radioactive atom

of beta radiation depends on its speed. It can travel several hundred feet in air and can be stopped by aluminum a few millimeters thick. The ionizing power of beta radiation is much less than that of alpha radiation.

Gamma Radiation

Gamma radiation is true electromagnetic radiation, which travels at the speed of light. It is similar to X-ray radiation but has a shorter wavelength and therefore greater penetrating power, which increases as the wavelength decreases. Proper shielding from gamma radiation requires a barrier of lead that is several centimeters thick or concrete several feet thick. The unit of gamma radiation is the *photon*.

Unit of Radioactivity

The measurement of radioactivity disintegration is expressed in *curies*. Formerly, one unit of radioactivity was considered to be the number of disintegrations occurring per second in one gram of pure radium. Because the constants for radium are subject to revision from time to time, the International Radium Standard Commission has recommended the use of a fixed value, 3.7×10^{10} disintegrations per second, as the *standard curie* (Ci).

The curie is used mainly to define quantities of radioactive materials. A curie of an alpha emitter is the quantity that releases 3.7×10^{10} alpha particles per second. A curie of a beta emitter is the quantity of material that releases 3.7×10^{10} beta particles per second, and a curie of a gamma emitter is the quantity of material that releases 3.7×10^{10} photons per second. The curie represents such a large number of disintegrations per second that the *millicurie* (mCi), *microcurie* (µCi), and *picocurie* (pCi)—corresponding to 10^{-3}, 10^{-6}, and 10^{-9} Ci, respectively—are more commonly used.

The *roentgen* is a unit of gamma or X-ray radiation intensity. It is of value in the study of the biological effects that result from ionization induced within cells by radiation. The roentgen is defined as the amount of gamma or X-ray radiation that will produce in one cubic centimeter of dry air, at 0°C (32°F) and 760 mm of pressure, one electrostatic unit (esu) of electricity. This is equivalent to 1.61×10^{12} ion pairs per gram of air and corresponds to the absorption of 83.8 ergs of energy.

The roentgen is a unit of the total quantity of ionization produced by gamma radiation or X-rays. Dosage rates for these radiations are expressed in terms of roentgens per unit of time.

With the advent of atomic energy involving exposure to neutrons, protons, and alpha and beta particles—which also have effects on living tissue—it has become necessary to have other means of expressing ionization produced in cells. Three methods of expression have been used.

The **roentgen equivalent physical (rep)** is defined as the quantity of radiation (other than X-rays or other generated radiation) that produces in one gram of human tissue ionization equivalent to the quantity produced in air by one roentgen of radiation or X-rays (equivalent to 83.8 ergs of energy). The rep has been replaced largely by the term **radiation absorption dose (rad)**, which has wider application.

The rad is a unit of radiation corresponding to an energy absorption of 100 ergs per gram of any medium. It can be applied to any type and energy of radiation that leads to the production of ionization. Studies of the radiation of biological materials have shown that the roentgen is approximately equivalent

roentgen equivalent physical (rep)
The quantity of radiation (other than X-rays or other generated radiation) that produces in one gram of human tissue ionization equivalent to the quantity produced in air by one roentgen of radiation or X-rays (equivalent to 83.8 ergs of energy).

radiation absorption dose (rad)
A measure of the dose absorbed by the body from radiation (100 ergs of energy in 1 g of tissue).

to 100 ergs/g of tissue; it can be equivalent to 90–150 ergs/g of tissue, depending on the energy of the X-ray radiation and type of tissue. The rad, therefore, is more closely related to the roentgen than is the rep, in terms of radiation effects on living tissues, and is the term biologists prefer.

The rad represents such a tremendous radiation dosage, in terms of permissible amounts for human beings, that another unit—**roentgen equivalent man (rem)**—has been developed specifically for humans. The rem unit corresponds to the amount of radiation that will produce an energy dissipation in the human body that is biologically equivalent to one roentgen of radiation of X-rays, or approximately 100 ergs/g. The recommended maximum permissible dose for radiation workers is 5 rem/year; for nonradiation workers, it is 0.5 rem/year.

Radioactive Contaminants in Water

Humans receive a radiation dose of about 200 millirems (mrem) or 0.2 rem from all sources each year, and USEPA estimates that on average as much as 3 percent of this dose comes from drinking water. Local conditions can, of course, greatly alter this proportion.

The following are some of the radioactive substances currently listed for testing as potential drinking water contaminants:

- Radium
- Uranium
- Radon
- Artificial radionuclides

Radium   Radium is the most common radionuclide of concern in drinking water. Naturally occurring radium leaches into groundwater from rock formations, so it is present in water sources in those parts of the country where there is radium-bearing rock. It may also be found in surface water as a result of runoff from mining and industrial operations where radium is present in the soil. The three *isotopes* (variations) of radium of concern in drinking water are radium 226, which emits principally alpha particles; radium 228, which emits beta particles and alpha particles from its daughter decay products; and radium 224, which has a very short half-life of about 3.6 days compared with radium 226 and radium 228, whose half-lives are measured in years. Currently, federal regulations ignore radium 224, but some states require monitoring for this isotope even though the sampling, shipping, and testing requirements make it difficult to obtain meaningful results.

Uranium   Naturally occurring uranium is found in some groundwater supplies as a result of leaching from uranium-bearing sandstone, shale, and other rock. Uranium may also occasionally be present in surface water, carried there in runoff from areas with mining operations. Uranium may be present in a variety of complex ionic forms, depending on the pH of the water.

Radon   Radon is a naturally occurring radioactive gas that cannot be seen, smelled, or tasted. Radon comes from the natural breakdown (radioactive decay) of uranium. It is the direct radioactive-decay daughter of radium 226. The highest concentrations of radon are found in soil and rock containing uranium.

roentgen equivalent man (rem)

A quantification of radiation in terms of its dose effect on the human body; the number of rads times a quality factor.

Significant concentrations, from a health standpoint, may be found in groundwater from any type of geologic formation, including unconsolidated formations.

Outdoors, radon emitted from the soil is diluted to such low concentrations that it is not of concern. However, when it is liberated inside a confined space, such as a home or office building, radon can accumulate to relatively high levels, and inhalation of the gas is considered a health danger. Most cases of excessive levels of radon in buildings are caused by the gas seeping through cracks in concrete floors and walls. In areas where high levels of radon in the soil are a problem, foundation ventilation should be installed to reduce the concentration of radon entering buildings.

The problem from a public water supply standpoint is that, if radon is present in the water, a significant amount of the gas will be liberated into a building as water is used. Showers, washing machines, and dishwashers are particularly efficient in transferring radon gas into the air. The radon released from the water adds to the radon that seeps into a building from the soil, adding to the health risk.

Artificial Radionuclides   Significant levels of artificial radionuclides have been recorded in surface waters as a result of atmospheric fallout following nuclear testing, leaks, and disasters. Otherwise, surface water generally contains little or no radioactivity. Potential sources of serious water contamination are accidental discharges from facilities using radioactive materials, such as power stations, industrial plants, waste-disposal sites, or medical facilities. State and federal nuclear regulatory agencies monitor all uses of radioactive materials to prevent such discharges. If an accidental discharge of artificial radionuclides takes place, the elements most likely to be present are strontium 90 and tritium.

Adverse Health Effects of Radioactivity

The effects of excessive levels of radioactivity on the human body include developmental problems, nonhereditary birth defects, genetic effects that might be inherited by future generations, and various types of cancer. All radionuclides are considered to be carcinogens.

Radium is chemically similar to calcium, so about 90 percent of naturally occurring radium that is ingested goes to the bones. Consequently, the primary risk from radium ingestion is bone cancer. Although uranium has not definitively been proven carcinogenic, its potential to accumulate in the bones, much like radium 228, has prompted USEPA, as a policy matter, to consider uranium a carcinogen. Thus, USEPA has set the MCLG at zero. The principal adverse effect of uranium is toxicity to human kidneys.

Inhaled radon is considered to be a cause of lung cancer. Radon is also thought to have some noncarcinogenic effects on internal body organs when ingested. Although the proportion of radon added to a building by the water supply is usually relatively small in comparison with the amount that seeps into the building from the soil, the issue of radon in drinking water is still significant because of the many people being exposed. USEPA estimates that between one and five million homes in the United States may have significantly high levels of radon contamination and that between 5,000 and 20,000 lung cancer deaths a year may be attributed to all sources of radon. USEPA has not set, as of this writing, the MCL for radon in drinking water.

Study Questions

1. Which of the following are the ideal indicator for pathogens?
   a. *Salmonella* species
   b. Coliform group bacteria
   c. Gram-negative cocci
   d. Gram-negative coccobacilli

2. Acids, bases, and salts lacking carbon are
   a. ketones.
   b. aldehydes.
   c. organic compounds.
   d. inorganic compounds.

3. The organisms used to indicate the likelihood that pathogenic bacteria may be present are
   a. *Salmonella* bacteria.
   b. enteric viruses.
   c. coliform bacteria.
   d. *Pseudomonas* group bacteria.

4. A physical property, as opposed to a chemical property, important to water treatment is
   a. turbidity.
   b. pH.
   c. dissolved solids.
   d. electrical conductivity.

5. Which of the following are the two principal chemicals that cause water hardness?
   a. Aluminum and iron
   b. Aluminum and calcium
   c. Iron and manganese
   d. Calcium and magnesium

6. Which of the following statements about viruses is *not* correct?
   a. Viruses have no independent metabolism and depend on living cells for reproduction.
   b. Viruses range in diameter from 10 to 25 nanometers (nm), which is smaller than can be seen with an optical microscope.
   c. Viruses cannot survive in the environment for any length of time outside of a human's or an animal's body.
   d. Some types of viruses can cause acute epidemics of gastroenteritis.

7. Which of the following are commonly used as an indicator of drinking water quality?
   a. Protozoan parasites
   b. Coliform bacteria
   c. *Cryptosporidium* oocysts
   d. Viruses

8. What is the term for the smallest particle that retains the characteristics of the element that it helps form?

9. What is a radical?

10. What measurements are used to express the weight of solute dissolved in a given volume of solution?

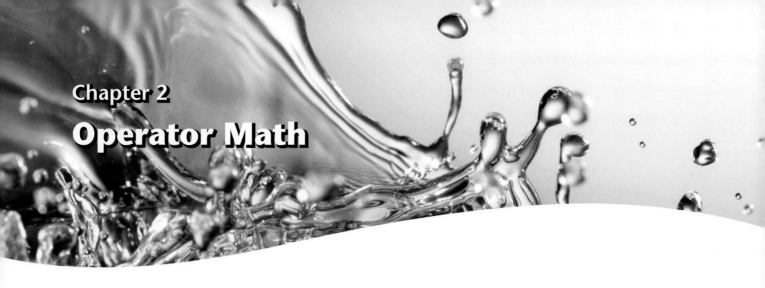

Chapter 2
Operator Math

Powers and Scientific Notation

Two common methods of expressing a number—powers notation and scientific notation—will be used in this chapter. Let's begin with an overview of each method.

Powers Notation

The most basic form of powers notation is merely a shorthand method of writing multiplication. For example, 5×5 can be written as

$$5^2$$

This term is read *5 to the second power*, or *5 squared*. The small 2 is the exponent, or power. It tells you how many 5s are to be multiplied together: two. In expanded form,

$$5^2 = (5)(5)$$

The expression *5 to the third power* (usually called *5 cubed*) is written as

$$5^3$$

In expanded form, this notation means

$$5^3 = (5)(5)(5)$$

The following examples further illustrate this concept of powers notation.

Example 1

How is the term 5^3 written in expanded form?

The power (or exponent) of 3 means the number is multiplied by itself three times:

$$5^3 = (5)(5)(5)$$

Example 2

How is the term ft^2 written in expanded form?

The power or exponent of 2 means the term is multiplied by itself two times:

$$ft^2 = (ft)(ft)$$

Scientific Notation

Scientific notation is a method by which any number can be expressed as a term multiplied by a power of 10. The term itself is greater than or equal to 1 but less than 10. Examples of numbers written in scientific notation include the following:

$$5.4 \times 10^1$$

$$1.2 \times 10^3$$

$$9.789 \times 10^4$$

$$3.62 \times 10^{-2}$$

The numbers can be taken out of scientific notation by performing the indicated multiplication. For example,

$$5.4 \times 10^1 = (5.4)(10) = 54$$

$$1.2 \times 10^3 = (1.2)(10)(10)(10) = 1,200$$

$$9.789 \times 10^4 = (9.789)(10)(10)(10)(10) = 97,890$$

$$3.62 \times 10^{-2} = (3.62)\frac{1}{10^2} = (3.62)\frac{(1)}{(10)(10)} = \frac{3.62}{(10)(10)} = 0.0362$$

An easier way to take a number out of scientific notation is to move the decimal point the number of places indicated by the exponent.

Rule 1

When a number is taken out of scientific notation, a positive exponent indicates a decimal point move to the right, and a negative exponent indicates a decimal point move to the left.

Let's rework the expressions in the preceding list, this time using the decimal point move instead of the multiplication method. The first example is

$$5.4 \times 10^1$$

The *positive* exponent of 1 indicates that the decimal point in 5.4 should be moved one place to the *right*:

$$5.4 = 54$$

The next example is

$$1.2 \times 10^3$$

The *positive* exponent of 3 indicates that the decimal point in 1.2 should be moved three places to the *right*:

$$1.200 = 1,200$$

The next example is

$$9.789 \times 10^4$$

The *positive* exponent of 4 indicates that the decimal point should be moved four places to the *right*:

$$9.7890 = 97,890$$

The final example is

$$3.62 \times 10^{-2}$$

scientific notation
A method by which any number can be expressed as a number between 1 and 9 multiplied by a power of 10.

The *negative* exponent of 2 indicates that the decimal point should be moved two places to the *left*:

$$03.62 = 0.0362$$

Dimensional Analysis

Dimensional analysis is a tool that you can use to determine whether you have set up a problem correctly. In checking a math setup using dimensional analysis, you work only with the dimensions or units of measure and not with the numbers themselves.

To use the dimensional analysis method, you must know three things:

- How to express a horizontal fraction (such as gal/ft³) as a vertical fraction $\left(\text{such as } \dfrac{\text{gal}}{\text{ft}^3}\right)$
- How to divide by a fraction
- How to divide out or cancel terms in the numerator and denominator of a fraction

These techniques are reviewed briefly below.

When you are using dimensional analysis to check a problem, it is often desirable to write any horizontal fractions as vertical fractions. Thus,

$$\text{ft}^3/\text{min} = \frac{\text{ft}^3}{\text{min}}$$

$$\text{s/min} = \frac{\text{s}}{\text{min}}$$

$$\frac{\text{gal/min}}{\text{gal/ft}^3} = \frac{\dfrac{\text{gal}}{\text{min}}}{\dfrac{\text{gal}}{\text{ft}^3}}$$

When a problem involves division by a fraction, the rule is to invert (or turn over) the terms in the denominator and then multiply. For example,

$$\frac{\dfrac{\text{gal}}{\text{min}}}{\dfrac{\text{gal}}{\text{ft}^3}} = \frac{\text{gal}}{\text{min}} \times \frac{\text{ft}^3}{\text{gal}}$$

$$\frac{\text{lb/d}}{\text{min/d}} = \frac{\dfrac{\text{lb}}{\text{d}}}{\dfrac{\text{min}}{\text{d}}} = \frac{\text{lb}}{\text{d}} \times \frac{\text{d}}{\text{min}}$$

$$\frac{\text{mm}^2}{\text{mm}^2/\text{m}^2} = \frac{\dfrac{\text{mm}^2}{1}}{\dfrac{\text{mm}^2}{\text{m}^2}} = \text{mm}^2 \times \frac{\text{m}^2}{\text{mm}^2}$$

Once the fractions in a problem, if any, have been rewritten in the vertical form, and division by a fraction has been re-expressed as multiplication, the terms can be divided out or canceled. For every term canceled in the numerator of a fraction, a similar term must be canceled in the denominator, and vice versa, as shown:

$$\frac{\cancel{gal}}{min} = \frac{ft^3}{\cancel{gal}} = \frac{ft^3}{min}$$

$$\frac{kg}{\cancel{d}} = \frac{\cancel{d}}{min} = \frac{kg}{min}$$

$$\cancel{mm^2} = \frac{m^2}{\cancel{mm^2}} = m^2$$

$$\frac{\cancel{ft^3}}{\cancel{s}} = \frac{gal}{\cancel{ft^3}} = \frac{\cancel{s}}{\cancel{min}} = \frac{\cancel{min}}{d} = \frac{gal}{d}$$

Suppose you wish to convert 2,500 ft³ volume to gallons, and suppose you know you will use 7.48 gal/ft³ in the conversion but that you don't know whether to multiply or divide by 7.48. Let's look at both possible ways and see how dimensional analysis can be used to choose the correct way. *Only the dimensions* will be used to determine if the math setup is correct. First, try multiplying the dimensions:

$$(ft^3)(gal/ft^3) = (ft^3)\left(\frac{gal}{ft^3}\right)$$

Then multiply the numerators and denominators to get

$$= \frac{(ft^3)(gal)}{ft^3}$$

and cancel common terms to get

$$= \frac{(\cancel{ft^3})(gal)}{\cancel{ft^3}}$$

$$= gal$$

Thus, by dimensional analysis you know that if you *multiply* the two dimensions (ft³ and gal/ft³), the answer you get will be in gallons, which is what you want. Therefore, because the math setup is correct, you would then multiply the numbers to obtain the number of gallons:

$$(2,500 \ ft^3)(7.48 \ gal/ft^3) = 18,700 \ gal$$

What would have happened if you had divided the dimensions instead of multiplying?

$$\frac{ft^3}{gal/ft^3} = \frac{ft^3}{\dfrac{gal}{ft^3}}$$

$$= ft^3\left(\frac{ft^3}{gal}\right)$$

Then multiply the numerators and denominators of the fraction to get

$$\frac{ft^6}{gal}$$

So had you *divided* the two dimensions (ft³ and gal/ft³), the units of the answer would have been ft⁶/gal, *not* gal. Clearly you do not want to divide in making this conversion.

Rounding and Estimating

The practice of approximating the size of the answer to a calculation helps you to anticipate the general scale of the answer, and thus avoid mathematical errors. For example, if you know in advance that a calculation should be somewhere in the thousands—say, 5,000—you will know at once that something is amiss when your calculations render 500,000. Perhaps you forgot to multiply or divide by a certain number, or maybe you punched a wrong button on the calculator. If you have an idea of what the approximate answer should be, then you can recognize an incorrect answer and recheck your arithmetic.

Rounding is the first step in approximating the answer of a calculation. Rounding involves changing the actual numbers to ones that can be more easily calculated. Estimating is the next step, in which the rounded numbers are calculated, yielding a rough idea of what may be expected once the actual numbers are calculated.

Rounding

Rounding means replacing the final digits of a number with zeros, thus expressing the number as tens, hundreds, thousands, etc., or tenths, hundredths, thousandths, etc. For example, 398 would be expressed as 400; 0.19 as 0.2; and 5,825,393 as 6,000,000. Equations using rounded numbers are often written with an approximate sign ($\approx$) instead of an equals sign ($=$) to show that the answer is an estimate.

The technique of rounding numbers is based on a particular place value in the decimal system. The various place values are reviewed in the following illustration. It is important to understand this concept before proceeding.

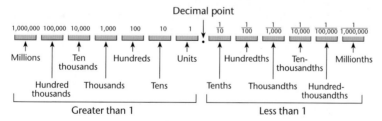

Suppose you want to round the number 3,321 to the nearest hundred. Rounding this number depends only on the *size of the digit just to the right* of the hundreds place:

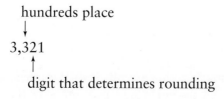

Similarly, if you want to round the number 323,772 to the nearest thousand, this rounding depends only on the *size of the digit just to the right* of the thousands place:

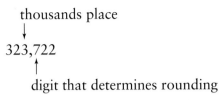

thousands place

323,722

digit that determines rounding

Now consider the rules for *rounding whole numbers*. The procedure depends on whether the digit just to the right of the rounding place is less than 5 or is greater than or equal to 5.

Rule 2

If the digit is less than 5: When rounding to any desired place, if the digit to the right of that place is less than 5, replace all digits to the right of the rounding place with zeros.

Rule 3

If the digit is 5 or greater than 5: When rounding to any desired place, if the digit to the right of that place is 5 or greater, increase the digit in the rounding place by 1 and replace all digits to the right of the increase with zeros.

The best way to understand rounding rules is to look at an example.

Example 3

Round 37,926 to the nearest hundred.

The procedure used in this rounding depends on the digit just to the right of the hundreds place:

37,926

hundreds place

Since the digit to the right of the hundreds place is less than 5, the 9 is not changed and all the digits to the right of the 9 are replaced with zeros:

37,926 ≈ 37,900 (rounded to the nearest hundred)

Estimating

When estimating the answer to a problem, you will find it helpful to round each number in the calculation so that only one digit remains, with the rest of the digits in the number either changed to zeros or dropped in accordance with the rounding rules. In this way the estimation can often be done in your head, or at least with a minimum of computing with pencil or calculator.

However, you should be aware that the more rounding you do in an estimation, the greater the difference may be between the digits of your estimated answer and those of the actual answer. Keep this principle in mind:

Rounding and estimating indicate the approximate size (place value) of a calculated answer but do not necessarily indicate the numerical value of the answer.

For instance, if the estimate to a problem is 40,000, you can expect the calculated answer to be in the tens of thousands (not hundreds or millions); but the value of the calculated answer could fall between 10,000 and 90,000.

Also consider what the place value of your answer could be if the digit in the estimated answer is 1 or 9. With an estimate of 900, the actual answer will probably be in the hundreds (somewhere between 100 and 900)—but it could also be a little more than 900 (such as 1,020). In contrast, if the estimate is 1,000, then the calculated answer could be in the thousands, or a little less than 1,000 (in the high hundreds).

Now let's look at the mechanics of estimating. Suppose you have rounded two numbers so that your estimate of the answer is 40 × 50. In making this estimate, first multiply the two digits (4 and 5):

$$(40)(50)$$
$$\downarrow \quad \downarrow$$
$$4 \times 5 = 20$$

Then count all the zeros in the calculation and put that number of zeros after the 20:

$$(40)(50) = 2000$$
$$\downarrow \quad \downarrow \qquad \downarrow\downarrow$$
$$\text{2 zeros} \quad \text{2 zeros}$$

The estimated answer is 2000, so the actual answer should be in the thousands.

Let's look at a couple more examples of this procedure.

Example 4

A calculation has been rounded so that it can be estimated. What is the estimated answer for the calculation?

$$(600)(3,000)$$

First the 6 and the 3 are multiplied, then the total number of zeros are added:

$$(600)(3,000) = \underbrace{18}_{6 \times 3} \quad \underbrace{00000}_{5 \text{ zeros}}$$

Therefore, the estimated answer for the calculation is 1,800,000; the actual answer should be in the millions.

Example 5

A calculation has been rounded to the numbers shown below. What is the estimated answer for the calculation?

$$(400)(70,000)$$

First the 4 and 7 are multiplied, then the total number of zeros are added:

$$(400)(70,000) = \underbrace{28}_{4 \times 7} \quad \underbrace{000000}_{6 \text{ zeros}}$$

The estimated answer is therefore 28,000,000; the actual answer should be in the ten millions.

Solving for the Unknown Value

In treatment plant operations, you may use equations for such calculations as the detention time of a tank, flow rate in a channel, filter loading rate, or chlorine dosage. To make these calculations, you must first know the values for all but one of the terms of the equation to be used.

For example, in making a flow rate calculation, you would use the equation

$$Q = AV$$

where

$$Q = \text{flow rate}$$

$$A = \text{area}$$

$$V = \text{velocity}$$

The terms of the equation are Q, A, and V. In solving problems using this equation, you would need to be given values to substitute for any two of the three terms. The term for which you do not have information is called the unknown value, or merely the unknown. The unknown value is often denoted by a letter such as x, but may be any other letter, such as Q, A, V, etc.

Suppose you are presented with the following problem:

$$46 = (x)(85)$$

You will need to determine the value of x. The rules that allow you to solve for x are discussed in this section. The discussion considers only what the rules are and how they work. If you are interested in why these rules work and how they came about, you should consult a book on elementary algebra.

Almost all problems in water treatment plant calculations can be solved by an equation that involves only multiplication (such as the one just shown) and/or division. There are occasional problems, however, that require equations involving addition and subtraction. The way to solve for the unknown in each of these types of equations is discussed in this section. Equations involving all four operations of multiplication, division, addition, and subtraction are encountered only in more advanced calculations and are thus beyond the scope of this text.

Equations Using Multiplication and Division

To solve for the unknown value in an equation using multiplication and division, you must rearrange the terms so that x is by itself on one side of the equation. This often involves two steps:

1. Move x to the numerator (top) of the fraction, if it is not already there.
2. Move any other terms away from x, to the other side of the equal sign, so that x stands alone.

To accomplish these two steps, follow this rule:

Rule 4

In equations using multiplication and division, to move a term from one side of the equation to the other, move the term from the numerator (top) of one side to the denominator (bottom) of the other side or from the denominator of one side to the numerator of the other side.

Although you rearrange only some of the terms in an equation when you solve for the unknown value, any of the terms in the equation may be moved if they are moved according to this rule. The following example shows how to rearrange terms.

Example 6

Given the following equation, rearrange the terms so that the x is alone on one side:

$$\frac{(x)(2)}{9} = \frac{3}{7}$$

According to the rearrangement rule, there is only one possible way to move the 9. It must be moved to the numerator of the right side of the equation:

$$\frac{(x)(2)}{9} = \frac{(3)}{7}$$

After making this move, the equation is

$$(x)(2) = \frac{(9)(3)}{7}$$

Next, the 2 must be moved to the opposite side. Although the left side of the equation is not currently in the form of a fraction, it is understood that the terms x and 2 function as a numerator (with the denominator understood to be 1). Thus, the 2 must move to the denominator on the other side of the equation:

$$x = \frac{(9)(3)}{(7)(2)}$$

From here, you can multiply and divide to solve for x, which is 1.93.

Equations Using Addition and Subtraction

As previously mentioned, most water treatment calculations involve equations using only multiplication and division. There are some, however, such as chlorine dosage problems, that involve addition and subtraction. To solve for the unknown value in an equation using addition and subtraction, you must rearrange the terms so that x is positive and is by itself. However, in this type of equation, there is neither a numerator nor a denominator, so the crisscross method of rearranging *cannot be used*. Instead, the terms are moved directly from one side of the equation to the other side, according to the following rule:

Rule 5

In equations using addition and subtraction, when a term is moved from one side of the equation to the other side, the sign of the term must be changed.

This rule means that if a term is positive on one side of the equation, it becomes negative when moved to the other side. Conversely, if a term is negative on one side of the equation, it becomes positive when moved to the other side.

If a term does not show either a plus or minus sign in front, it is assumed to be positive. For example, in the equation

$$7 - 2 - 5 + x = 24 - 3$$

both the 7 and the 24 are considered positive, although no plus sign is shown in front of them.

To solve an equation involving addition and subtraction, you must ask yourself two questions:

- Is x positive?
- Is x by itself?

The terms of the equation must be rearranged so that the answer to both questions is yes. It is important to understand, however, that although x as a term in the equation should be *positive*, the value of x in the answer could be positive or negative.

Ratios and Proportions

A **ratio** is the relationship between two numbers and may be written using a colon (1:2, 4:7, 3:5) or as a fraction (½, ⁴⁄₇, ³⁄₅). When the relationship between two numbers in a ratio is the same as that between two other numbers in another ratio, the ratios are said to be in **proportion**, or proportionate. Stated another way, proportionate ratios are mathematically equal.

A method used to determine if two ratios are in proportion is cross-multiplication. If the answers are the same when numbers diagonally across from each other are multiplied, then the ratios are proportionate.

$$\frac{2}{3} \quad \times \quad \frac{4}{6}$$

$$(3)(4) = 12 \qquad \boxed{(2)(6) = 12}$$

In this example, because the numerator and denominator are both 12 after cross-multiplying, we know that ⅔ is equal to ⁴⁄₆.

The next example uses the cross-multiplication method to determine whether ratios are proportionate.

ratio

A relationship between two numbers. A ratio may be expressed using colons (for example, 1:2 or 3:7), or it may be expressed as a fraction (for example, ½ or ³⁄₇).

proportion

The relationship between two numbers in a ratio. When it is the same as that between two other numbers in another ratio, the two ratios are said to be in proportion, or proportionate.

Example 7

Are 3/7 and 42/98 proportionate?

$$\frac{3}{7} \quad \times \quad \frac{42}{98}$$

$$(7)(42) = 294 \qquad \boxed{(98)(3) = 294}$$

Because the answers (products) of the cross-multiplication are the same (294), the ratios are proportionate.

Practical Applications

In practical application problems, the ratios will not be arranged as in the examples just given. You must know how to set up the proportion before you can solve for the unknown value. As previously explained, a proportion establishes a simple relation between two ratios. If any number in one of the ratios changes, then another must also change to maintain the equality.

In performing various treatment plant operations, you will find that a change in one operating condition produces a proportionate change in some other condition.

For example, changing the speed of a metering pump changes the quantity metered, or changing the amount of chemical added to a certain volume of water changes the strength of the solution. Whatever the scenario, if you can set up a relation (ratio) for a particular operating condition, then when one of the two quantities of that ratio changes, you can calculate what the new value of the other quantity should be. For example, suppose you know the speed of a metering pump and the corresponding quantity of water metered. If the speed is changed to a different (but known) value, then you may wish to determine the new quantity of water metered.

To set up a proportion, first analyze the problem to decide what is unknown. Then decide whether you would expect the unknown value to be larger or smaller than the known value of the same unit. For example, if the unknown in a particular problem is pounds, would you expect the unknown amount of pounds to be larger or smaller than the number of pounds given in the problem? Now write all values (including the unknown x) in fraction form, grouping values having the same units (pounds with pounds, time with time, liters with liters, and so on) and putting the smaller value in the numerator (top) of each fraction and the larger value in the denominator (bottom).

Use this arrangement:

$$\underbrace{\text{first kind of units}}_{\text{(for example, lb)}} \qquad \underbrace{\text{second kind of units}}_{\text{(for example, \$)}}$$

$$\frac{\text{smaller value}}{\text{larger value}} = \frac{\text{smaller value}}{\text{larger value}}$$

And follow these rules:

Rule 6

If the unknown is expected to be smaller than the known value, put an x in the numerator of the first fraction, and put the known value of the same unit in the denominator.

Rule 7

If the unknown is expected to be larger than the known value, put an x in the denominator of the first fraction, and put the known value of the same unit in the numerator.

Rule 8

Form the two remaining values of the problem into the second fraction (the smaller value in the numerator, the larger in the denominator).

The next example demonstrates this method of setting up proportions to solve typical problems.

Example 8

If 3 people can complete a job in 11 days, how many days will it take 5 people to complete it?

First, decide what is unknown. In this problem, a number of days is the unknown. If it takes 3 people 11 days to complete a job, then 5 people should complete the job in less time, or fewer than 11 days. Therefore, the unknown x should be smaller than the known (11 days). Now set up the proportion. Applying rule 6, set up a fraction with x as the numerator and 11 days as the denominator. Then set up the other side of the proportion according to rule 8, with 3 people as the numerator and 5 people as the denominator:

$$\frac{x \text{ days}}{11 \text{ days}} = \frac{3 \text{ people}}{5 \text{ people}}$$

Now solve for the unknown value:

$$x = \frac{(3)(11)}{5}$$

$$x = 6.6 \text{ days}$$

Averages

To assess the performance of a water treatment plant, much data must be collected and evaluated. Because there may be considerable variation in the information, it is often difficult to determine *trends* in performance.

The calculation of an **average** is a method to group the information so that trends in the information may be determined. When evaluating information based on averages, you must keep in mind that the "average" reflects the *general* nature of the group and does not necessarily reflect any one element of that group.

The **arithmetic mean** is the most commonly used measurement of average value. It is calculated as follows:

$$\text{average} = \frac{\text{total of all terms}}{\text{number of terms}}$$

Example 9

The following raw-water turbidities (measured in nephelometric turbidity units, or ntu) were recorded for a week: Monday, 8.2 ntu; Tuesday, 7.9 ntu; Wednesday, 6.3 ntu; Thursday, 6.5 ntu; Friday, 7.4 ntu; Saturday, 6.2 ntu; Sunday, 5.9 ntu. What was the average daily turbidity?

Monday	8.2
Tuesday	7.9
Wednesday	6.3
Thursday	6.5
Friday	7.4
Saturday	6.2
Sunday	5.9
Total	48.4 ntu

average

A method to group the information so that trends in the information may be determined.

arithmetic mean

A measurement of average value, calculated by summing all terms and dividing by the number of terms.

$$\text{average} = \frac{\text{total of all terms}}{\text{number of terms}}$$

$$= \frac{48.4 \text{ ntu}}{7}$$

$$= 6.91 \text{ ntu}$$

Percentages

The word **percent** (symbolized %) comes from the Latin words *per centum*, meaning "per one hundred." For example, if 62 percent of the voters are in favor of passing a bond issue, then 62 voters out of every 100 voters are in favor of the issue. Or if a student scores 87 percent on a test with 100 questions, that student has answered 87 of the 100 questions correctly.

There is a direct relationship between percentages, fractions, and decimal numbers. They are merely different ways of expressing the same mathematical proportions, as shown in the following examples:

$$20\% = \frac{20}{100} = 0.20$$

$$95\% = \frac{95}{100} = 0.95$$

$$5\% = \frac{5}{100} = 0.05$$

$$14.5\% = \frac{14.5}{100} = 0.145$$

$$24\% = \frac{24}{100} = 0.24$$

$$0.5\% = \frac{0.5}{100} = 0.005$$

Many problems involving percentages require converting from a fraction to a decimal number to a percentage. For example,

$$\frac{20}{100} = 0.20 = 20\%$$

$$\frac{85}{100} = 0.85 = 85\%$$

$$\frac{18}{60} = 0.30 = 30\%$$

$$\frac{4}{32} = 0.125 = 12.5\%$$

percent
The fraction of the whole expressed as parts per one hundred.

Note that to change from a decimal number to a percentage, the decimal point is moved two places to the right. (The result is the same as multiplying by 100.) To convert a percentage to a decimal, the decimal point is moved two places to the left (the same as dividing by 100).

A fraction is the key to calculating percentages. The fraction is divided out, resulting in a decimal number that is then multiplied by 100 to be expressed as a percentage. The formula for all percentage problems is

$$\text{percent} = \frac{\text{part}}{\text{whole}} \times 100$$

Remember that the *whole* is always the entire quantity; 100 percent of anything is the whole thing. For percentages less than 100, the *part* is less than the whole. For example, 50¢ is less than $1.00; in fact, it is 1/2 (or 50 percent) of the dollar. And $25.00 is less than $100.00; it is 1/4, or 25 percent, of the whole amount.

The following example illustrates how to use the percentage formula in solving a water treatment plant problem.

Example 10

A piece of equipment is having mechanical difficulties. If the equipment fails 6 times out of 25 tests, what is its failure percentage?

The equation to be used in solving percentage problems is

$$\text{percent} = \frac{\text{part}}{\text{whole}} \times 100$$

In this problem, *percent* is unknown, but information is given regarding the *part* and the *whole*. Fill this information into the equation:

$$\text{percent failure} = \frac{9 \text{ failed tests}}{36 \text{ tests}} \times 100$$

$$= 0.25 \times 100$$

$$= 25\% \text{ failure}$$

Linear Measurements

Linear measurements define the distance (or length) along a line. They can be expressed in customary or metric units. The customary units of linear measurement are inches, feet, yards, and miles; the metric units are centimeters, meters, and kilometers.

The focus of this section is on one particular linear measurement: the distance around the outer edge of a shape, called the *perimeter*. To determine the distance around the outer edge of an *angular shape*, such as a square, rectangle, or any other shape with sides that are straight lines, merely add the length of each side, as shown in the following examples:

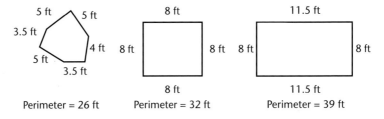

The mathematical equation for perimeter is

$$\text{perimeter} = \text{side}_1\text{length} + \text{side}_2\text{length} + \text{side}_3\text{length}\ldots\text{etc.}$$

Use this type of calculation if, for example, you must determine the length of wire needed for a fence.

Because the outside of a circle is not made up of straight lines, perimeter calculations for a circle are approached differently. The following diagram illustrates two of the linear terms associated with the circle:

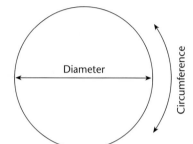

circumference = distance *around* the circle

diameter = distance through the center *across* the circle

As shown, the distance measured around the outside edge of a circle is called the circumference; this is just a special name for the perimeter of a circle. The diameter is a straight line drawn from one side of the circle *through the center* to the other side.

If you compare the diameter of any circle with the circumference of that same circle, you will find that the circumference is just a little more than three times the length of the diameter. In mathematics, this length comparison (or ratio) of circumference to diameter is represented by the Greek letter pi (π) and has a value of approximately 3.14:

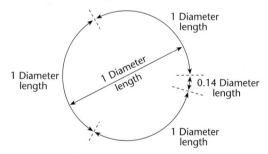

Because this relationship between the diameter length and circumference length is true for all circles, you can quickly estimate the circumference of any circle if you know the circle's diameter. For example, if you know the diameter of a circle is 30 ft, the distance around the circle (circumference) is roughly 3 × 30 ft, or about 90 ft. To be more precise, you would use the mathematical equation for circumference:

$$\text{circumference} = (3.14)(\text{diameter})$$

Thus:

$$(3.14)(30 \text{ ft}) = 94.2 \text{ ft}$$

Use this type of calculation if, for example, you must determine the circumference of a circular tank.

Area Measurements

Area measurements define the size of the *surface* of an object. The customary units most frequently used to express this surface space are square inches, square feet, and square yards; the metric units are square millimeters, square centimeters, and square meters.

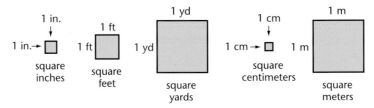

The fact that area measurements are expressed in square units does *not* mean that the surface must be a square to be measured. The surface of any shape can be measured. Although the shapes differ in the following illustration, the total surface area of each is the same:

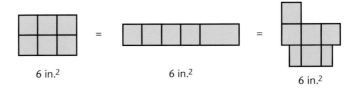

For area measurements in water treatment plant calculations, three shapes are particularly important—rectangles, triangles, and circles. Most problems involve one or two combinations of these shapes. Equations (formulas) for each of the three basic shapes are presented below. Because these formulas are used so often in treatment plant calculations, you should memorize them.

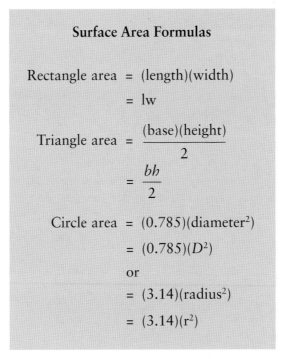

Use of these formulas is demonstrated in the examples that follow.

Area of a Rectangle

area of a rectangle = (length)(width)

= lw

Example 11

What is the area of the rectangle shown below?

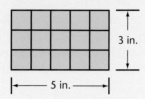

area of rectangle = (length)(width)

= (5 in.)(3 in.)

= 15 in.^{2} surface area

Area of a Triangle

area of a triangle = $\dfrac{(\text{base})(\text{height})}{2}$

As shown in the following example, the *height* of the triangle must be measured *vertically* from the horizontal base.

Example 12

What is the area of the triangle in the diagram below?

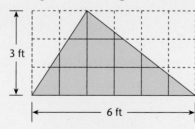

area = $\dfrac{(\text{base})(\text{height})}{2}$

= $\dfrac{(6 \text{ ft})(3 \text{ ft})}{2}$

= 9 ft^2 surface area

Area of a Circle

$$\text{area of circle} = (0.785)(\text{diameter}^2)$$

or

$$= (3.14)(\text{radius}^2)$$

The more familiar formula for the area of a circle is πr^2. The r stands for the *radius* of the circle; that is, the distance from the circle's center to its edge. The radius of any circle is exactly *half* of the diameter.

However, since the diameter rather than the radius is generally given for circular tanks and basins, the formula using diameter is preferred for water treatment plant calculations. The relationship between the two formulas is shown in the following equations:

$$\text{area} = \pi r^2$$

Because the radius is half the diameter, r^2 in the formula may be expressed as $(D/2)^2$, where D is the diameter:

$$\text{area} = (\pi)\left(\frac{D}{2}\right)^2$$

$$= (\pi)\left(\frac{D}{2}\right)\left(\frac{D}{2}\right)$$

or

$$= \frac{\pi D^2}{4}$$

And, because $\pi = 3.14$,

$$\text{area} = \left(\frac{3.14}{4}\right)(D^2)$$

The formula may be reexpressed as

$$\text{area} = (0.785)(D^2)$$

Another advantage of the formula using diameter is that it can be better understood by diagram than the formula using radius. The diameter formula describes a surface area that can be thought of as *a square with the corners cut off*.

Let's examine the relationship between a square and a circle to better understand the formula for circle area:

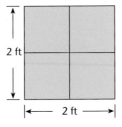

$$\text{area of square} = (\text{length})(\text{width})$$
$$= (2 \text{ ft})(2 \text{ ft})$$
$$= 4 \text{ ft}^2 \text{ surface area}$$

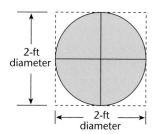

$$\text{area of circle} = (0.785)(D)^2$$
$$= (0.785)(2 \text{ ft})(2 \text{ ft})$$

or

$$= (0.785)(\text{area of square})$$
$$= (0.785)(4 \text{ ft}^2)$$
$$= 3.14 \text{ ft}^2 \text{ surface area}$$

When a circle with a 2-ft diameter is drawn inside the 2-ft square, you can see that the surface area of the circle is less than that of the square. However, it is not necessary to construct a square around each circle that is being measured. Mathematically, the $D2$ (diameter squared) of the formula represents the square. Therefore, in finding the area of the circle, 0.785 is essential to the formula, because it is this factor that "cuts off the corners" of the square.

Example 13

Calculate the area of the circle shown below.

$$\text{area of circle} = (0.785)(D)^2$$
$$= (0.785)(5 \text{ ft})(5 \text{ ft})$$
$$= 19.63 \text{ ft}^2 \text{ surface area}$$

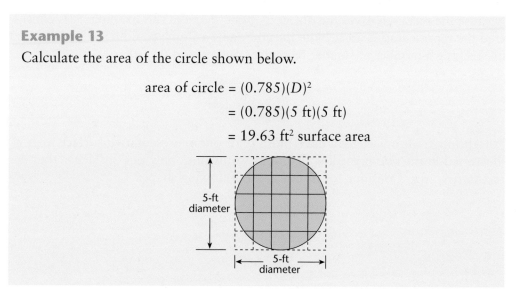

Volume Measurements

A volume measurement defines the amount of space that an object occupies. The basis of this measurement is the *cube*, a square-sided box with all edges of equal length, as shown in the diagram below. The customary units commonly used in volume measurements are cubic inches, cubic feet, cubic yards, gallons, and acre-feet. The metric units commonly used to express volume are cubic centimeters, cubic meters, and liters.

The calculations of surface area and volume are closely related. For example, to calculate the surface area of one of the below cubes, you would multiply two of the dimensions (length and width) together. To calculate the volume of that cube, however, a *third dimension* (depth) is used in the multiplication.

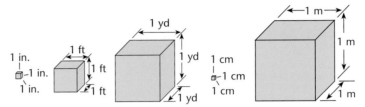

The concept of volume can be simplified as follows:

volume = (area of surface)(third dimension)

The *area of surface* to be used in the volume calculation is the *representative surface* area, the side that gives the object its basic shape. For example, suppose you begin with a rectangular area. Notice the shape that would be created by stacking a number of those same rectangles one on top of the other:

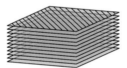

Because the rectangle gives the object its basic shape in this example, it is considered the representative area. Note that the same volume could have been created by stacking a number of smaller rectangles one behind the other:

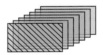

Although an object may have more than one representative surface area as illustrated in the two preceding diagrams, sometimes only one surface is the representative area. Consider, for instance, the following shape:

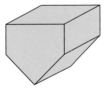

Let's compare two different sides of this shape—the top and the front—to determine if they are representative areas. In the first case, a number of the top shapes (rectangles) stacked together does not result in the same shape volume. Therefore, this rectangular area is not a representative area. In the second case, however, a number of front shapes (pentagons) stacked one behind the other results in the same shape volume as the original object. Therefore, the pentagonal area may be considered a representative surface area.

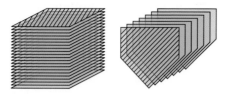

Rectangles, Triangles, and Circles

For treatment plant calculations, representative surface areas are most often rectangles, triangles, circles, or a combination of these. The following diagrams illustrate the three basic shapes for which volume calculations are made.

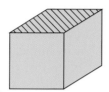

In the first diagram, the rectangle defines the shape of the object; in the second diagram, the triangle, rather than the rectangle, gives the trough its basic shape; in the third, the surface that defines the shape of the cylinder is the circle.

The formulas for calculating the volume of each of these three shapes are given below. Note that they are closely associated with the area formulas given previously.

Volume Formulas

Rectangle tank volume $= \left(\begin{array}{c}\text{area of}\\\text{rectangle}\end{array}\right)\left(\begin{array}{c}\text{third}\\\text{dimension}\end{array}\right)$

$= lw \left(\begin{array}{c}\text{third}\\\text{dimension}\end{array}\right)$

Trough volume $= \left(\begin{array}{c}\text{area of}\\\text{rectangle}\end{array}\right)\left(\begin{array}{c}\text{third}\\\text{dimension}\end{array}\right)$

$= \left(\dfrac{bh}{2}\right)\left(\begin{array}{c}\text{third}\\\text{dimension}\end{array}\right)$

Cylinder volume $= \left(\begin{array}{c}\text{area of}\\\text{rectangle}\end{array}\right)\left(\begin{array}{c}\text{third}\\\text{dimension}\end{array}\right)$

$= (0.785\ D^2)\left(\begin{array}{c}\text{third}\\\text{dimension}\end{array}\right)$

Cone volume $= 1/3(\text{volume of a cylinder})$

Sphere volume $= \left(\dfrac{\pi}{6}\right)(\text{diameter})^3$

Conversions

In making the conversion from one unit to another, you must know the following:

- The number that relates the two units
- Whether to multiply or divide by that number

For example, in converting from feet to inches, you must know that in 1 ft there are 12 in., and you must know whether to multiply or divide the number of feet by 12.

Although the number that relates the two units of a conversion is usually known or can be looked up, there is often confusion about whether to multiply or divide. *Dimensional analysis*, discussed previously, is one method to help decide whether to multiply or divide for a particular conversion.

Conversion Tables

Usually the fastest method of converting units is to use a conversion table, and to follow the instructions indicated by the table headings. For example, if you want to convert from feet to inches, look in the *Conversion* column of the table for *From* "feet" *To* "inches." Read across this line and perform the operation indicated by the headings of the other columns; that is, multiply the number of feet by 12 to get the number of inches.

Suppose, however, that you want to convert inches to feet. Look in the *Conversion* column for *From* "inches" *To* "feet," and read across this line. The headings tell you to multiply the number of inches by 0.08333 (which is the decimal equivalent of 1/12) to get the number of feet. Multiplying by either 1/12 or 0.08333 is the same as dividing by 12.

The instruction to *multiply* by certain numbers (called conversion factors) is used throughout the conversion table. There is no column headed *Divide by* because the fractions representing division (such as 1/12) were converted to decimal numbers (such as 0.08333) when the table was prepared.

To use the conversion table, remember the following three steps:

1. In the *Conversion* column, find the units you want to change *From* and *To*. (Go *From* what you have *To* what you want.)
2. Multiply the *From* number you have by the conversion factor given.
3. Read the answer in *To* units.

Example 14

Convert 288 in. to feet.

In the *Conversion* column of the table, find *From* "inches" *To* "feet." Reading across the line, perform the multiplication indicated; that is, multiply the number of inches (288) by 0.08333 to get the number of feet:

$$(288 \text{ in.})(0.08333) = 24 \text{ ft}$$

Example 15

A tank holds 50 gal of water. How many cubic feet of water is this, and what does it weigh?

First, convert gallons to cubic feet. Using the table, you find that to convert *From* "gallons" *To* "cubic feet," you must multiply by 0.1337:

$$(50 \text{ gal})(0.1337) = 6.69 \text{ ft}^3$$

Note that this number of cubic feet is actually a rounded value (6.685 is the actual calculated number). Rounding helps simplify calculations.

Next, convert gallons to pounds of water. Using the table, you find that to convert *From* "gallons" *To* "pounds of water," you must multiply by 8.34:

$$(50 \text{ gal})(8.34) = 417 \text{ lb of water}$$

Notice that you could have arrived at approximately the same weight by converting 6.69 ft³ to pounds of water. Using the table, we get

$$(6.69 \text{ ft}^3)(62.4) = 417.46 \text{ lb of water}$$

This slight difference in the two answers is due to rounding numbers both when the conversion table was prepared and when the numbers are used in solving the problem. You may notice the same sort of slight difference in answers if you have to convert from one kind of unit to two or three other units, depending on whether you round intermediate steps in the conversions.

Box Method

Another method that may be used to determine whether multiplication or division is required for a particular conversion is called the *box method*. This method is based on the relative sizes of different squares ("boxes"). The box method can be used when a conversion table is not available (such as during a certification exam). This method of conversion is often slower than using a conversion table, but many people find it simpler.

Because multiplication is usually associated with an *increase* in size, moving from a smaller box to a larger box corresponds to using multiplication in the conversion:

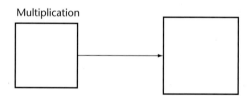

Division, on the other hand, is usually associated with a *decrease* in size. Therefore, moving from a larger box to a smaller box corresponds to using division in the conversion:

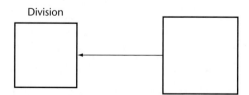

To use the box method to determine whether to multiply or divide in making a conversion, set up and label the boxes according to the following procedure:

1. Write the equation that relates the two types of units involved in the conversion. One of the two numbers in the equation must be a 1 (for example, 1 ft = 12 in., or 1 ft = 0.305 m).
2. Draw a small box on the left and a large one on the right, then connect them with a line.

3. In the smaller box, write the name of the units associated with the 1 (for example, 1 ft = 12 in.—*ft* should be written in the smaller box). Note that the name of the units next to the 1 must be written in the *smaller* box; otherwise the box method will give incorrect results.

4. In the larger box, write the name of the remaining units. Those units will also have a number next to them, a number that is not 1. Write that number over the line between the boxes.

Suppose, for example, that you want to make a box diagram for feet-to-inches conversions. First, write the equation that relates feet to inches:

$$1 \text{ ft} = 12 \text{ in.}$$

Next, draw the conversion boxes (smaller box on the left) and the connecting line:

Now label the diagram. Because the number 1 is next to the units of feet (1 ft), write *ft* in the smaller box. Write the name of the other units, inches (*in.*), in the larger box. And write the number that is next to inches, 12, over the line between the boxes.

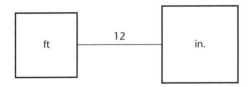

To convert from feet to inches, then *multiply* by 12 because you are moving from a smaller box to a larger box. And to convert from inches to feet, *divide* by 12 because you are moving from a larger box to a smaller box.

Let's look at another example of making and using the box diagram. Suppose you want to convert cubic feet to gallons. First write down the equation that relates these two units:

$$1 \text{ ft}^3 = 7.48 \text{ gal}$$

Then draw the smaller and larger boxes and the connecting line; label the boxes, and write in the conversion number:

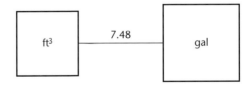

The smaller box corresponds to cubic feet and the larger box to gallons. To convert from cubic feet to gallons according to this box diagram, *multiply* by 7.48 because you are moving from a smaller to a larger box. And to convert from gallons to cubic feet, *divide* by 7.48 because you are moving from a larger to a smaller box.

Conversions of US Customary Units

This section discusses important conversions between terms expressed in US customary units (based on the box method).

Conversions From Cubic Feet to Gallons to Pounds

In making the conversion from cubic feet to gallons to pounds of water, you must know the following relationships:

$$1 \text{ ft}^3 = 7.48 \text{ gal}$$
$$1 \text{ gal} = 8.34 \text{ lb}$$

You must also know whether to multiply or divide, and which of the above numbers are used in the conversion. The following box diagram should assist in making these decisions:

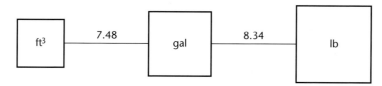

Example 16

Convert 1 ft³ to pounds.
   First write down the diagram to aid in the conversion:

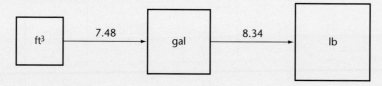

When you are converting from cubic feet to pounds, you are moving from smaller to larger boxes. Therefore, *multiplication* is indicated in both conversions:

$$(1 \text{ ft}^3)(7.48 \text{ gal/ft}^3)(8.34 \text{ lb/gal}) = 62.38 \text{ lb}$$

This total can be rounded to 62.4 lb, the number commonly used for water treatment calculations.

Example 17

A tank has a capacity of 60,000 ft³. What is the capacity of the tank in gallons?

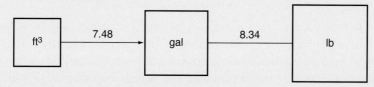

When converting from cubic feet to gallons, you are moving from a smaller to a larger box. Therefore, *multiplication* by 7.48 is indicated:

$$(60,000 \text{ ft}^3)(7.48 \text{ gal/ft}^3) = 448,800 \text{ gal}$$

Example 18

A tank will hold 1,500,000 lb of water. How many cubic feet of water will it hold?

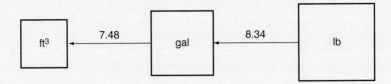

A move from larger to smaller boxes indicates *division* in both conversions:

$$\frac{1,500,000 \text{ lb}}{(8.34 \text{ lb/gal})(7.48 \text{ gal/ft}^3)} = 24,045 \text{ ft}^3$$

Flow Conversions

The relationships among the various US customary flow units are shown by the following diagram. Note the abbreviations commonly used in discussing flow:

- gps = gallons per second
- gpm = gallons per minute
- gpd = gallons per day

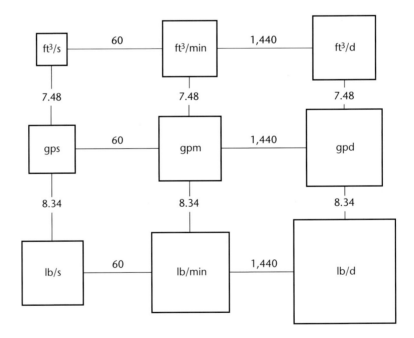

Because flows of cubic feet per hour, gallons per hour, and pounds per hour are less frequently used, they have not been included in the diagram. However, some chemical feed rate calculations require converting from or to these units.

The lines that connect the boxes and the numbers associated with them can be thought of as *bridges* that relate two units directly and all other units in the diagram indirectly. The relative sizes of the boxes are an aid in deciding whether multiplication or division is appropriate for the desired conversion.

The relationship among the boxes should be understood, not merely memorized. The principle is basically the same as that described in the preceding section. For example, notice how every box in a single vertical column has the same *time* units; a conversion in this direction corresponds to a change in volume units. Every box in a single horizontal row has the same *volume* units; a conversion in this direction corresponds to a change in time units.

Although you need not draw the nine boxes each time you make a flow conversion, it is useful to have a mental image of these boxes to make the calculations. For the examples that follow, however, the boxes are used in analyzing the conversions.

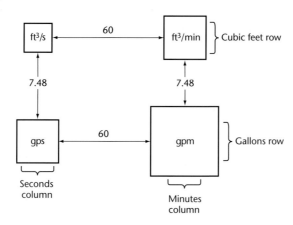

Example 19

The flow rate in a water line is 2.3 ft³/s. What is this rate expressed as gallons per minute? (Assume the flow is steady and continuous.)

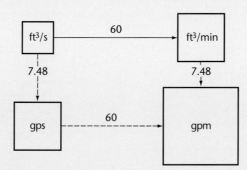

There are two possible paths from cubic feet per second to gallons per minute. Either will give the correct answer. Notice that each path has factors of 60 and 7.48, with only a difference in order. In each case, you are moving from a smaller to a larger box, and thus *multiplication* by both 60 and 7.48 is indicated:

$$(2.3 \text{ ft}^3/\text{s})(60 \text{ s/min})(7.48 \text{ gal/ft}^3) = 1,032 \text{ gpm}$$

Notice that you can write both multiplication factors into the same equation; you do not need to write one equation for converting cubic feet per second to cubic feet per minute and another for converting cubic feet per minute to gallons per minute.

Example 20

The flow rate to a sedimentation basin is 2,450,000 gpd. At this rate, what is the average flow in cubic feet per second?

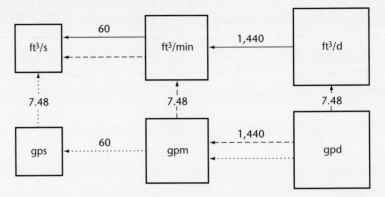

There are three possible paths from gallons per day to cubic feet per second. In each case, you would be moving from a larger to a smaller box, thus indicating *division* by 7.48, 1,440, and 60 (in any order):

$$\frac{2{,}450{,}000 \text{ gpd}}{(7.48 \text{ gal/ft}^3)(1{,}440 \text{ min/d})(60 \text{ s/min})} = 3.79 \text{ ft}^3/\text{s}$$

Again, the divisions are all written into one equation.

Example 21

The flow rate in a water line is 200,000 gpd. What is this rate expressed as pounds per minute?

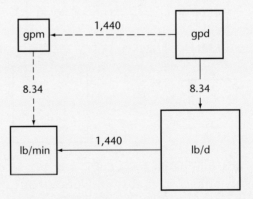

There are two possible paths from gallons per day to pounds per minute. The only difference in these paths is the order in which the numbers appear. The answer is the same in either case. In the following explanation, the solid-line path of the diagram is used.

Converting from gallons per day to pounds per day, you are moving from a smaller box to a larger box. Therefore, *multiplication* by 8.34 is indicated. Then from pounds per day to pounds per minute, you are moving from a larger to a smaller box, which indicates *division* by 1,440. These multiplication and division steps are combined into one equation:

$$\frac{(200{,}000 \text{ gpd})(8.34 \text{ lb/gal})}{1{,}440 \text{ min/d}} = 1{,}158 \text{ lb/min}$$

Linear Measurement Conversions

Linear measurement defines the distance along a line; it is the measurement between two points. The US customary units of linear measurement include the inch, foot, yard, and mile. In most treatment plant calculations, however, the mile is not used. Therefore, this section discusses conversions of inches, feet, and yards only. The box diagram associated with these conversions is

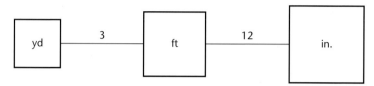

Example 22

The maximum depth of sludge drying beds is 14 in. How many feet is this?

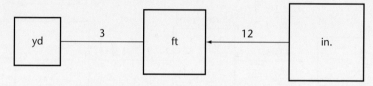

In converting from inches to feet, you are moving from a larger to a smaller box. Therefore, *division* by 12 is indicated:

$$\frac{14 \text{ in.}}{12 \text{ in./ft}} = 1.17 \text{ ft}$$

Example 23

During backwashing, the water level drops 0.6 yd during a given time interval. How many feet has it dropped?

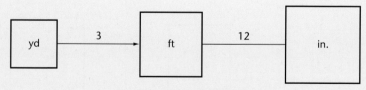

Moving from a smaller to a larger box indicates *multiplication* by 3:

$$(0.6 \text{ yd})(3 \text{ ft/yd}) = 1.8 \text{ ft}$$

Area Measurement Conversions

To make area conversions in US customary units, you work with units such as square yards, square feet, or square inches. These units are derived from the following multiplications:

$$(\text{yards})(\text{yards}) = \text{square yards, or yd}^2$$

$$(\text{feet})(\text{feet}) = \text{square feet, or ft}^2$$

$$(\text{inches})(\text{inches}) = \text{square inches, or in.}^2$$

By examining the relationship of yards, feet, and inches in linear terms, you can recognize the relationship between yards, feet, and inches in square terms. For example,

$$
\begin{aligned}
1 \text{ yd} &= 3 \text{ ft} \\
(1 \text{ yd})(1 \text{ yd}) &= (3 \text{ ft})(3 \text{ ft}) \\
1 \text{ yd}^2 &= 9 \text{ ft}^2
\end{aligned}
$$

This method of comparison may be used whenever you wish to compare linear terms with square terms.

Compare the diagram used for linear conversions with that used for square measurement conversions:

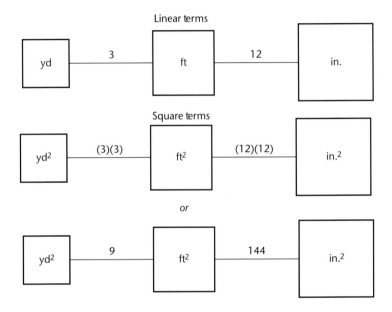

Example 24

The surface area of a sedimentation basin is 170 yd². How many square feet is this?

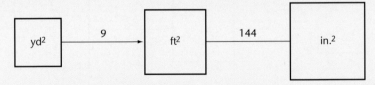

When converting from square yards to square feet, you are moving from a smaller to a larger box. Therefore, *multiplication* by 9 is indicated:

$$(170 \text{ yd}^2)(9 \text{ ft}^2/\text{yd}^2) = 1{,}530 \text{ ft}^2$$

Example 25

The cross-sectional area of a pipe is 64 in². How many square feet is this?

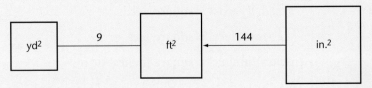

Converting from square inches to square feet, you are moving from a larger to a smaller box. *Division* by 144 is indicated:

$$\frac{64 \text{ in.}^2}{144 \text{ in.}^2/\text{ft}^2} = 0.44 \text{ ft}^2$$

One other area conversion important in treatment plant calculations is that between square feet and acres. This relationship is expressed mathematically as

$$1 \text{ acre} = 43,560 \text{ ft}^2$$

A box diagram can be devised for this relationship. However, the diagram should be separate from the diagram relating square yards, square feet, and square inches because you usually wish to relate directly with square feet. As in the other diagrams, the relative sizes of the boxes are important.

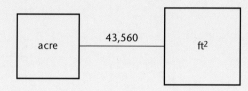

Example 26

A treatment plant requires 0.2 acre for drying beds. How many square feet are required?

Converting acres to square feet, you are moving from a smaller to a larger box. *Multiplication* by 43,560 is therefore indicated:

$$(0.2 \text{ acre})(43,560 \text{ ft}^2/\text{acre}) = 8,712 \text{ ft}^2$$

Volume Measurement Conversions

To make volume conversions in US customary unit terms, you work with such units as cubic yards, cubic feet, and cubic inches. These units are derived from the following multiplications:

$$(\text{yards})(\text{yards})(\text{yards}) = \text{cubic yards, or yd}^3$$

$$(\text{feet})(\text{feet})(\text{feet}) = \text{cubic feet, or ft}^3$$

$$(\text{inches})(\text{inches})(\text{inches}) = \text{cubic inches, or in.}^3$$

By examining the relationship of yards, feet, and inches in linear terms, you can recognize the relationship between yards, feet, and inches in cubic terms. For example,

$$1 \text{ yd} = 3 \text{ ft}$$

$$(1 \text{ yd})(1 \text{ yd})(1 \text{ yd}) = (3 \text{ ft})(3 \text{ ft})(3 \text{ ft})$$

$$1 \text{ yd}^3 = 27 \text{ ft}^3$$

The box diagram associated with these cubic conversions is

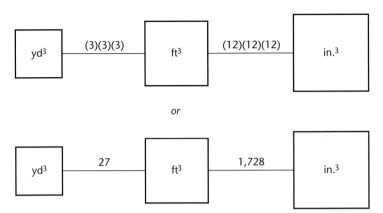

or

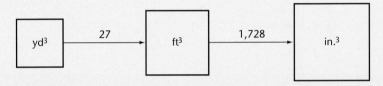

Example 27

Convert 15 yd³ to cubic inches.

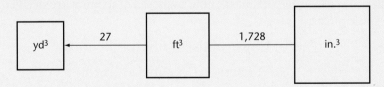

In converting from cubic yards to cubic feet and from cubic feet to cubic inches, you are moving from smaller to larger boxes. Thus, *multiplication* by 27 and 1,728 is indicated:

$$(15 \text{ yd}^3)(27 \text{ ft}^3/\text{yd}^3)(1{,}728 \text{ in.}^3/\text{ft}^3) = 699{,}840 \text{ in.}^3$$

Example 28

The required volume for a chemical is 325 ft³. What is this volume expressed as cubic yards?

When you move from a larger to a smaller box, *division* is indicated:

$$\frac{325 \text{ ft}^3}{27 \text{ ft}^3/\text{yd}^3} = 12.04 \text{ yd}^3$$

Another volume measurement important in treatment plant calculations is that of acre-feet. A reservoir with a surface area of 1 acre and a depth of 1 ft holds exactly 1 acre-ft:

$$1 \text{ acre-ft} = 43{,}560 \text{ ft}^3$$

The relative sizes of the boxes are again important:

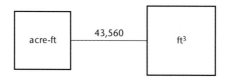

Example 29

The available capacity of a reservoir is 220,000 ft³. What is this volume expressed in acre-feet?

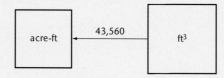

When you move from the larger to the smaller box, *division* by 43,560 is indicated:

$$\frac{220{,}000 \text{ ft}^3}{43{,}560 \text{ ft}^3/\text{acre-ft}} = 5.05 \text{ acre-ft}$$

Concentration Conversions

A milligrams-per-liter (mg/L) concentration can also be expressed in terms of grains per gallon (gpg) or parts per million (ppm). However, of the three, the preferred unit of concentration is milligrams per liter.

Milligrams per Liter to Grains per Gallon

Conversions between milligrams per liter and grains per gallon are based on the relationship

$$1 \text{ gpg} = 17.12 \text{ mg/L}$$

As with any other conversion, often the greatest difficulty in converting from one term to another is deciding whether to multiply or divide by the number given. The following box diagram should help in making this decision:

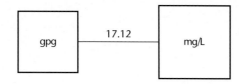

Example 30

Convert 25 mg/L to grains per gallon.

In this example, you are converting from milligrams per liter to grains per gallon. Therefore, as shown below, you are moving from the larger to the smaller box:

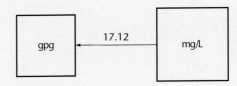

Larger to smaller indicates *division* by 17.12:

$$\frac{25 \text{ mg/L}}{17.12 \text{ mg/L/gpg}} = 1.46 \text{ gpg}$$

Example 31

Express a 20-gpg concentration in terms of milligrams per liter.

In this example, you are converting from grains per gallon to milligrams per liter. Therefore, you are moving from the smaller to the larger box:

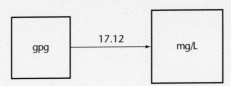

Smaller to larger indicates multiplication by 17.12:

$$(20 \text{ gpg})(17.12 \text{ mg/L/gpg}) = 342.4 \text{ mg/L}$$

Example 32

If the dosage rate of alum is 1.5 gpg, what is the dosage rate expressed in milligrams per liter?

The desired conversion is from grains per gallon to milligrams per liter:

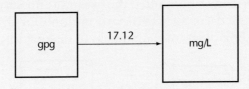

Smaller to larger indicates *multiplication* by 17.12:

$$(1.5 \text{ gpg})(17.12 \text{ mg/L/gpg}) = 25.68 \text{ mg/L}$$

Milligrams per Liter to Parts per Million

The concentration of impurities in water is usually so small that it is measured in milligrams per liter. This means the impurities in a standard volume (a liter) of water are measured by weight (milligrams). Concentrations in the range of 0–2,000 mg/L are roughly equivalent to concentrations expressed as the same number of parts per million (ppm). For example, "12 mg/L of calcium in water" expresses roughly the same concentration as "12 ppm calcium in water." However, milligrams per liter are the preferred units of concentration.

Metric System Conversions

In order to convert from the system of US customary units to the metric system, or vice versa, you must understand how to convert within the metric system. This requires a knowledge of the common metric prefixes. *These prefixes should be learned before any conversions are attempted.*

As shown in Table 2-1, the metric system is based on *powers*, or multiples of 10, just like the decimal system is. These prefixes may be associated with positions in the place value system.

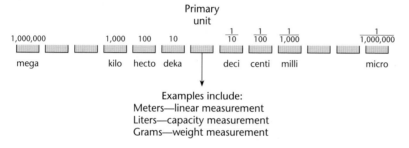

Understanding the position of these prefixes in the place value system is important because the method discussed below for metric-to-metric conversions is based on this system.

It is also important to understand the abbreviations used for metric terms. The basic measurement terms and their abbreviations are meters (m), liters (L),

Table 2-1 Metric system notations

Prefix	Abbreviation	Mathematical Value	Power Notation
giga	G	1,000,000,000	10^9
mega	M	1,000,000	10^6
kilo	k	1,000	10^3
hecto*	h	100	10^2
deka*	da	10	10^1
(none†)	(none)	1	10^0
deci*	d	1/10 or 0.1	10^{-1}
centi*	c	1/100 or 0.01	10^{-2}
milli	m	1/1,000 or 0.001	10^{-3}
micro	m	1/1,000,000 or 0.000001	10^{-6}
nano	n	1/1,000,000,000 or 0.000000001	10^{-9}

*Use of these units should be avoided when possible.

†Primary units, such as meters, liters, grams

and grams (g). The prefixes added to the basic measurement terms may also be abbreviated (as shown in Table 2-1). For example,

$$1 \text{ megaliter} = 1 \text{ ML}$$

$$1 \text{ millimeter} = 1 \text{ mm}$$

$$1 \text{ kilogram} = 1 \text{ kg}$$

Use of these abbreviations greatly simplifies expressions of measurement.

Metric-to-Metric Conversions

When conversions are being made for linear measurement (meters), volume measurement (liters), and weight measurement (grams), each change in prefix place value represents one decimal point move. This system of conversion is demonstrated by the following examples.

Example 33

Convert 1 m to decimeters (dm).

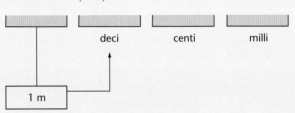

Converting from meters to decimeters requires moving the decimal point from its present position to *one place to the right*.

$$1.0 = \boxed{10 \text{ decimeters}}$$

Example 34

Convert 1 g to (a) decigrams, (b) centigrams, and (c) milligrams.

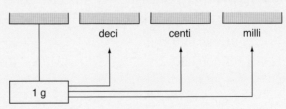

(a) Move the decimal point one place to the right.

$$1.0 = \boxed{10 \text{ decigrams}}$$

(b) Move the decimal point two places to the right.

$$1.00 = \boxed{100 \text{ centigrams}}$$

(c) Move the decimal point three places to the right.

$$1.000 = \boxed{1,000 \text{ milligrams}}$$

In the preceding examples, the units are being converted from a primary unit (meter and gram) to a smaller unit (decimeter, decigram, etc.). Note that this system of conversion applies regardless of the initial type of unit and regardless of whether the number is increasing or decreasing, as shown in the following examples.

Example 35

Convert 1 dL to milliliters.

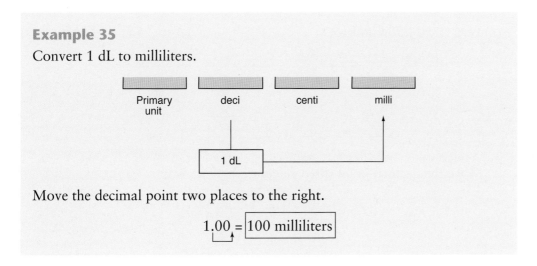

Move the decimal point two places to the right.

$$1.00 = \boxed{100 \text{ milliliters}}$$

This system of conversion applies whether the number you are converting is a whole number—such as in the preceding examples, which use the number 1—or any other number.

Example 36

Convert 3.5 kg to grams.

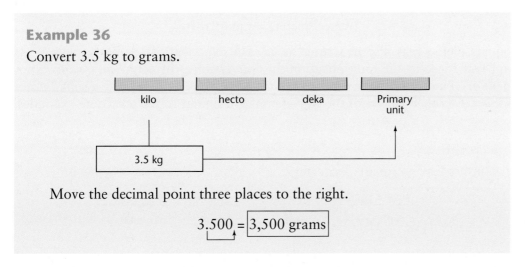

Move the decimal point three places to the right.

$$3.500 = \boxed{3,500 \text{ grams}}$$

Example 37

Convert 0.28 cm to meters.

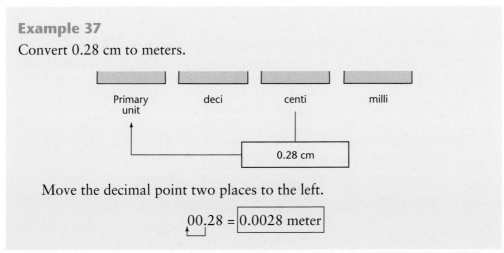

Move the decimal point two places to the left.

$$00.28 = \boxed{0.0028 \text{ meter}}$$

Most metric conversion errors are made in moving the decimal point to the left. You must be very careful in moving the decimal point from its present position, counting every number (including zeros) to the left as a decimal point move.

Example 38

Convert 1,750 L to kiloliters.

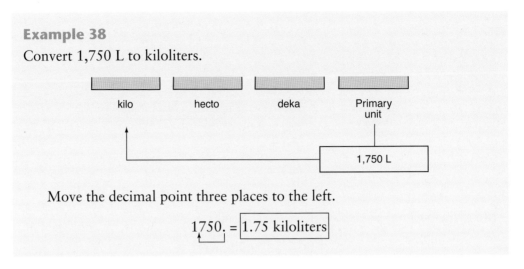

Move the decimal point three places to the left.

$$1750. = \boxed{1.75 \text{ kiloliters}}$$

In the examples just given, there were no conversions of square or cubic terms. However, area and volume measurements can be expressed as square and cubic meters, centimeters, kilometers, and so on. The following discussion shows the special techniques needed for converting between these units.

Square meters indicates the mathematical operation:

$$(\text{meter})(\text{meter}) = \text{square meters}$$

Square meters may also be written as m^2. The exponent of 2 indicates that *meter* appears twice in the multiplication. In conversions, the term *square* (or exponent of 2) indicates that *each prefix place value move requires two decimal point moves*. All other aspects of the conversions are similar to the preceding examples.

Example 39

Convert 1 m^2 to square decimeters.

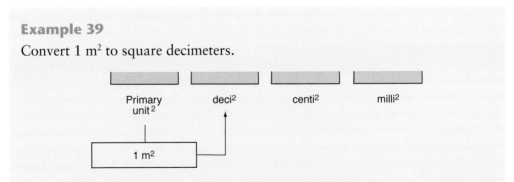

Converting from square meters to square decimeters requires moving one place value to the right. In square terms, *each prefix place move requires two decimal point moves*. Making the move in groups of two may be easier:

$$1.00 = \boxed{100 \text{ dm}^2}$$

Now check this conversion. From example 31, you know that 1 m = 10 dm. Squaring both sides of the equation, we get

$$(1 \text{ m})(1 \text{ m}) = (10 \text{ dm})(10 \text{ dm})$$

$$1 \text{ m}^2 = 100 \text{ dm}^2$$

Example 40

Convert 32,000 m² to square kilometers.

Three place value moves to the left correspond to six total decimal point moves to the left:

$$032{,}000. = 0.032 \text{ square kilometer}$$

Cubic meters indicates the following mathematical operation:

$$(\text{meters})(\text{meters})(\text{meters}) = \text{cubic meters}$$

Cubic meters may also be written as m³. The exponent of 3 indicates that *meter* appears three times in the multiplication. When you are converting cubic terms, *each prefix place value move requires three decimal point moves.* Again, it may be easier to make the decimal point moves in groups—groups of three for cubic-term conversions as opposed to groups of two for square-term conversions.

Example 41

Convert 1 m³ to cubic decimeters.

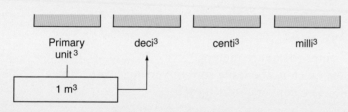

Converting from cubic meters to cubic decimeters requires moving one place value to the right. In cubic terms, *each prefix place value move requires three decimal point moves:*

$$1.000 = 1{,}000 \text{ cubic decimeters}$$

Now check this conversion. From example 33, you know that 1 m = 10 dm. Cubing both sides of the equation, we get

$$(1 \text{ m})(1 \text{ m})(1 \text{ m}) = (10 \text{ dm})(10 \text{ dm})(10 \text{ dm})$$

$$1 \text{ m}^3 = 1{,}000 \text{ dm}^3$$

Example 42

Convert 155,000 mm³ to cubic meters.

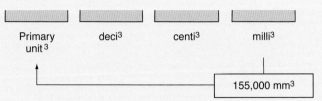

Three place value moves to the left indicate three *groups of three* decimal point moves to the left:

$$000115,000. = 0.000155 \text{ cubic meter}$$

Cross-System Conversions

For conversions from the US customary unit system to the metric system, or vice versa, the conversion table appearing in Appendix A and discussed at the beginning of this chapter is useful.

Example 43

Convert 20 gal to liters.

The factor given in the table to convert *From* "gallons" *To* "liters" is 3.785. This means there are 3.785 L in 1 gal. Therefore, the conversion is

$$(20 \text{ gal})(3.785) = 75.7 \text{ L}$$

Example 44

Convert 3.7 acres to square meters.

The factor given in the table for converting *From* "acres" *To* "square meters" is 4,047. The conversion is therefore

$$(3.7 \text{ acre})(4,047) = 14,974 \text{ m}^2$$

Example 45

Convert 0.8 m/s to ft/min.

The factor given in the table for converting *From* "meters per second" *To* "feet per minute" is 196.8. Therefore, the conversion is

$$(0.8 \text{ m/s})(196.8) = 157.44 \text{ ft/min}$$

Occasionally, when making cross-system conversions, you may not find the factor in the table for the two terms of interest. For example, suppose you wish to convert from inches to decimeters but the table gives factors only for converting from inches to centimeters or inches to millimeters. Or suppose you wish to convert cubic centimeters to gallons but the table gives factors only for converting cubic meters to gallons.

In such situations, it is usually easiest to make sure that the US customary system unit is in the desired form and then make any necessary changes to the metric unit (e.g., changing inches to centimeters, then centimeters to decimeters). As shown in the example problems for metric-to-metric conversions, changing units in the metric system requires only a decimal point move.

The following two examples illustrate how the cross-system conversion may be made when the table does not give the precise units you need.

Example 46

The water depth in a channel is 1.2 ft. How many decimeters is this?

First check the conversion table in Appendix A to see if a factor is given for converting feet to decimeters. The conversion factor is given only for feet to kilometers, meters, centimeters, or millimeters.

To make the conversion from feet to decimeters then, first convert from feet to the closest metric unit to decimeters given in the table (centimeters); then convert that answer to decimeters. The conversion from feet to centimeters is

$$(1.2 \text{ ft})(30.48) = 36.58 \text{ cm}$$

Then converting from centimeters to decimeters, we get

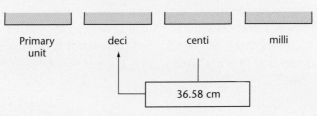

Move the decimal point one place to the left:

$$36.58 \text{ cm} = 3.658 \text{ dm}$$

Example 47

If you use 0.12 kg of a chemical to make up a particular solution, how many ounces of that chemical are used?

First, check the conversion table in Appendix A to determine if a factor is given for converting kilograms to ounces. No such conversion factor is given.

Try to find a conversion in the table from some other metric unit (such as milligrams or grams) to ounces. The conversion from grams to ounces is given in the table. Therefore, first convert the 0.12 kg to grams, then convert grams to ounces:

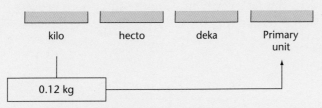

Move the decimal point three places to the right:

$$0.12 \text{ kg} = 120 \text{ g}$$

Then

$$(120 \text{ g})(0.03527) = 4.23 \text{ oz}$$

Temperature Conversions

The formulas used for Fahrenheit and Celsius temperature conversions are

$$°C = 5/9(°F - 32)$$

$$°F = (9/5)°C + 32$$

These formulas are difficult to remember unless used frequently. There is, however, another method of conversion that is perhaps easier to remember because the following three steps are used for both Fahrenheit and Celsius conversions:

1. Add 40°.
2. Multiply by the appropriate fraction (5/9 or 9/5).
3. Subtract 40°.

The only variable in this method is the choice of 5/9 or 9/5 in the multiplication step. To make this choice, you must understand the relative values of the two scales. As shown in Figure 2-1, on the Fahrenheit scale the freezing point of water is 32°, whereas it is 0° on the Celsius scale. The boiling point of water is 212° on the Fahrenheit scale and 100° on the Celsius scale.

Thus for the same temperature, higher numbers are associated with the Fahrenheit scale and lower numbers with the Celsius scale. This information helps you decide whether to multiply by 5/9 or 9/5. Let's look at a few conversion problems to see how the three-step process works.

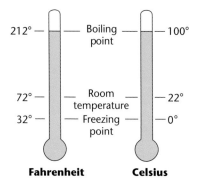

Figure 2-1 Fahrenheit and Celsius temperature scales

Example 48

Convert 212°F to Celsius.

From the sketch of the two scales in Figure 2-1, you know that the answer should be 100°C. But let's verify it using the three-step process.

The first step is to add 40°:

$$\begin{array}{r} 212° \\ + 40° \\ \hline 252° \end{array}$$

Next, 252° must be multiplied by either 5/9 or 9/5. Since the conversion is to the Celsius scale, you will be moving to a number *smaller* than 252. Multiplying by 9/5 is roughly the same as multiplying by 2, which would double 252 rather than make it smaller. In comparison, multiplying by 5/9 is about the same as multiplying by 1/2, which would cut 252 in half.

In this problem, since you wish to move to a smaller number, you should multiply by 5/9:

$$\left(\frac{5}{9}\right)(252°) = \frac{1,260°}{9}$$

$$= 140°$$

The problem can now be completed using step 3 (subtract 40°):

$$\begin{array}{r} 140° \\ -\ 40° \\ \hline 100° \end{array}$$

Therefore, 212°F = 100°C.

Example 49

Convert 0°C to Fahrenheit.

The sketch of the two scales in Figure 2-1 indicates that 0°C = 32°F. Let's verify this conversion using the three-step method.

First, add 40°:

$$\begin{array}{r} 0° \\ +\ 40° \\ \hline 40° \end{array}$$

In this problem, you are going from Celsius to Fahrenheit. Therefore you will be moving from a smaller number to a larger number, and 9/5 should be used in the multiplication:

$$\left(\frac{9}{5}\right)(40°) = \frac{360°}{5}$$

$$= 72°$$

Subtract 40°:

$$\begin{array}{r} 72° \\ -\ 40° \\ \hline 32° \end{array}$$

Thus, 0°C = 32°F.

Example 50

A thermometer indicates that the water temperature is 15°C. What is this temperature expressed in degrees Fahrenheit?

First, add 40°:

$$\begin{array}{r} 15° \\ +\ 40° \\ \hline 55° \end{array}$$

Moving from a smaller number (Celsius) to a larger number (Fahrenheit) indicates multiplication by 9/5:

$$\left(\frac{9}{5}\right)(55°) = \frac{495°}{5}$$

$$= 99°$$

Subtract 40°:

$$\begin{array}{r} 99° \\ -\ 40° \\ \hline 59° \end{array}$$

Therefore, 15°C = 59°F.

Although it is useful to know how to make these temperature conversion calculations, in practical applications you may wish to use a temperature conversion table such as the one in Appendix A. Let's look at a couple of example conversions using the table.

Example 51

Normal room temperature is considered to be 68°F. What is this temperature expressed in degrees Celsius?

Use the Fahrenheit-to-Celsius temperature conversion table. Coming down the Fahrenheit column to 68°, you can see that 68°F = 20°C.

Example 52

Convert 90°C to degrees Fahrenheit.

Use the Celsius-to-Fahrenheit temperature conversion table. Coming down the Celsius column to 90°, you can see that 90°C = 194°F.

 WATCH THE VIDEOS
Operator Math 1 and Operator Math 2 (www.awwa.org/wsovideoclips)

Study Questions

1. Convert 35.1 cfs to gpm.
   a. 14,200 gpm
   b. 15,800 gpm
   c. 17,600 gpm
   d. 18,300 gpm

2. Convert 7.7 million gallons a day (mgd) into cubic feet per second (cfs).
    a. 11 cfs
    b. 12 cfs
    c. 15 cfs
    d. 19 cfs

3. How many million gallons (mil gal) are there in 318 acre-ft?
    a. 104 mil gal
    b. 107 mil gal
    c. 110 mil gal
    d. 116 mil gal

4. If 8.25 pounds of soda ash are mixed into 45 gallons of water, what is the percentage of soda ash in the slurry?
    a. 2.0% soda ash slurry
    b. 2.1% soda ash slurry
    c. 2.2% soda ash slurry
    d. 2.3% soda ash slurry

5. Calculate the area of a circular reservoir in ft², with a diameter of 411 ft.
    a. 108,000 ft²
    b. 112,000 ft²
    c. 125,000 ft²
    d. 133,000 ft²

6. Replacing the final digits of a number with zeros, thus expressing the number as tens, hundreds, thousands, etc., is referred to as
    a. estimating.
    b. squaring.
    c. rounding.
    d. guesstimating.

7. In solving for an unknown value, you must
    a. know the values for all but one of the terms of the equation to be used.
    b. move all positive numbers to the left side of the equation.
    b. know the values for all of the terms in the equation.
    c. divide all unknown values by a known value.

8. What is the purpose of scientific notation?

9. In performing treatment plant operations, what can you expect to happen if one of the operating conditions changes?

10. What is linear measurement?

Chapter 3
USEPA Water Quality Regulations Overview

Regulations that govern US water supply and treatment are developed by the US Environmental Protection Agency (USEPA) under the Safe Drinking Water Act (SDWA). Most states administer USEPA regulations after adopting regulations that are no less stringent than federal rules; and in some cases, states have adopted stricter regulations or have developed regulations for additional contaminants not regulated by USEPA.

This chapter discusses current and anticipated USEPA regulations and the challenges that operators face in their efforts to comply with the regulations. Water system operators should consult their local and state regulatory agencies to verify applicable regulations that may be different than the federal regulations listed in this chapter. The chapter concludes with a discussion of selected contaminants that are commonly found in water, their significance, and the methods for their removal.

Types of Water Systems

The SDWA defines a **public water system (PWS)** as a supply of piped water for human consumption that has at least 15 service connections, or serves 25 or more persons 60 or more days each year. By that definition, private homes, groups of homes with a single water source but having fewer than 25 residents, and summer camps with their own water source that operate less than 60 days per year are not PWSs. They may, however, be subject to state or local regulations. Such systems may also be subject to state and local well construction and water quality requirements.

PWSs are classified into three categories based on the type of customers served:

- *Community PWS:* a system whose customers are full-time residents
- *Nontransient noncommunity PWS:* an entity having its own water supply, serving an average of at least 25 persons who do not live at the location but who use the water for more than 6 months per year
- *Transient noncommunity PWS:* an establishment having its own water system, where an average of at least 25 people per day visit and use the water occasionally or for only short periods of time

These classifications are based on the differences in exposure to contaminants experienced by persons using the water. Most chemical contaminants are believed

public water system (PWS)

A supply of piped water for human consumption that has at least 15 service connections, or serves 25 or more persons 60 or more days each year.

to potentially cause adverse health effects from long-term exposure. Short-term exposure to low-level chemical contamination may not carry the same risk as long-term exposure.

Therefore, the monitoring requirements for both community and noncommunity water systems apply to all contaminants that are considered a health threat. The transient and nontransient noncommunity systems must monitor only for nitrite and nitrate, as well as biological contamination (those sources that pose an immediate threat from brief exposure). The remaining community systems, about 52,000 in the United States, have more stringent and frequent monitoring requirements.

Before examining the specific regulations that govern contaminants, the operator needs to know the difference between the two concepts used in the contaminant monitoring process: the maximum contaminant level goal (MCLG) and the maximum contaminant level (MCL) (recall also the previous discussion of MCL and MCLG in Chapter 1).

- The MCLG is set for most substances at a level where there are no known, or anticipated, health effects. For those substances that are suspected carcinogens, the MCLG is set at zero.
- The MCL is set as close as feasible to the MCLG for substances regulated under the SDWA. The MCL is a level that is reasonably and economically achievable. This is the enforceable regulated level. Water systems that exceed an MCL must take steps to install treatment to reduce the contaminant concentration to below the MCL. Where USEPA has found it impractical to set an MCL, a treatment technique has been established instead of an MCL.

With these concepts in mind, the various regulations can be examined. This discussion is not meant to be all-inclusive. Because the regulatory process is an ever-evolving one, the reader is cautioned that some of the stated facts presented in this discussion may have changed since the writing of this chapter. For up-to-date information, it is best to contact the local office of the regulatory authority in the district or state where the utility operates.

Table 3-1 contains some of the more common regulated contaminants and their respective MCL or treatment technique descriptions. These standards are provided for illustration only and are not intended to be used for regulatory purposes (see the official USEPA regulatory information on the agency website).

Operations personnel are expected to know the regulatory limits for compounds encountered in their water supply. However, the number and variety of regulated substances make it unlikely that operators would know all of the regulatory limits. Operators must rely on current references for the most accurate information. These are available from the regulatory agency responsible for the location of the treatment plant.

Disinfection By-product and Microbial Regulations

Drinking water treatment, including use of chemical disinfectants such as chlorine, ozone, and chlorine dioxide, has been an important step in protecting drinking water consumers from exposure to harmful microbial contaminants. However, these chemical disinfectants can also react with organic and inorganic substances in the water to produce by-products that may be harmful to

Table 3-1 Selected USEPA drinking water standards

Contaminant	MCL or Treatment Technique (mg/L)*
Total coliform	5% (monthly positives)
Turbidity	0.3 ntu monthly or 1 ntu†
Chlorite	1.0
Haloacetic acids (HAA5)	0.060
Total trihalomethanes (TTHM)	0.080
Chloramines (as Cl_2)	4.0
Chlorine (as Cl_2)	4.0
Chlorine dioxide (as ClO_2)	0.8
Arsenic	0.010
Copper	Treatment technique, action level = 1.3
Cyanide (as free cyanide)	0.2
Fluoride	4.0
Lead	Action level = 0.015
Mercury (inorganic)	0.002
Nitrate (measured as nitrogen)	10
Nitrite (measured as nitrogen)	1
Radium 226 and 228 (combined)	5 pCi/L
Uranium	10 µg/L

*The listed standards are numerical representations of the current USEPA drinking water standard and do not include the sample frequency or location and other important compliance information. For a complete definition of the standards, consult USEPA Drinking Water Standards.

†Turbidity less than or equal to 0.3 nephelometric turbidity units (ntu) for the combined filter effluent for 95% of the monthly samples. At no time can turbidity be above 1 ntu.

drinking water consumers, particularly some susceptible segments of the population. Therefore, drinking water treatment using chemical disinfectants involves a delicate balancing act—i.e., adding enough disinfectant to control harmful microorganisms but not enough to produce unacceptably high levels of regulated **disinfection by-products (DBPs)**.

USEPA has enacted several regulations impacting microbial control and production of DBPs in groundwater and surface water supplies for small and large public drinking water systems. These rules are referred to collectively as the Microbial/Disinfection By-products (M/DBP) Rules. Microbial protection for consumers of drinking water from public supplies is provided by provisions of current or pending rules listed below and discussed in more detail later in this chapter:

- Filter Backwash Recycling Rule (FBRR)
- Ground Water Rule (GWR)
- Interim Enhanced Surface Water Treatment Rule (IESWTR)
- Long-Term 1 Enhanced Surface Water Treatment Rule (LT1ESWTR)
- Long-Term 2 Enhanced Surface Water Treatment Rule (LT2ESWTR)
- Stage 1 Disinfectants and Disinfection By-products Rule (Stage 1 DBPR)
- Stage 2 Disinfectants and Disinfection By-products Rule (Stage 2 DBPR)
- Surface Water Treatment Rule (SWTR)
- Total Coliform Rule (TCR)

disinfection by-products (DBPs)
A new chemical compound formed by the reaction of disinfectants with organic compounds in water. At high concentrations, many DBPs are considered a danger to human health.

Provisions of the Disinfectants and Disinfection By-products Rule (DBPR) are intended to protect drinking water consumers against the unintended public health consequences associated with consumption of treated drinking water containing residual disinfectants and DBPs produced from degradation of these residual disinfectants or reaction of disinfectants with organic and inorganic DBP precursors.

More details regarding the DBPR, including the current Stage 1 DBPR and Stage 2 DBPR, are described in this chapter. Also included in the DBPR description is a brief discussion of some currently unregulated DBPs that are being heavily researched and may be the subject of future regulation. In the following discussion, the DBPR will be discussed first, followed by the microbial protection rules (SWTR, GWR, and TCR).

Disinfectants and Disinfection By-products Rule (DBPR)

The Stage 1 DBPR and Stage 2 DBPR requirements discussed in the following sections focus first on two specific contaminants (TTHM and HAA5) and then on other aspects of these regulations dealing with control or removal of DBP precursors ("enhanced coagulation"), bromate, chlorite, and residual disinfectants.

Stage 1 DBPR—HAA5 and TTHM Provisions

The Stage 1 DBPR was published in 1998 and established an MCL of 0.080 mg/L for TTHM (the sum of four trihalomethanes, which are chloroform, bromodichloromethane, dibromochloromethane, and bromoform) and 0.060 mg/L for HAA5 (the sum of five specific haloacetic acids, which are mono-, di-, and trichloroacetic acids plus mono- and dibromoacetic acids). Although the MCLs for TTHM and HAA5 were officially written as 0.080 mg/L and 0.060 mg/L, respectively, the limits are commonly referred to as "80/60," or 80 µg/L and 60 µg/L. While knowing the numerical value of each MCL is important in understanding compliance with the DBPR, it is equally important to understand the methodology, in all its subtleties, used to calculate the compliance value that will be compared to this MCL.

For TTHM and HAA5, the compliance value is determined by monitoring the distribution system. Compliance monitoring locations need to be representative of the distribution system. Systems serving more than 10,000 persons who use surface water sources are required to monitor at least four locations per plant, meaning that distribution systems fed by more than one treatment plant must have at least four monitoring locations designated for each plant entry point.

The compliance monitoring location for systems with only one monitoring point must be representative of maximum residence time in the distribution system. A minimum of one out of every four compliance monitoring locations for systems with more locations must also be representative of maximum residence time. The other locations must be far enough away from the plant entry points to be representative of average residence time in the distribution system.

Unlike acute toxicity risks, for which the exposure could be a single glass of water, cancer risks like those believed to be linked to TTHM and HAA5 involve longer periods of exposure (daily glasses of water spanning decades). For chronic exposures such as these, exposure to an excessively high concentration of a given cancer-causing agent will not necessarily result in the consumer getting cancer from this source. Conversely, a consumer exposed to a lower concentration every day for a lifetime could be more likely to develop cancer. Therefore, regulation of DBPs to reduce cancer risks is *not* based on limiting exposure to a single incident (i.e., not a "single hit"), but rather is aimed at reducing the repeated exposure over time. In other words, DBP exposure needs to be evaluated on an average basis over time.

Under the Stage 1 DBPR, the compliance value for TTHM and HAA5 is determined by calculating a running annual average (RAA) during the previous 12 months for each DBP for all monitoring locations at each plant. Most systems are required to monitor quarterly (i.e., 4 times per year), although small groundwater systems (<10,000 persons) may be allowed to sample once a year. Typically, the RAA is based on 4 monitoring locations sampled quarterly, meaning RAA will be the average of 16 monitoring results each for HAA5 and TTHM.

Table 3-2 illustrates one facility's calculations of RAA for HAA5 that were used for Stage 1 compliance (this table also shows calculation of values for Stage 2 DBPR, which will be discussed later). It is important to reemphasize that compliance is based solely on the RAA, not on a single quarterly result at any one monitoring location. Consequently, it is *not* correct to refer to a single quarterly monitoring result above 60 µg/L for HAA5 or above 80 µg/L for TTHM as being above the MCL. Therefore, even though several individual monitoring values in Table 3-2 are greater than 60 µg/L, the facility is in compliance with the HAA5 MCL because the RAA is 45 µg/L for HAA5.

Utility personnel should be consistent and rigorous in their use of terminology when dealing with the general public or with state and local health officials, and should ensure that all people participating in these discussions are consistent in applying the MCL only to RAA values and do not make the common mistake of referring to a single quarterly monitoring value as being "above the MCL."

Stage 2 DBPR—HAA5 and TTHM Provisions

The Stage 2 DBPR, published in 2006, is now in effect. This rule tightened requirements for DBPs, but compliance is not achieved by modifying the numerical value of the MCLs or by requiring monitoring of new constituents. Instead, the rule makes compliance more challenging than under the Stage 1 DBPR by (1) changing the way the compliance value is calculated and (2) changing the compliance monitoring locations to sites representative of the greatest potential for THM and HAA formation. These changes were made to ensure uniform compliance with the DBP standards across all areas of the distribution system; that is, compliance is required at each sampling location.

The compliance value in the Stage 2 DBPR is called the *locational running annual average* (LRAA), and it is calculated by separately averaging the four quarterly samples at each monitoring location. Compliance is based on the maximum

Table 3-2 Example RAA and LRAA calculations for Stage 1 DBPR and Stage 2 DBPR

| Year | Quarter | Sampling Location, µg/L | | | |
		A	B	C	D
1	3rd	52	68	63	66
1	4th	35	42	38	41
2	1st	47	49	42	43
2	2nd	18	42	45	37
LRAA		38	50	47	47
Maximum LRAA			50		
RAA			45		

LRAA value (see Table 3-2). Furthermore, the Stage 2 DBPR included several interim steps that led to the replacement of many existing Stage 1 DBPR monitoring locations with new locations representative of the greatest potential for consumer exposure to high levels of TTHM and HAA5.

The Stage 2 DBPR required that facilities maintain compliance with the Stage 1 DBPR using the existing monitoring locations during the first three years after the final version of the Stage 2 DBPR was published. In the time period between the third and sixth year after the Stage 2 DBPR was published, compliance continues to be based on maintaining 80/60 (TTHM and HAA5) or lower for RAA; it also includes a requirement for maximum LRAA at existing Stage 1 monitoring locations. The long-term goal of the Stage 2 DBPR was to identify locations within the distribution system with the greatest potential for either TTHM or HAA5 formations and then base compliance on the LRAA at or below 80/60 for each of these locations. Many of these locations were identified during the initial distribution system evaluation (IDSE).

The IDSE included monitoring, modeling, and/or other evaluations of drinking water distribution systems to identify locations representative of the greatest potential for consumer exposure to high levels of TTHM and HAA5. The goal of the IDSE was to evaluate a number of potential monitoring locations to justify selection of monitoring locations for long-term compliance (i.e., Stage 2B) with the Stage 2 DBPR.

One item to note regarding the Stage 2 DBPR as it applies to TTHM and HAA5 is that the goal was to find the locations in the distribution system where average annual levels of these DBPs are highest. TTHM formation increases as contact time with free or combined chlorine increases, although formation in the presence of combined chlorine is limited. Therefore, establishing points in the distribution system with the highest potential for TTHM formation is related to knowing the points with maximum water age. Utilities that have not performed a tracer study in the distribution system to determine water age should consider doing so.

By contrast, peak locations for HAA5 are more complicated because microorganisms in biofilm attached to distribution system pipe surfaces can biodegrade HAA5. Consequently, increasing formation of HAA5 over time is offset by biodegradation, eventually reaching a point where HAA5 levels decrease over time, even to the point where they drop to zero. Figure 3-1 shows a gradual reduction in HAA5 formation over time in a distribution system, followed by an eventual decrease of HAA5 as water age increases (water age measured in tracer test). In chloramination systems, HAA5 formation is limited. In fact, ammonium chloride is added as a quenching agent in HAA5 compliance samples in order to halt HAA5 formation prior to analysis (*Standard Methods for the Examination of Water and Wastewater*, latest edition). Therefore, little additional HAA5 formation occurs after chloramination to offset HAA5 biodegradation occurring in the distribution system.

Enhanced Coagulation Requirement of the Stage 1 DBPR and Stage 2 DBPR

The enhanced coagulation requirement has been developed to promote optimization of coagulation processes in conventional surface water treatment systems as required to improve removal of organic DBP precursors. The focus of the SWTR is separate from that of the enhanced coagulation requirement, with the former directed toward optimizing particle removal and the latter toward optimizing removal of natural organic matter (DBP precursors). Both promote efforts by water utilities to properly control and optimize coagulation processes and reduce DBP formation.

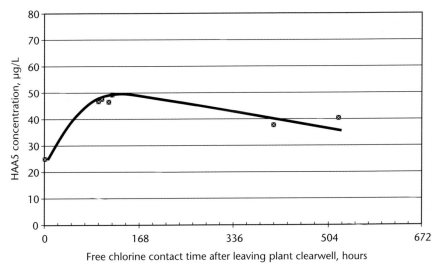

Figure 3-1 Formation and decay of HAA5 in a distribution system (time estimated by fluoride tracer test—T_{100})

Under the enhanced coagulation requirements, treatment plants must remove specific percentages of total organic carbon (TOC) based on their source water TOC and alkalinity levels. Facilities must meet the enhanced coagulation requirements unless they meet any of the following exemptions (USEPA Stage 1 DBPR Guidance):

1. The PWS's source water TOC level is <2.0 mg/L, calculated quarterly as an RAA.

2. The PWS's treated water TOC level is <2.0 mg/L, calculated quarterly as an RAA.

3. The PWS's source water TOC level is <4.0 mg/L, calculated quarterly as an RAA; the source-water alkalinity is >60 mg/L (as calcium carbonate [$CaCO_3$]), calculated quarterly as an RAA; and either the TTHM and HAA5 RAAs are no greater than 0.040 mg/L and 0.030 mg/L, respectively, or the PWS has made a clear and irrevocable financial commitment to use technologies that will limit the levels of TTHMs and HAA5 to no more than 0.040 mg/L and 0.030 mg/L, respectively.

4. The PWS's TTHM and HAA5 RAAs are no greater than 0.040 mg/L and 0.030 mg/L, respectively, and the PWS uses only chlorine for primary disinfection and maintenance of a residual in the distribution system.

5. The PWS's source water specific ultraviolet absorption at 254 nm (SUVA), prior to any treatment and measured monthly, is ≤2.0 L/mg-m, calculated quarterly as an RAA.

6. The PWS's finished-water SUVA, measured monthly, is ≤2.0 L/mg-m, calculated quarterly an RAA.

Additionally, alternative compliance criteria for softening systems include the following:

7. Softening results in lowering the treated water alkalinity to <60 mg/L (as $CaCO_3$), measured monthly and calculated quarterly as an RAA.

8. Softening results in removing at least 10 mg/L of magnesium hardness (as $CaCO_3$), measured monthly and calculated quarterly as an RAA.

Utilities that cannot meet these avoidance criteria should know their enhanced coagulation endpoint, identified as the coagulant dosage and/or pH value that, when achieved, no longer produces significant TOC reduction. Specifically, when the source water TOC is not reduced by at least 0.3 mg/L with an incremental dosage increase of 10 mg/L alum (or equivalent ferric salt) and the pH value of the source reaches a value listed in Table 3-3, the enhanced coagulation endpoint has been reached.

If a utility is not exempt, a number of steps have to be evaluated relating to TOC removal, alkalinity of source water, range of source water TOC, required TOC removal for given source water characteristics, and several other factors.

Bromate

The bromate MCL from the Stage 1 DBPR remained at 0.010 mg/L for the Stage 2 DBPR. Bromate can be present in systems using ozone that have bromide present at the ozone application point. Bromate is also potentially formed during manufacture and storage of sodium hypochlorite. Consequently, systems using ozone for oxidation or disinfection are required to monitor once a month at a distribution system entry point for bromate, but systems without ozone are not required to perform this monitoring. Systems that use ozone and that also add sodium hypochlorite will need to closely monitor the quality of these sodium hypochlorite products for bromate content.

Chlorite

Similar to bromate, chlorite monitoring is required only for systems using chlorine dioxide as an oxidant or disinfectant. Chlorite is a degradation product of chlorine dioxide. Chlorate is also a degradation product of chlorine dioxide but is not currently regulated. Chlorite and chlorate are potential degradation products of sodium hypochlorite, but systems using sodium hypochlorite are not required to monitor for chlorite unless they also use chlorine dioxide.

Monitoring for chlorite is more complicated than for bromate because chlorine dioxide will degrade and chlorite formation will increase over time. Therefore, chlorite monitoring requirements include daily monitoring at the distribution system entry point and monthly samples at three locations in the distribution system (first customer, average residence time, maximum residence time). Unlike the health risks for bromate, TTHM, and HAA5, the risk for chlorite requires compliance based on the average of the three chlorite-monitoring locations each month. The Stage 1 DBPR MCL for chlorite is 1.0 mg/L.

Residual Disinfectants

The maximum residual disinfectant level (MRDL) for combined or total chlorine is 4.0 mg/L as Cl_2. These values are based on the same data used to monitor

Table 3-3 Target pH values for coagulation when TOC removal rates are not sufficient

Alkalinity	pH Value
0–60	5.5
>60–120	6.3
>120–240	7.0
>240	7.5

minimum free and combined chlorine levels in the distribution system as required by the SWTR, using the same monitoring locations used for the TCR. Chlorine dioxide residual also has an MRDL of 0.8 mg/L as ClO_2, based on daily samples at the treatment plant.

 WATCH THE VIDEO
Disinfection By-products (www.awwa.org/wsovideoclips)

Surface Water Treatment Rule (SWTR)

IESWTR and LT1ESWTR

The goal of the IESWTR is to limit human exposure with harmful organisms, including *Cryptosporidium*, by promoting achievement of particle and turbidity removal targets for surface water treatment systems. Among the IESWTR requirements that apply to surface water treatment plants are the following:

- Combined filter effluent turbidity must be ≤0.3 ntu for 95 percent of samples collected each month, including none with >1 ntu. Compliance is based on combined filter effluent samples collected at 4-hour intervals during the entire month.

- The utility must monitor each individual filter for turbidity at 15-minute intervals and must report results, including a filter profile (graphical representation of filter performance), if either of the following two conditions are met: (1) turbidity in any filter for two consecutive 15-minute intervals exceeds 1 ntu or (2) turbidity during the first 4 hours of a given filter run exceeds 0.5 ntu for two consecutive 15-minute samples. Results must be reported within 10 days of the end of the month.

- Any newly constructed finished water reservoirs must include covers to keep out dust, debris, birds, etc.

- The utility must complete a sanitary survey every 3 years. Existing surveys conducted after December 1995 can be used if they meet minimum requirements. Variances can be granted to decrease frequency to 5 years. The IESWTR explicitly requires that sanitary surveys include efforts to evaluate and control *Cryptosporidium*, in addition to other target organisms.

- Systems where the average of quarterly TTHM or HAA5 values exceeds 64 and 48 µg/L, respectively, need to complete disinfection profiling and benchmarking. *Profiling* involves determination of $C \times T$ values (concentration of disinfectant × contact time) for each segment of the treatment plant (see later discussion). *Benchmarking* involves determining the lowest monthly average during 12-month monitoring of *Giardia* and virus inactivation. This procedure is required for any systems that are considering a major change to their disinfection practice. Consultation with the primacy agency is also required before any disinfection change.

- Turbidity monitoring records must be maintained for a minimum of 3 years.

Facilities in compliance with these requirements, chiefly the turbidity monitoring provisions, are designated by the IESWTR to have provided 2-log virus removal, 2.5-log *Giardia* removal, and 2-log *Cryptosporidium* removal. Literature and other information cited in the IESWTR final rule indicate that these credits are conservative, and most facilities meeting these requirements are probably achieving far greater levels of virus, *Giardia*, and *Cryptosporidium* removal than

C × T value
The product of the residual disinfectant concentration *C*, in milligrams per liter, and the corresponding disinfectant contact time *T*, in minutes. Minimum *C* × *T* values are specified by the Surface Water Treatment Rule as a means of ensuring adequate kill or inactivation of pathogenic microorganisms in water.

the minimum credits previously cited. The level of *Cryptosporidium* protection cited is sufficient to meet all requirements of the IESWTR, but the rule requires a total of 3.0 credits for *Giardia* and 4.0 credits for viruses. The additional credits (0.5-log for *Giardia* and 2-log for viruses) are required to be achieved by disinfection with free chlorine, chloramines, ozone, or chlorine dioxide by meeting contact time requirements described later in this chapter.

Provisions of the IESWTR apply to large systems (>10,000 persons) using surface water sources. However, similar provisions are applied to smaller surface water systems (<10,000 persons), as outlined in the LT1ESWTR. The objectives of the LT1ESWTR and IESWTR are identical, though some of the compliance deadlines and other regulatory provisions are slightly different based on greater financial and personnel resources for larger systems.

Sanitary Surveys

Sanitary surveys are a requirement of the Interim Enhanced Surface Water Treatment Rule (IESWTR). A sanitary survey is "an onsite review of the water source, facilities, equipment, operation, and maintenance of the public water system for the purpose of evaluating the adequacy of such source, facilities, equipment, operation, and maintenance for producing and distributing safe drinking water." Surveys are usually performed by the state primacy agency and are required of all surface water systems and groundwater systems under the direct influence of surface water.

These surveys are typically divided into eight main sections, although some state primacy groups may have more:

1. Water sources
2. Water treatment process
3. Water supply pumps and pumping facilities
4. Storage facilities
5. Distribution systems
6. Monitoring, reporting, and data verification
7. Water system management and operations
8. Operator compliance with state requirements

Sanitary surveys are required on a periodic basis, usually every 3 years. Surveys may be comprehensive or focused according to the regulatory agency requirements.

C × T Requirements

Every water system that uses surface water as a source must meet treatment technique requirements for the removal and/or inactivation of *Giardia*, viruses, *Legionella*, and other bacteria. Because these pathogens are not easily identified in the laboratory on a routine basis, USEPA has set quality goals in lieu of MCLs in this instance. Meeting SWTR treatment technique goals demonstrates all or part of the required microbial protection, as previously noted, but additional protection is required through the use of approved disinfection treatment chemicals. The effectiveness of disinfection depends on the type of disinfectant chemical used, the residual concentration, the amount of time the disinfectant is in contact with the water, the water temperature, and, when chlorine is used, the pH of the water.

According to USEPA, a combination of the residual concentration, *C*, of a disinfectant (in milligrams per liter) multiplied by the contact time, *T* (in minutes), can be used as a measure of the disinfectant's effectiveness in killing or inactivating microorganisms. For water plant operators, this means that high residuals held for a short amount of time or low residuals held for a long period of time will produce similar results. Water plants are required to provide this computation daily, and the measure must always be higher than the required minimum value.

Long-Term 2 Enhanced SWTR (LT2ESWTR)

The LT2ESWTR supplements the SWTR requirements contained in the IESWTR for large surface water systems (>10,000 persons) and the LT1ESWTR for small systems (<10,000 persons). Details of the rules can be reviewed in the *Federal Register* or at the USEPA website (http://water.epa.gov/drink/index.cfm). One of the key elements of the LT2ESWTR was the use of *Cryptosporidium* monitoring results to classify surface water sources into one of four USEPA-defined risk levels called "bins." Facilities in the lowest bin (bin 1) are required to maintain compliance with the current IESWTR. Facilities in higher bins (bins 2 to 4) are required to either (1) provide additional *Cryptosporidium* protection from new facilities or programs not currently in use at a facility or (2) demonstrate greater *Cryptosporidium* protection capabilities of existing facilities and programs using a group of USEPA-approved treatment technologies, watershed programs, and demonstration studies, referred to collectively as the *Microbial Toolbox*.

Implementation of the LT2ESWTR was phased over many years according to system size. Four separate size categories were established (schedules 1–4, with 4 being the smallest at <10,000 population) for implementing the rule. The rule for schedule-4 systems allows filtered supplies to perform initial monitoring for fecal coliform to determine if *Cryptosporidium* monitoring is required.

Filter Backwash Recycle Rule (FBRR)

The FBRR currently applies to systems of all sizes and is intended to help utilities minimize potential health risks associated with recycle, particularly associated with respect to *Giardia* and *Cryptosporidium*. Other contaminants of concern in the recycle stream include suspended solids (turbidity), dissolved metals (especially iron and manganese), and dissolved organic carbon. Plants that control recycle will also help minimize operational problems.

Prior to the FBRR, no USEPA regulation governed recycle. Regulations within the United States regarding recycle had been established by the states, if at all. State regulatory approaches varied from a requirement of equalization of two backwashes in Illinois to 80 percent solids removal prior to recycle and maintaining recycle flows at less than 10 percent of raw water flow in California. Virginia discourages recycling.

Key components of the FBRR include (1) recycle must reenter the treatment process *prior* to primary coagulant addition, (2) direct filtration plants must report their recycle practices to the state and may need to treat their recycle streams, and (3) a self-assessment must be done at those plants that use direct recycle (i.e., no separate equalization and/or treatment of recycle stream) and that operate fewer than 20 filters. The goal of the self-assessment is to determine if the design capacity of the plant is exceeded due to recycle practices.

WATCH THE VIDEO
Filter Backwash (www.awwa.org/wsovideoclips)

Ground Water Rule (GWR)

USEPA promulgated the final GWR in October 2006 to reduce the risk of exposure to fecal contamination that may be present in PWSs that use groundwater sources. The rule establishes a risk-targeted strategy to identify groundwater systems that are at high risk for fecal contamination. The GWR also specifies when corrective action (which may include disinfection) is required to protect consumers who receive water from groundwater systems from bacteria and viruses.

A sanitary survey is required, by the state primacy agency, at regular intervals depending on the condition of the water system as determined in the initial survey. Systems found to be at high risk for fecal contamination are required to provide 4-log inactivation of viruses. Increased monitoring for fecal contamination indicators may be required by the regulatory authority.

Total Coliform Rule (TCR) and Revised Total Coliform Rule (RTCR)

The objective of the TCR is to promote routine surveillance of distribution system water quality to search for fecal matter and/or disease-causing bacteria. All points in a distribution system cannot be monitored, and complete absence of fecal matter and disease-causing bacteria cannot be guaranteed. The TCR is an attempt to persuade water utilities to implement monitoring programs sufficient to verify that public health is being protected as much as possible, as well as allowing utilities to identify any potential contamination problems in their distribution system. The rule requires monthly sampling at each distribution sampling point.

The TCR, and the RTCR that was finalized in 2013, impact all PWSs. The RTCR requires PWSs that are vulnerable to microbial contamination to identify and fix problems. The RTCR also established criteria for systems to qualify for and stay on reduced monitoring, thereby providing incentives for improved water system operation.

The RTCR rule established an MCLG and an MCL for *Escherichia coli* (*E. coli*) and eliminated the MCLG and MCL for total coliform, replacing it with a treatment technique for coliform that requires assessment and corrective action. The rule establishes an MCLG and an MCL of zero for *E. coli*, a more specific indicator of fecal contamination and potentially harmful pathogens than total coliform. USEPA removed the MCLG and MCL of zero for total coliform. Many of the organisms detected by total coliform methods are not of fecal origin and do not have any direct public health implication.

Under the treatment technique for coliform, total coliform serves as an indicator of a potential pathway of contamination into the distribution system. A PWS that exceeds a specified frequency of total coliform occurrence must conduct an assessment to determine if any sanitary defects exist and, if found, correct them. In addition, a PWS that incurs an *E. coli* MCL violation must conduct an assessment and correct any sanitary defects found.

The RTCR also changed monitoring frequencies. It links monitoring frequency to water quality and system performance and provides criteria that well-operated small systems must meet to qualify and stay on reduced monitoring. It also requires increased monitoring for high-risk small systems with unacceptable compliance history and establishes some new monitoring requirements for seasonal systems such as state and national parks.

The revised rule eliminated monthly public notification requirements based only on the presence of total coliforms. Total coliforms in the distribution system may indicate a potential pathway for contamination but in and of themselves do not indicate a health threat. Instead, the rule requires public notification when an *E. coli* MCL violation occurs, indicating a potential health threat, or when a PWS fails to conduct the required assessment and corrective action.

The rule requires that PWSs collect total coliform samples at sites representative of water quality throughout the distribution system according to a written plan approved by the state or primacy agency. Samples are collected at regular intervals monthly. Positive total coliform samples must be tested for *E. coli*. If any positive total coliform sample is also positive for *E. coli* the state must be notified by the end of the day on which the result was received. Repeat samples are required within 24 hours of any total coliform–positive routine sample. Three repeat samples are required, one at the site of the positive sample and one within five service taps both upstream and downstream of the positive site. Any positive total coliform samples must be tested for *E. coli*. Any positive *E. coli* (EC+) samples must be reported by the end of the day. Any positive total coliform (TC+) samples require another set of repeat samples.

A Level 1 or Level 2 sanitary assessment and corrective action is triggered to occur within 30 days if there is indication of coliform contamination. A Level 1 assessment by the PWS is triggered if more than 5 percent of the routine/repeat monthly samples (if at least 40 are required) are total coliform positive or a repeat sample is not taken for a total coliform positive result. A Level 2 assessment conducted by the state or its representative is triggered if the PWS has an *E. coli* violation or repeated Level 1 assessment triggers.

Major violations of the RTCR are MCL violations and treatment technique violations. A PWS will receive an *E. coli* MCL violation when there is any combination of an EC+ sample result with a routine/repeat TC+ or EC+ sample result, as follows:

E. coli MCL Violation Occurs With the
Following Sample Result Combination

Routine	Repeat
EC+	TC+
EC+	Any missing sample
EC+	EC+
TC+	EC+
TC+	TC+ (but no *E. coli* analysis)

A PWS will receive a treatment technique violation given any of the following conditions:

- Failure to conduct a Level 1 or Level 2 assessment within 30 days of a trigger.
- Failure to correct all sanitary defects from a Level 1 or Level 2 assessment within 30 days of a trigger or in accordance with the state-approved time frame.
- Failure of a seasonal system to complete state-approved start-up procedures prior to serving water to the public.

 WATCH THE VIDEO
Coliform Sampling 2 (www.awwa.org/wsovideoclips)

Lead and Copper Rule (LCR)

The objective of the LCR is to control corrosiveness of the finished water in drinking water distribution systems to limit the amount of lead (Pb) and copper (Cu) that may be leached from certain metal pipes and fittings in the distribution system. Of particular concern are pipes and fittings connecting the household tap to the distribution system service line at individual homes or businesses, especially because water can remain stagnant in these service lines for long periods of time, increasing the potential to leach Pb, Cu, and other metals. Although the utility is not responsible for maintaining and/or replacing these household connections, they are responsible for controlling pH and corrosiveness of the water delivered to the consumers.

Details of the LCR include the following:

- The LCR became effective December 7, 1992.
- The action level for Pb is 0.015 mg/L and for Cu is 1.3 mg/L.
- A utility is in compliance at each sampling event (frequency discussed below) when <10 percent of the distribution system samples are above the action levels for Pb and Cu (i.e., 90th percentile value for sampling event must be below action level).
- Utilities found not to be in compliance must modify water treatment until they are in compliance. The term *action level* is used rather than *MCL* because noncompliance (i.e., exceeding an action level) triggers a need for modifications in treatment.

After identifying sampling locations and determining initial tap water Pb and Cu levels at each of these locations, utilities must also monitor other water quality parameters (WQPs) at these same locations as needed to monitor and evaluate corrosion control characteristics of treated water. The only exemptions from analysis of these WQPs are systems serving less than 50,000 people for which Pb and Cu levels in initial samples are below action levels.

Pb, Cu, and WQPs are initially collected at 6-month intervals; this frequency can be reduced if action levels are not exceeded and optimal water treatment is maintained. Systems that are in noncompliance and are performing additional corrosion-control activities must continue to monitor at 6-month intervals, plus they must collect WQPs from distribution system entry points every 2 weeks.

Each utility must complete a survey and evaluate materials that comprise their distribution system, in addition to using other available information, to target homes that are at high risk for Pb/Cu contamination.

Revisions to the LCR were enacted in 2007. These clarifications to the existing rule were made in seven areas:

- Minimum number of samples required
- Definitions for compliance and monitoring periods
- Reduced monitoring criteria
- Consumer notice of lead tap water monitoring results
- Advanced notification and approval of long-term treatment changes
- Public education requirements
- Reevaluation of lead service lines

Consult your local regulatory agency for those revisions that are applicable to your system.

WATCH THE VIDEOS
Lead and Copper Sampling, Water Quality and Household Plumbing,
and Water Quality and Faucets (www.awwa.org/wsovideoclips)

Phase I, II, and V Contaminants

The Phase I, II, and V regulations were finalized in 1989, 1992, and 1995, respectively, and include various inorganic and organic contaminants. Sampling and reporting frequency vary with constituent, though sampling is typically required once every 3 years after the initial sampling period. Variances or waivers are possible for a number of constituents based on analytical results and/or a vulnerability assessment.

Public Notification Rule

USEPA has implemented a regulation called the *Public Notification Rule*. This rule is separate from the Consumer Confidence Report (CCR) Rule. The Public Notification Rule includes requirements for reporting certain water quality monitoring violations and other water quality incidents, as well as requirements for the timing, distribution, and language of the public notices. For example, the Public Notification Rule includes requirements that some incidents be reported within 24 hours, others within 30 days, and others included as part of the annual CCR. Some of these reporting requirements are more stringent than those currently required by USEPA. The regulation also includes requirements regarding how notices are to be distributed/broadcast (i.e., TV, radio, newspaper, hand delivery, regular mail, etc.), the format of the notices, the wording of certain items in the notice, and the need to include information in languages other than English.

Public notification according to the rule might include the following:

- Templates, or model notices, to be available for adaptation for certain potential incidents
- Consolidated and updated lists of phone numbers and contacts for government (local, county, state), regulatory agencies, hospitals, radio and TV, newspapers, etc., that should be contacted per requirements of the Public Notification Rule
- Checklists and flow diagrams outlining activities that would need to be completed for certain potential events outlined in the regulation
- Identification of key personnel and what their roles and responsibilities would be to respond as required by the regulation
- A plan to periodically review and update all lists, templates, and other aspects of a response plan every year or when/if the Public Notification Rule is modified by future federal or state regulations

Unregulated Contaminant Monitoring Rule (UCMR)

The 1996 amendments to the SDWA require USEPA to establish criteria for a monitoring program for currently unregulated contaminants to generate data that USEPA can use to evaluate and prioritize contaminants that could potentially be regulated in the future. USEPA has developed three cycles of the UCMR:

1. UCMR1 in 1999
2. UCMR2 in 2007
3. UCMR3 in 2012

Failing to (1) perform required sampling and analysis, (2) use the appropriate analytical procedures, or (3) report these results is a violation of the UCMR. However, the numerical results of these analytical efforts cannot result in a violation because none of the constituents in the UCMR are currently regulated (i.e., no MCLs, action levels, or other standards apply).

Although the UCMR contaminants have no standards associated with them, the data from this monitoring will need to be reported in the annual CCR. Therefore, the CCR will need to address implications of any constituents found above detection limits. Reporting UCMR results in the CCR would also fulfill the notification requirements for "unregulated contaminants" included in the recently promulgated Public Notification Rule.

Note that the UCMR is an ongoing part of the regulatory development process that will be repeated every 5 years. Utilities will be performing similar mandatory sampling for a new list of constituents every 5 years.

UCMR3 was signed by USEPA Administrator Lisa P. Jackson on April 16, 2012. As finalized, UCMR3 requires monitoring for 30 contaminants using USEPA and/or consensus organization analytical methods during 2013–2015. Together, USEPA, states, laboratories, and PWSs will participate in UCMR3.

Operator Certification

Amendments to the 1996 SDWA required USEPA to develop national guidance for operator certification. The final rule was published on February 5, 1999, and became effective on February 5, 2001. State operator certification programs were required to address nine baseline standards, including operator qualifications, certification renewal, and program review. Indirect impacts of the rule on most water utilities include availability of Drinking Water State Revolving Fund (DWSRF) money and perhaps some slight modifications in paperwork/record-keeping requirements.

Arsenic MCL

The MCL for arsenic was reduced from 50 µg/L to 10 µg/L in the *Federal Register* published on January 22, 2001. This was the second time USEPA has established an MCL that was higher than the technically feasible level (3 µg/L), with the first being the uranium rule in 2000. The original SDWA required the MCL to be set as close to the health goal (zero for arsenic and all other suspected carcinogens) as technically feasible. Amendments to the SDWA allowed USEPA the discretion to set the MCL above the technically feasible level.

The final rule, including the revised MCL, became effective 3 years after the rule was published.

Radionuclides Rule

The Radionuclide Rule was published in December 2000. In the final rule, USEPA maintained the gross alpha MCL at 15 pCi/L MCL, 4 mrem/yr for beta emitters, 4 mrem/yr for photon emitters, and 5 pCi/L for combined radium 226 and 228 isotopes, and an MCL for uranium of 30 µg/L.

Analytical Methods

Each of the individual USEPA regulations contains its own information regarding analytical methods approved for compliance monitoring. These and other approved analytical methods are compiled in a final rule titled "Analytical Methods for Chemical and Microbiological Contaminants and Revisions to Laboratory Certification Requirements," published December 1, 1999. These analytical methods were approved for compliance monitoring effective January 3, 2000. The USEPA-approved methods include analytical procedures developed by USEPA, plus procedures developed by others that USEPA endorses, including specific procedures developed by the American Society for Testing and Materials (ASTM) and some specific procedures included in *Standard Methods for the Examination of Water and Wastewater*, published jointly by the American Public Health Association (APHA), AWWA, and the Water Environment Federation (WEF).

Currently, only approved analytical methods can be used for compliance monitoring. In the future, USEPA hopes to implement a performance-based measurement system that will allow utilities to use alternative screening methods instead of requiring only USEPA-approved reference methods. The 1996 SDWA amendments require USEPA to review new analytical methods that may be used for the screening and analysis of regulated contaminants. After this review, USEPA may approve methods that may be more accurate or cost-effective than established methods for compliance monitoring. These screening methods are expected to provide flexibility in compliance monitoring and may be better and/or faster than existing analytical methods.

The approval of new drinking water analytical methods can be announced through an expedited process in the *Federal Register*. This allows laboratories and water systems more timely access to new alternative testing methods than the traditional rule-making process. If alternate test procedures perform the same as or better than the approved methods, they can be considered for approval using the expedited process.

Study Questions

1. Provisions of which regulation are intended to protect drinking water consumers against the unintended public health consequences associated with consumption of treated drinking water containing residual disinfectants and disinfection by-products?
   a. Filter Backwash Recycling Rule
   b. Ground Water Rule
   c. Disinfectants and Disinfection By-products Rule
   d. Surface Water Treatment Rule

2. Under the Stage 1 DBPR, the compliance value for TTHM and HAA5 is determined by calculating a _____ during the previous 12 months for each DBP for all monitoring locations at each plant.
   a. running annual average
   b. maximum contaminant level
   c. locational annual average
   d. $C \times T$ value

3. Which of the following is *not* typically a section covered in a sanitary survey?
   a. Water sources
   b. Storage facilities
   c. Fire department hydrants
   d. Water system management and operations

4. The maximum contaminant level for arsenic
   a. is not specified in most states because it's too difficult to control.
   b. is constantly changing.
   c. has increased in recent years.
   d. is higher than the technically feasible level.

5. List the MCL for the following: Nitrate, Nitrite, Fluoride, TTHM, HAA5, Arsenic

6. List and explain the treatment technic requirements for the following: Copper, Lead

7. Explain the regulations for microbiological contaminates included in the total coliform rule and its revisions.

8. Explain the CT disinfection requirements.

9. What is a sanitary survey?

10. How does the SDWA define a public water system?

Chapter 4
Water Sources and Treatment Options

Water Supply Hydrology

Hydrology is the study of the properties, distribution, and circulation of water and its constituents as it moves through the atmosphere, across the earth's surface, and below the earth's surface. In the context of drinking water supply operations, hydrology is primarily concerned with the factors that affect the availability and the quality of water needed to meet user demands. This chapter introduces those factors and presents some terms that are commonly used in the drinking water supply industry to describe the volume and flow of water.

The Hydrologic Cycle

The continuous circulation of water above, below, and across the surface of the earth is called the water cycle or, more commonly, the **hydrologic cycle**. Illustrated in Figure 4-1, the hydrologic cycle includes the following processes:

1. **Evaporation**: Water moves off land and water surfaces and into the atmosphere.
2. **Transpiration**: Water is released into the air by plants, primarily through their leaves.
3. **Advection**: Water moves with the air currents in the atmosphere.
4. **Condensation**: Water vapor in the air forms tiny droplets.
5. **Precipitation**: Water falls out of the atmosphere as rain, snow, or ice.
6. **Interception**: Some precipitation lands on vegetation and does not reach the ground.
7. **Infiltration**: Some of the rain that reaches the ground soaks into it.
8. **Subsurface flow**: Below the surface, water movement is influenced by gravity and the presence of natural barriers in the rock or soil.
9. **Runoff**: A portion of the water that reaches the ground flows toward nearby bodies of water.
10. **Channel flow**: Runoff eventually flows into small channels that feed into larger channels that carry rivers and streams.
11. **Storage**: Water is taken out of circulation because it is frozen, held in a lake aboveground, or held in an aquifer belowground.
12. **Snowmelt**: Water that has collected as snow or ice is released as liquid.

Each of these processes is explained further below.

---

hydrology
The science dealing with the properties, distribution, and circulation of water and its constituents in the atmosphere, on the earth's surface, and below the earth's surface.

hydrologic cycle
The movement of water to and from the surface of the earth.

evaporation
Water that moves off land and water surfaces and into the atmosphere.

transpiration
The release of water into the air by plants, primarily through their leaves.

advection
Water movement with the air currents in the atmosphere.

condensation
Water vapor in the air that forms tiny droplets.

precipitation
Water that falls out of the atmosphere as rain, snow, or ice.

interception
The process of rain water landing on vegetation, not reaching the ground.

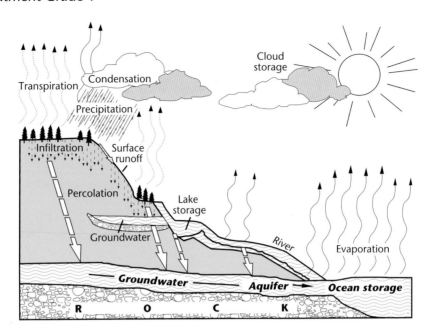

Figure 4-1 The hydrologic cycle

infiltration
The process of rain water reaching the ground soaking through the soil.

subsurface flow
Water movement below the surface, influenced by gravity and the presence of natural barriers in the rock or soil.

runoff
Water that reaches the ground and flows toward nearby water bodies.

channel flow
Runoff that flows into small channels that feed into larger channels that carry rivers and streams.

storage
The removal of water from circulation because it is frozen, held in a lake aboveground, or held in an aquifer belowground.

snowmelt
Water that has collected as snow or ice and been released as liquid.

Evaporation

Evaporation occurs when liquid water changes to an invisible gas or vapor. Through evaporation, a wet towel dries out when it is hung up, for example, and a wet driveway dries after a rain shower. Evaporation is more rapid from surfaces that have been warmed by the sun or other heat sources. Across the earth, enormous amounts of water are evaporated from oceans, lakes, and streams, as well as from the land surface. The water vapor then moves with the air vertically or horizontally above the earth.

Transpiration

Transpiration also moves water into the air. Water in the soil is taken up by the roots of plants. It then moves up into the plants' leaves and is released into the air through tiny pores in the leaves called stomata.

Advection

Advection, the movement of water vapor as it is carried by air currents, redistributes water evaporated from water and land surfaces.

Condensation

Most of us have observed condensation. On a hot summer day, for example, a glass of cold liquid is quickly covered with very tiny drops of water that eventually combine and run down the glass. When conditions are right, this process of condensation happens in the atmosphere: water vapor condenses on microscopic particles in the air and forms clouds that are made up of tiny water droplets or ice crystals.

Precipitation

As water droplets collide and combine or as ice crystals grow, they become too heavy to stay airborne and fall to the earth as drizzle, rain, hail, sleet, or snow. This process is called precipitation. The world's freshwater supply depends entirely on the various forms of precipitation.

Interception

When it first starts to rain during a storm event, the initial rainfall might not reach the ground as it encounters vegetation or other structures above ground level. The amount of rainfall that is intercepted above the ground can be substantial in wooded areas. Interception can keep relatively small storm events from increasing moisture in the ground.

Infiltration

Some of the rain or snow that falls on the ground during a storm event soaks into the soil. The movement of water through the earth's surface into the soil is called infiltration. How quickly the water moves through the soil surface depends on several factors, including the type of soil, how dry it is to begin with, and whether or not a crust has formed on its surface.

Subsurface Flow

After the water penetrates into the ground, it can move in several different directions. Relatively close to the surface, water can be taken up by the roots of plants.

Another portion of the infiltrated water can be drawn back up to the surface because of the capillary action of the soil. Capillary action is the force that causes water to rise above a water surface through porous soil. The capillary rise in coarse sand is only about 5 in. (125 mm), but it may be as much as 40 in. (1,000 mm) in some silty soil.

Most of the remaining infiltrated water continues to move downward below the root zone to a water-saturated area. This downward movement of water is called percolation.

In the subsurface, water can move toward stream channels and emerge to feed the streams. This kind of water movement is what keeps water flowing in streams as the base flow between storm events.

Runoff

During a storm event, when the precipitation rate exceeds the infiltration capacity of the soil, the excess precipitation flows downhill over the land surface. This process is called overland flow or surface runoff.

Surface runoff flows along the path of least resistance and often moves toward a primary watercourse or channel.

Channel Flow

Downhill from the land surfaces where runoff is first generated, the water typically begins to flow into channels. As these channels combine, the size of channels carrying the water increases until the water is flowing in a permanent channel such as a stream or river, or until it reaches a wetland or lake. Eventually, much of the water carried in channels of various sizes and shapes reaches the oceans or inland seas (such as the Dead Sea and the Great Salt Lake).

Storage

Water does not move continuously at the same rate around the globe but may be stored for a while and then released after a short time or a very long time. Water in the atmosphere is stored as vapor that may become visible as clouds. Surface water may be stored in ponds, natural lakes, and artificial reservoirs. Belowground, large aquifers may store water for a few years to thousands of years. At high elevations and in polar regions, water may be stored as ice and snow.

Snowmelt

Snow is a very important form of water storage. Snowmelt greatly prolongs the flow in many streams. If rainfall were the only source of water for surface water bodies, many streams would have very low flows or, in some cases, no flow during dry periods.

Many water supply systems, including most of those in the western United States and Canada, are dependent on the seasonal accumulating and melting of snow and glacial ice to provide an adequate water supply. The amount of available surface water in the spring and summer is affected by the amount of snow that accumulates in the winter and by spring temperatures. Climate warming trends can, in the short term, result in higher rates of glacial melt and an associated increase in the amount of water available downstream over several years in the near term. But over the long term, the amount of water released will decrease unless a sufficient amount of water accumulates as snow and ice each winter.

Groundwater

Groundwater accumulates as the result of percolation of water down to the water table through the void spaces in the soil and cracks in rock formations. (See Chapter 5 for more information on groundwater sources.) The place where groundwater accumulates is called an aquifer. An aquifer is defined as any porous water-bearing geologic formation. The size, thickness, and depth of aquifers can vary considerably. The largest aquifer in the United States is the Ogallala Aquifer, which underlies 147,000 square miles (380,728 square kilometers) across eight states.

An easy way to visualize groundwater is to fill a glass bowl halfway with sand, as shown in Figure 4-2. If water is poured onto the sand, it infiltrates into the sand and percolates down through the voids until it reaches the watertight (impermeable) bottom of the bowl. As more water is added, the sand becomes saturated and the water surface in the sand rises. The water in this saturated sand is equivalent to groundwater in an aquifer.

When the sand in the bowl is partially saturated with water, the level of the water surface can be found by poking a hole or cutting a stream channel in the sand. As illustrated in Figure 4-3, the level of water in the channel is the same as the level of the water surface throughout the sand. This level is called the water table. The water table may also be called the top of the groundwater, the top of the zone of saturation, or the top of the aquifer.

groundwater
Subsurface water occupying the saturation zone, from which wells and springs are fed. In a strict sense, the term applies only to water below the water table.

aquifer
A porous, water-bearing geologic formation. Generally restricted to materials capable of yielding an appreciable supply of water.

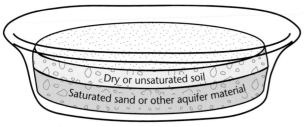

Figure 4-2 Simplified example of groundwater

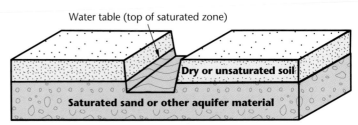

Figure 4-3 Illustration of a water table

Aquifers and Confining Beds

Groundwater occurs in two different kinds of aquifers: unconfined aquifers and confined aquifers.

Unconfined Aquifers

When the upper surface of the saturated zone is free to rise and fall, the aquifer is referred to as an unconfined aquifer or water-table aquifer (Figure 4-4). Wells that are constructed to reach only an unconfined aquifer are usually referred to as water-table wells. The water level in these wells indicates the level of the water table of the associated aquifer. The amount of water that the water-table well can produce may vary widely as the water table rises and falls in relation to the amount of rainfall that feeds or recharges the aquifer through percolation.

Confined Aquifers

A confined aquifer, or artesian aquifer, is a permeable layer that is confined between upper and lower layers that have low permeability. These layers, called confining beds (also known as aquitards or aquicludes), may consist of consolidated rock or clay. They restrict the movement of groundwater into or out of the aquifers.

As illustrated in Figure 4-5, the recharge area (the location where water enters the aquifer) is at a higher elevation than the main portion of the artesian aquifer.

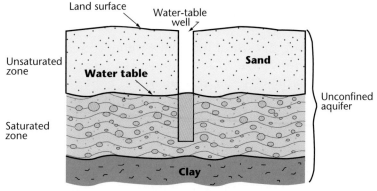

Figure 4-4 Cross section of an unconfined aquifer

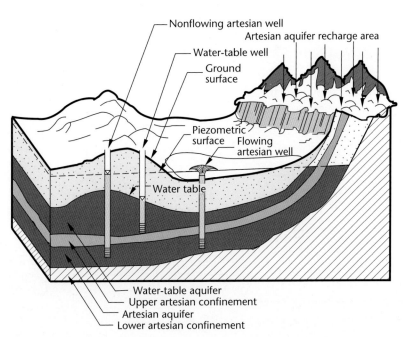

Figure 4-5 Cross section of a confined aquifer

As a result, the water is usually under pressure. Consequently, when a well is drilled through the upper confining layer, the pressure in the aquifer forces water to rise up above the confining layer. In some cases, the water rises above the ground surface, producing a flowing artesian well. In most cases, it does not rise as high as the ground surface and produces a nonflowing artesian well.

The height to which water will rise in wells located in an artesian aquifer is called the piezometric surface. This surface may be higher than the ground surface at some locations and lower than the ground surface at other points of the same aquifer.

There can be more than one aquifer beneath any particular point on the ground. For instance, there may be a layer of gravel, a layer of clay, another layer of sand or gravel, and another layer with low permeability. Some wells are constructed to tap several different aquifers. In locations where the water quality among aquifers varies, a well may be constructed to draw water only from the aquifer with the best quality.

Aquifer Materials

Aquifers may be made up of a variety of water-bearing materials. One characteristic that is important from the standpoint of water supply is the porosity, which represents the fraction of void space within a given amount of the material. The porosity determines how much water the material can hold. The other important characteristic is how easily water will flow through the material, a feature known as its permeability, or hydraulic conductivity. Both of these factors determine the amount of water an aquifer will yield. Figure 4-6 illustrates common aquifer materials.

Aquifers composed of material with individual grains such as sand or gravel are called *unconsolidated* formations. The range of sizes and the arrangement of the grains in the material are important. For example, two aquifers—one composed of fine sand and one of coarse sand—may contain the same amount of water, but the water flows faster through the coarse sand. A well in the coarse sand can therefore be pumped at a higher rate, and the pumping costs will be less.

Limestone and fractured-rock formations are *consolidated* formations. These formations produce water from channels, fractures, and cavities in the rock. Some fractured-rock formations can produce very large quantities of water. Limestone and fractured-rock formations with rapid flows are also more vulnerable to microbiological contamination.

Groundwater Movement

Water naturally moves downhill (downgradient) toward the lowest point. In the examples shown in Figures 4-3 and 4-4, the water will not move in any direction because the water table is flat. However, water tables are not usually flat.

porosity
An indication of the volume of space within a given amount of a material.

permeability
The characteristic of how easily water will flow through a material.

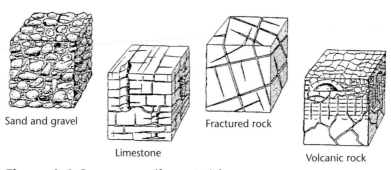

Sand and gravel

Limestone

Fractured rock

Volcanic rock

Figure 4-6 Common aquifer materials

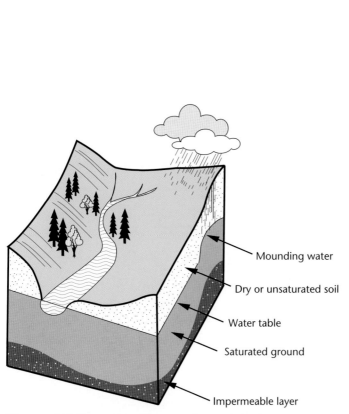

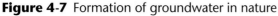

Figure 4-7 Formation of groundwater in nature

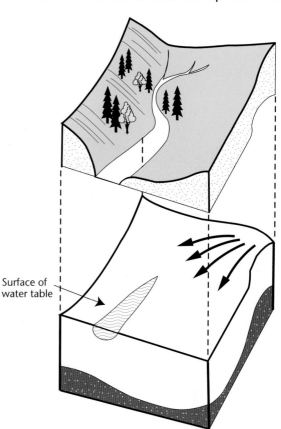

Figure 4-8 Groundwater movement

Figure 4-7 illustrates how a water table might actually occur in nature. When rain falls on the watershed, some of the rain infiltrates into the soil and percolates downward to the water table. A mound of water within the aquifer is then built up above the level of the rest of the water table. The water within this mound slowly flows downgradient, increasing the level of the water table slightly and, if the water table is high enough, draining into the stream channel. In most areas, more rain occurs before the mound completely drains off, so the water table never becomes level.

The movement of groundwater is illustrated further in Figure 4-8, in which a cutaway view shows a section of the ground surface. The water table is continuous and sloped, and the groundwater moves downgradient toward the lowest point—the stream channel. In this example, the water table is above the level of the stream channel. Consequently, water will flow into the stream. But, if the water table is below the streambed, water will infiltrate from the stream to the aquifer.

Springs

Springs occur where the water table intersects the surface of the ground or where the water-bearing crevices of fractured rock come to the surface (Figure 4-9). Springs flowing out of sand or soil often come from a source that is relatively close. Springs flowing out of fractured rock can come from more distant locations, and their origin is usually difficult to determine.

Because of the difficulty in determining where spring water is coming from, springs should generally be considered contaminated until proven otherwise. Many supposed "springs" have stopped flowing after a broken underground water pipe was repaired.

spring

A location where groundwater emerges on the surface of the ground.

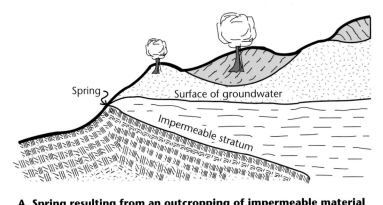

A. Spring resulting from an outcropping of impermeable material

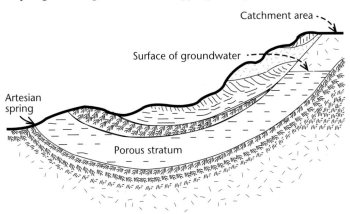

Figure 4-9 Common types of springs

B. Spring resulting from a recharged porous stratum

WATCH THE VIDEO
Aquifers (www.awwa.org/wsovideoclips)

Surface Water

Surface water in lakes and streams provides a source of water for many public water supply systems. (See Chapter 6 for more information on surface water sources.) The amount of surface water available varies widely by region of the country and also by season of the year.

The quality of the surface water available for water system use also varies. Some locations are fortunate to have very clean water available; in other areas, the only available sources require extensive treatment to make the water safe and palatable for human consumption.

Chemical Constituents of Rain and Snow

Precipitation in the form of rain or snow is the source of water for most surface-water supplies. The amount of foreign material in rain and snow is minimal in comparison with the amount that the water will later pick up as it moves over land or through the ground. In general, precipitation dissolves the gases in the atmosphere as the water falls to the ground, and it also collects dust and other solid materials suspended in the air. Once on the ground, flowing water picks up soil particles and microbes and dissolves various chemicals it comes in contact with.

surface water
All water on the surface, as distinguished from groundwater.

Atmospheric deposition is the process whereby airborne particles and gases are deposited on the earth's surface. Because the particles and gases in the atmosphere are from natural sources such as forest fires, volcanoes, and oceanic salt and from human-induced windblown soil and materials released into the air from combustion, industrial processes, motor vehicles, and other sources, there is considerable variation in the constituents of rain and snow. In general, precipitation without the impact of human activities is chemically very soft, is low in total solids and alkalinity, has a pH slightly below neutral (pH 7), and is corrosive to most metals.

There is considerable variability in the constituents of precipitation, depending on local conditions. The National Atmospheric Deposition Program monitors the chemistry of precipitation at more than 200 sites nationwide. Annual average concentrations of the constituents of precipitation are shown in Table 4-1.

Constituents Added During Runoff

Precipitation that falls on the ground surface and does not infiltrate into the soil or evaporate into the air travels over the land surface to a surface water body. As it travels, a variety of materials may be dissolved into the water or taken into suspension. Consequently, the type and amount of various constituents reflect both the surface characteristics and the geology of the area.

The presence of soluble formations near the surface (such as gypsum, rock salt, and limestone) has a marked effect on the chemical characteristics of surface water. In contrast, where the geological formations are less soluble, as is the case with sandstone or granite, the composition of the surface water in the area tends to be more similar to the composition of local rain.

If water flowing over the ground surface is exposed to decomposing organic matter in the soil, the carbon dioxide level of the water is increased. An increase in carbon dioxide causes the formation of additional carbonic acid and lowers the pH of the water. Consequently, the water becomes more corrosive. This corrosiveness in turn increases the amount of mineral matter dissolved by the water.

Groundwater Augmentation of Surface Water

Figure 4-10 illustrates how streamflow is augmented by groundwater. If the water table adjacent to the stream is at a higher level than the water surface of the stream, water from the water table will flow to the stream (a gaining stream). This is referred to as groundwater discharge. Conversely, when the water table is below the stream surface, water from the stream infiltrates into the ground (a losing stream). The recharge of groundwater from a stream is illustrated in Figure 4-11.

Table 4-1 Annual average concentrations of the constituents of precipitation

Calcium	0.02–1.27 mg/L as calcium (Ca^{2+} ions)
Magnesium	4–105 µg/L as magnesium (Mg^{2+} ions)
Sodium	15–980 µg/L as sodium (Na^+ ions)
Ammonium	0.01–0.95 mg/L as ammonium (NH_4^+ ions)
Chloride	0.03–1.639 mg/L as chloride (Cl^- ions)
Sulfate	0.1–2.6 mg/L as sulfate (SO_4^{2-} ions)
Nitrate	0.2–2.2 mg/L as nitrate (NO_3^- ions)
pH	4.3–6.3
Mercury	3.6–19.4 ng/L as mercury (Hg)

Source: National Atmospheric Deposition Program (NADP) 2000 Annual Summary. 2001.
Additional data are available at the NADP Internet site: http://nadp.sws.uiuc.edu.

drainage basin
An area from which surface runoff is carried away by a single drainage system. Also called *catchment area*, *watershed*, or *watershed drainage area*.

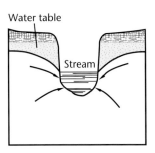

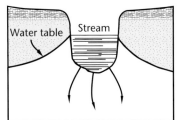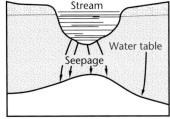

A. High water table　　**B. Low water table**

Figure 4-10 Surface flow from groundwater seepage

Figure 4-11 Streamflow recharging groundwater

Surface Runoff

The drainage basin or watershed is the land surface that contributes water to area streams and water bodies. The amount and flow rate of surface runoff through the drainage basin are highly variable, depending on both natural conditions and human influences. In some cases, water is held on the surface for a relatively long time. This is generally good from a water resources standpoint because it allows more water to infiltrate into the ground and recharge aquifers. If water runs off slowly, it also generally causes less erosion and creates less flooding. At the same time, the longer the water is in contact with the soil, the greater the mineral content of the water will be. Surface water running quickly off land may be expected to have all of the opposite effects.

As shown in Figure 4-12, a drainage basin or watershed is surrounded by high ground—a divide—that separates one watershed from another. The land area of the drainage basin or watershed is sloped toward a watercourse.

Watercourses

Typical natural watercourses include brooks, creeks, streams, and rivers. There are also many human-made features that are constructed to hasten the flow of surface water or to divert it in a direction different than it would flow under

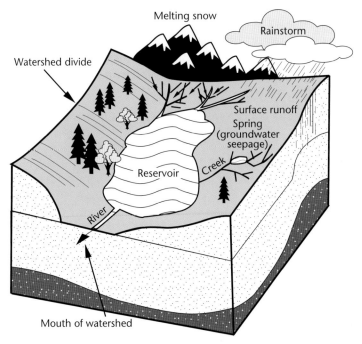

Figure 4-12 Schematic of a typical watershed

natural conditions. Such structures include ditches, channels, canals, aqueducts, conduits, tunnels, and storm sewers.

 WATCH THE VIDEO
Surface Water Sources (www.awwa.org/wsovideoclips)

Introduction to Water Treatment

Most groundwater and surface water sources contain contaminants. The types and concentrations of these contaminants determine the treatment (if any) necessary to provide safe and potable water to the public. The waterworks industry is tasked with providing drinking water that is acceptable for human consumption, compliant with federal drinking water standards, and aesthetically acceptable. Each day, this industry supplies 40 billion gallons of safe drinking water to people in the United States.

Health-Related Treatment

In recent years, the American public began to question the safety of its drinking water. The concept of the risk of illness caused by drinking water has replaced the concept of safe drinking water. To be acceptable for human consumption, water must be free of harmful organic and inorganic substances, radionuclides, and organisms capable of causing disease. Chemicals, though, are sometimes added to drinking water to benefit public health. For example, the benefit of maintaining fluoride in drinking water to reduce the incidence of cavities in children's teeth is well documented. When treatment chemicals are added to the water, a risk trade-off may be created. When this happens, operators are required to weigh the risks against the benefits in an effort to serve the greater good.

Aesthetic-Related Treatment

Drinking water should be aesthetically acceptable—i.e., palatable. Palatable drinking water should be free of turbidity, unpleasant taste, odor, and color. It should not contain high concentrations of hardness, dissolved solids, or minerals, such as iron and manganese, which can stain clothes.

Iron and manganese are removed using oxidation and subsequent filtration, as discussed in Chapters 12, 14, and 17. Lime–soda softening (Chapter 16) and ion exchange (Chapter 17) are used to soften hard water. The turbidity of surface water is reduced to aesthetically acceptable levels using conventional coagulation–flocculation and sedimentation together with filtration, or coagulation with direct filtration, or by membrane processes alone or in combination with pretreatment.

Treatment Required by Regulations

Advancements in health effects research combined with improved technologies for water quality analysis and water treatment have increased the complexity of the current drinking water regulatory environment. Pending drinking water regulations and recent modifications to existing regulations will significantly impact US drinking water utility planning and operations during the next decade and beyond. Among the general trends in regulatory developments that drinking water treatment and distribution operators have recently experienced, and that will

palatable
Pleasing to the taste.

probably continue into the foreseeable future, are (a) increasing complexity in attaining compliance, (b) increasing complexity in proving and documenting compliance, and (c) increasing reliance on "treatment technique" approaches (e.g., as used in the Surface Water Treatment Rule, Lead and Copper Rule, and so forth) as opposed to the more traditional "MCL" approach (e.g., using the limits set for arsenic and other metals except lead and copper, trichloroethylene and other organic contaminants, and so forth).

The history and development of drinking water standards is summarized in *Water Quality and Treatment* (2011, 6th edition). The reader is encouraged to review the "Reg Watch" each month in the *Journal AWWA* for recent updates in the compliance environment. The *Federal Register* publishes all proposed and final rules and regulations.

Water Treatment Process Selection

The selection of a water treatment process or processes to produce drinking water acceptable for human consumption is usually governed by the water supply source and the lifecycle costs involved in the production of an acceptable finished water. Most engineers agree that the choice of processes depends on the

- water supply source (groundwater or surface water),
- required finished water quality,
- capital and operating costs,
- process footprint versus land availability,
- residuals' disposal, and
- applicability to the multiple-barrier approach.

Groundwater Sources

Groundwater is water located below the water table in aquifers. It is a source of drinking water retrieved by the construction of wells or similar underground structures. There are 140,000 public water systems in the United States that rely on groundwater alone. These systems serve a population of about 100 million people. About 40,300 of the public groundwater systems are classified as "community water systems."

The US Environmental Protection Agency (USEPA) updated the Groundwater Rule in October 2006, and compliance with it was due in December 2009. This rule focuses on fecal contamination and requires groundwaters whose sources may be at risk to provide 4-log inactivation of viruses.

The quality and temperature of groundwater remain relatively constant from year to year but may exhibit variability from well to well. Groundwater quality is usually superior to that of surface water with regard to turbidity, harmful microorganisms, and total organic matter. A groundwater's mineral content, however, is often undesirable. High hardness (calcium and magnesium) and high iron and manganese concentrations are usually associated with groundwater. Dissolved gases, such as hydrogen sulfide, are often found in groundwaters. Trace concentrations of organic chemicals, such as pesticides and other synthetic organic chemicals, can be a concern.

Pumping costs associated with groundwater are higher than those associated with surface water.

WATCH THE VIDEO
Groundwater Sources (www.awwa.org/wsovideoclips)

Surface Water Sources

Surface water is considered to be all water exposed to the atmosphere, as distinguished from subsurface waters and groundwaters. Examples of surface waters are streams, rivers, lakes, and reservoirs. USEPA states that there are about 11,670 surface water systems in the United States classified as "community water systems." Surface water systems serve about 70 percent of the total population that receives drinking water.

USEPA considers all surface water to be contaminated by disease-causing microorganisms and has mandated that this water receive adequate treatment to reduce to an acceptable level the risk of illness to the public. USEPA has also mandated that surface waters' turbidity be reduced to specified levels.

Compared to groundwater, surface water is subject to rapid changes in water quality, especially during periods of heavy rains, spring runoff, or accidental spills. Surface water is also susceptible to algae blooms, which can cause changes in source water turbidity, alkalinity, taste, odor, and pH.

Other Considerations

Required finished water quality is governed by federal regulations and aesthetic water quality considerations. Capital and operating costs, process footprint requirements, and disposal of residuals are engineering decisions discussed in detail in following chapters.

Multiple-Barrier Approach

The multiple-barrier approach is a proven concept that continues to influence how the design of water treatment plants is regulated in the United States. The term multiple-barrier approach, when applied to the task of providing clean, safe drinking water, refers to the ability of the water industry to maintain a protected water source; to provide appropriate and adequate treatment; to provide, operate, and maintain a distribution system; and to provide adequate monitoring of regulated contaminants. This historically proven and reliable concept has been used for many years. It adopts the European "precautionary" principle and has been embraced by the USEPA Federal Advisory Committee on Microbial/Disinfection By-products in their approach to control *Cryptosporidium parvum*—i.e., source water protection, physical removal, and inactivation of the barriers. The multiple-barrier approach to water treatment is the foundation of optimizations programs like the Partnership for Safe Water.

Water treatment systems are evaluated by performance (log removals of a target organism, such as *C. parvum* or virus) and by reliability (online time). A multiple-barrier water treatment train incorporates multiple unit operations that provide a high level of performance such that the treatment train meets the targeted removal even if the most effective single unit process fails.

The following example (Forbes 2000) best explains the concept:

> A water treatment engineer is considering two different treatment trains. Alternative 1 incorporates a single unit process that, when properly operated, achieves 6-log removal of the target organism. Alternative 2 incorporates three independent unit operations in series, each of which achieves 2-log removal. Assume that each process fails 1 percent of the time and during that time provides zero removal.

Both alternatives provide 6-log removal, but the multiple-barrier alternative reduces the risk of total failure. The single-barrier alternative provides 6-log reduction 361 days of the year and zero-log reduction for 5 days. The three-barrier alternative provides 6-log removal for 350 days of the year and zero-log removal for only 32 seconds each year. The single barrier exposes the population to zero treatment for 5 days of the year. The multiple-barrier alternative provides at least

2-log removal except for 32 seconds of the year. The risk is significantly less for the multiple-barrier alternative.

Selection of Treatment Methods

The types of water treatment that are regularly used to improve water quality, remove microorganisms, and reduce the level of toxic substances fall into the following general categories.

Air Stripping and Aeration

Air stripping and aeration (Chapter 17) are processes used in water treatment to remove dissolved gases (carbon dioxide and hydrogen sulfide), taste-and-odor compounds, and volatile organic compounds. Aeration is used to oxidize iron and manganese and to prevent septic conditions.

Coagulation Processes—Mixing and Flocculation

The coagulation processes (Chapter 8) are used in water treatment to aggregate small particles, such as clay, turbidity, and natural organic matter, into larger particles that can be removed from the water using processes such as sedimentation, conventional filtration, or membrane processes. Other constituents removed by coagulation processes include microorganisms, iron, manganese, and organic chemicals that are removed by adsorption onto the particles.

Ion Exchange

Ion exchange (Chapter 17) with zeolites and synthetic ion exchange resins is a process used to exchange unwanted ions (constituents that ionize), such as calcium and magnesium, that cause hardness for another ion, such as sodium–ion exchange softening. Unwanted ions, such as arsenic, barium, radium, and nitrate, are removed using the ion exchange process. Total organic carbon (TOC) can be removed by a specific type of ion exchange, which is discussed in Chapter 17. The largest application of ion exchange in municipal water treatment is sodium softening. Ion exchange is used in industrial water treatment to demineralize water and exchange all cations for hydrogen and all anions for hydroxide.

Chemical Precipitation

The process of chemical precipitation is discussed in three chapters, Lime Softening Basics (Chapter 16), Introduction to Iron and Manganese Treatment (Chapter 12), and Fluoridation (Chapter 13). Lime precipitation is the most common form of chemical precipitation and uses the same processes as iron and manganese control and fluoridation—i.e., rapid-mix, coagulation–flocculation, and sedimentation.

Iron and manganese are commonly removed from water after oxidation with oxidizing agents, such as potassium permanganate, oxygen, and chlorine. Filtration is used to remove the precipitated iron and manganese.

Membrane Processes

Membrane processes (Chapter 17) include microfiltration for removal of particles, such as turbidity and disease-causing microorganisms; ultrafiltration for removal of large-molecular-weight organics; nanofiltration for the removal of divalent ions—another effective softening technology—and reverse osmosis for demineralization. Microfiltration processes enhance and, in some cases, replace conventional water treatment technologies. Microfiltration also provides high water quality to reverse osmosis systems for water reuse and aquifer recharge. Nanofiltration is replacing conventional lime softening.

Disinfection

Disinfection (Chapter 11) of municipal water includes chemical oxidation with the most common oxidants used in water treatment—i.e., chlorine, chloramines, ozone, chlorine dioxide, and permanganate. It also discusses the emerging technology of ultraviolet disinfection of waters.

Adsorption

Adsorption (Chapter 17) in water treatment uses powdered or granular activated carbon for the removal of dissolved organics, color, and taste-and-odor-causing compounds.

Disposal of Treatment Wastes

Prior to enactment of the Clean Water Act in 1987 and the environmental protection laws that followed, residuals created in water treatment processes (e.g., slurries and brines) were generally disposed of in the easiest way possible and at a relatively low cost. Under increasingly stringent regulations and public scrutiny, disposal of water treatment residuals is now a major consideration in the selection of which processes to use, and it is a significant cost of plant operation. As such, this edition will include a separate chapter on treatment of wastes produced by the drinking water treatment process (Chapter 17).

Study Questions

1. The movement of water from leaves, grasses, and other plants to the atmosphere is called
   a. organic evaporation.
   b. condensation.
   c. transpiration.
   d. capillary action.

2. A term used to describe cloud formation is
   a. transpiration.
   b. evaporation.
   c. condensation.
   d. precipitation.

3. An artesian aquifer could occur in a(n)
   a. confined aquifer.
   b. unconfined aquifer.
   c. water table aquifer.
   d. shale formation.

4. The process whereby water moves with the air currents in the atmosphere is called
   a. transpiration.
   b. evaporation.
   c. interception.
   d. advection.

5. The place where groundwater accumulates is called a(n)
   a. ground source.
   b. water table.
   c. channel.
   d. aquifer.

6. Drinking water that is aesthetically acceptable is considered
   a. palatable.
   b. sterile.
   c. potable.
   d. harmless.

7. Providing several treatment processes that can each remove a water contaminant is an example of what?

8. Which function of the hydrologic cycle is described as water moving with the air currents in the atmosphere?

9. Which function of the hydrologic cycle is described as water that has collected as snow or ice being released as liquid?

10. In what direction does water naturally move?

Chapter 5
Groundwater Quality and Wells

Groundwater Quality

Groundwater is not as vulnerable to direct pollution and contamination as surface water, but given such conditions as leaky underground storage tanks, chemical spills, failure of on-site waste treatment systems, underground injection of wastes, inadequate well protection, leaching from landfills, and overfertilization of crops, contamination can become a serious problem.

Aquifer Contamination

Because of the protective soil cover and the natural filtration provided by aquifer material, the biological characteristics of groundwater are generally very good. Because harmful bacteria do not penetrate very far into the soil, wells more than 50 ft (15 m) deep are generally free of harmful organisms. Some exceptions to this are aquifers with large voids in fractured rock or aquifers with conduits (such as improperly abandoned wells) that provide pathways for contaminants to enter the aquifers.

Many cases of groundwater contamination (Figure 5-1) are a result of either poor well construction or poor waste disposal practices on the land overlying the aquifer. Other sources of contamination may include recharge from nearby surface waters or excessive pumping near coastal areas, resulting in saltwater

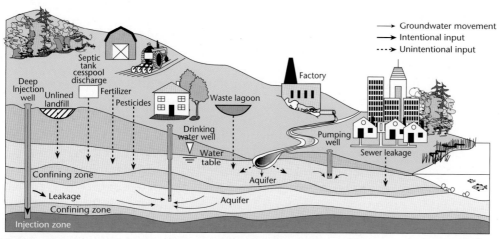

Figure 5-1 Sources of groundwater contamination

Source: *Monitoring and Assessing Water Quality, National Water Quality Inventory: 1998 Report to Congress*, Chapter 7, page 6, USEPA.

intrusion into the groundwater resources. The movement of water in the ground can treat water naturally. Many water supply systems, especially in European countries, employ riverbank-filtered water as their source of supply.

Chemical Characteristics

Groundwater acquires its chemical characteristics in two ways: from contact with soil and rock underground and from incorporation of surface water that percolates into the aquifer. Typically, aquifers are recharged by the rain that falls on the aquifer recharge area. This water is generally free of anthropogenic contaminants if the rain falls on land that is free from pollution; but the water can become contaminated if it carries undesirable chemicals from the landscape. In agricultural areas, for example, water that percolates down into an aquifer can be contaminated with nitrates, herbicides, or pesticides.

Not all contamination of groundwater comes from surface contamination. In coastal areas, saltwater intrusion presents a major concern. Under natural conditions, the boundary between subsurface fresh water and subsurface salt water near the coast is generally in equilibrium and moves very little. When well operation removes the fresh water faster than it is replenished, the salt water moves underground toward the wells. Where saltwater intrusion is a threat, wells may still be used, but withdrawal rates must be limited to prevent saltwater from reaching the wells.

Several natural contaminants affect the potability of groundwater. Some elements and compounds are beneficial or harmless in low concentrations; they become troublesome or harmful only when found in high concentrations. Some contaminants, such as barium, arsenic, and various radionuclides, are harmful at even very low levels. Gases that are undesirable in groundwater include hydrogen sulfide, methane, and radon. Common groundwater contaminants and their associated problems are listed in Table 5-1.

Chemical Contaminants

Synthetic organic compounds in the vicinity of public water supply wells are a very serious concern. Chemicals that have been carelessly disposed of on the ground or buried in unlined pits have been found in many well supplies. Some of these chemicals are considered a health threat at concentrations far less than can be detected by taste or smell. The only way they can be detected is by relatively complicated and expensive tests.

One common contaminant that makes groundwater unfit to drink is gasoline, which is a complex mixture of toxic organic compounds. Thousands of wells, mostly private individual home wells (but some public supplies, too), have been contaminated because of leaking underground gasoline tanks. Less widespread, but not uncommon, is contamination from underground fuel oil storage.

If chemical contamination of a well is detected, it is generally best to abandon the well and use another water source. If no alternative source is available, the chemicals can usually be removed from the water by aeration or carbon adsorption processes. But it is much more desirable to prevent groundwater contamination in the first place than to have to treat the contaminated water indefinitely.

Table 5-1 Common groundwater quality problems

Constituent	Source	Type of Problem	USEPA Primary Drinking Water Standards*	USEPA Secondary Drinking Water Standards†
Inorganic Constituents				
Arsenic	Naturally occurring‡	Toxic	0.05 mg/L	—
Fluoride	Naturally occurring	Stains teeth, can cause tooth damage at high levels	4.0 mg/L	—
Hydrogen sulfide	Naturally occurring	Offensive odor, flammable, corrosive	—	0.05 mg/L
Iron	Naturally occurring	Stains plumbing fixtures and laundry, causes tastes	—	0.3 mg/L
Manganese	Naturally occurring	Discolors laundry and plumbing fixtures, causes tastes	—	0.05 mg/L
Nitrate	Fertilizer and fecal matter	Toxic to infants	10 mg/L (as nitrogen)	—
Radioactivity	Naturally occurring	Cancer causing	Gross alpha activity (15 pCi/L) Radium 226 and 228 (5 pCi/L)	—
Sodium	Naturally occurring	May contribute to high blood pressure	—	Being investigated
Sulfate	Naturally occurring‡	Laxative effect	—	250 mg/L
Total dissolved solids	Naturally occurring‡	Associated with tastes, scale formation, corrosion, and hardness	—	500 mg/L
Organic Constituents				
Pesticides and herbicides	Agricultural and industrial contamination	Many are toxic; cause tastes and odors	Several are regulated	—
Solvents	Industrial contamination	Many are toxic; cause tastes and odors	Being developed	—
Microbiological Constituents				
Disease-causing microorganisms	Fecal contamination	Cause variety of illnesses	Coliform bacteria are regulated as indicator organism	—
Iron bacteria	Contamination from surface	Produce foul-smelling slimes, which plug well screens, pumps, and valves	—	—
Sulfate-reducing bacteria	Contamination from surface	Produce foul-smelling and corrosive hydrogen sulfide	—	—

Note: USEPA = US Environmental Protection Agency

*State regulations may be more restrictive.

†Not enforceable at federal level.

‡The naturally occurring elements can also be present as a result of contamination by humans.

Source: *Basics of Well Construction Operator's Guide.*

Water Well Terminology

Wells are the most common means of accessing groundwater. This section describes the various parts of a well and defines some common terms associated with wells.

Parts of a Well

Although wells come in many varieties and brands, some components are common to all types (Figure 5-2). At the surface, all wells should have a **sanitary seal**, which prevents contamination from entering the **well casing**. The seal is generally a metal plate with a rubberized gasket around its perimeter that fits snugly into the top of the well casing. It has openings into the well for the discharge pipe, the pump power cable, and an air vent to let air into the casing as the water level drops. A sanitary seal for a small well with a submersible pump is illustrated in Figure 5-3.

The well casing is simply a liner placed in the borehole to prevent the surrounding rock and soil from collapsing into the shaft and blocking it. The casing (generally made of steel or plastic pipe) may not be necessary where the well extends into solid rock that has little risk of collapsing into the well. Where the well extends into solid rock, the casing is generally extended from the ground surface through the soil or seated into the rock to prevent soil from falling into the shaft.

sanitary seal

A well feature that prevents contamination from entering the well.

well casing

The metal pipe used to line the borehole of a well.

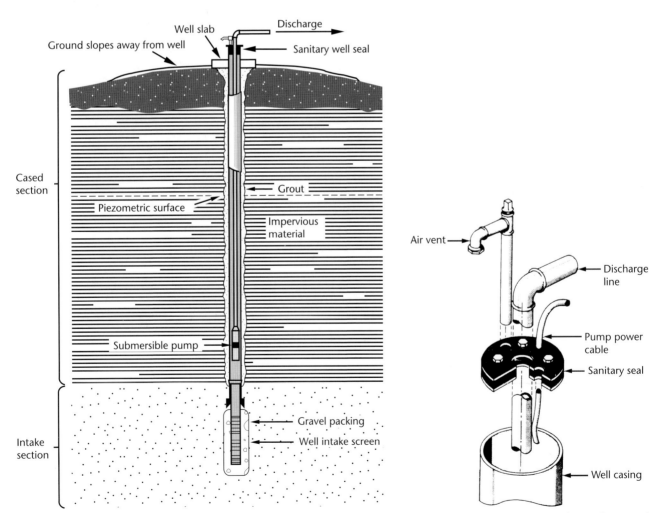

Figure 5-2 Parts of a typical well

Figure 5-3 Components of a sanitary seal

The space between the casing and the borehole above the production zone (i.e., where groundwater is withdrawn from the aquifer) is filled with grout to help prevent water from traveling along the outside of the casing and to support the casing. Where a well penetrates several aquifers, the grout also keeps water from flowing between aquifers along the outside of the well casing.

A **well screen** (intake screen) may be placed in a formation or highly fractured rock aquifer at intervals along the well where water intake is desired. The well screen prevents rock and soil from entering the well while letting in water. Often in a well that is screened in soil, sand is packed between the screen and the soil to fill the area and keep out sediment that would otherwise get into the well. Where the well has been drilled through solid rock, water may enter the well mainly through fractures in the rock rather than through the pores of the rock. In this case, the fractured zones may be screened to prevent rock chips around the fracture from falling into the well.

The **well slab** is a concrete area placed around the casing of some wells to support pumping equipment and to help prevent surface water from contaminating the well water.

Well Terms

Hydraulic characteristics of a well that are important during well operation are as follows:

- Static water level
- Pumping water level
- Drawdown
- Cone of depression
- Zone of influence
- Residual drawdown
- Well yield
- Specific capacity

The following discussion describes these characteristics. Several are illustrated in Figure 5-4.

Static Water Level

The **static water level** in a well is the level of the water surface in the well when no water is being taken from the aquifer. It is normally measured as the

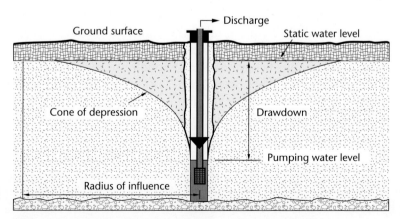

Figure 5-4 Hydraulic influence of a well on an aquifer

depth from the ground surface to the water surface and may be converted to elevation for comparison with information about other wells in the area. This is an important measurement because it is the basis for monitoring changes in the water table.

In some areas, the water table is just below the ground surface; usually, it is several feet below the surface. In other areas, there is no groundwater near the surface, and a well may not pass through any water until an aquifer is intercepted at hundreds or even thousands of feet below the surface.

Pumping Water Level

When water is pumped out of a well, the water level usually drops below the level in the surrounding aquifer and eventually stabilizes at a lower level, called the pumping level. The level varies depending on the pumping rate. The water intake or submerged pump must be located below this level. It is also preferred to limit the pumping rate so that this level is above the screened portion of the well (or, in an open rock well, above water-bearing fractures) to prevent water from continually cascading down the sides of the well.

Drawdown

The drop in water level between the static water level and the pumping water level is called the drawdown of the well.

Cone of Depression

In unconfined aquifers, water flows from all directions toward the well during pumping. The free water surface in the aquifer then takes the shape of an inverted cone or curved funnel called the cone of depression. In a confined aquifer, the water pressure within the aquifer will also be much less at the well than at some distance from the well. A graph of the pressure versus distance from the well will also have the shape of a curved funnel that is centered on the well.

Zone of Influence

The size of the area that is affected by drawdown depends on the porosity, conductivity, and other properties of the aquifer. When drawdown occurs, the water table (or pressure, in the case of an unconfined aquifer) is affected significantly out to some distance away from the well. That horizontal distance is called the radius of influence (Figure 5-4), and the entire affected area is called the zone of influence.

If the aquifer is composed of material that transmits water easily, such as coarse sand or gravel, the cone of depression may be almost flat and the zone of influence relatively small. If the material in the aquifer transmits water slowly, the cone will usually be quite steep and the zone of influence large.

If possible, wells should be situated far enough apart that their zones of influence do not overlap. The effect on the cones of depression of two wells located close together is illustrated in Figure 5-5. Pumping a single well reduces the water level in the other well, and pumping both simultaneously creates an undesirable interference in the drawdown profiles.

Residual Drawdown

After the pumping of a well has stopped, the water level in the well rises back up toward the static water level. If the water level does not quite reach the original level, the distance it falls short is called the residual drawdown.

---

water table
The upper surface of the zone of saturation closest to the ground surface.

drawdown
The difference between the static water level and the pumping water level in a well.

cone of depression
The cone-shaped depression in the groundwater level around a well during pumping.

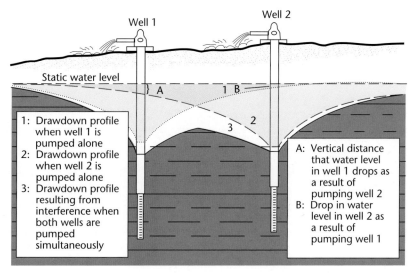

Figure 5-5 Overlapping cones of depression of two wells

Well 1

Well 2

Static water level

1: Drawdown profile when well 1 is pumped alone
2: Drawdown profile when well 2 is pumped alone
3: Drawdown profile resulting from interference when both wells are pumped simultaneously

A: Vertical distance that water level in well 1 drops as a result of pumping well 2
B: Drop in water level in well 2 as a result of pumping well 1

Well Yield

Well yield is the rate of water withdrawal that a well can supply over a long period of time. The yield of small wells is usually measured in gallons per minute (liters per minute) or gallons per hour (liters per hour). For large wells, it may be measured in cubic feet per second (cubic meters per second).

When more water is taken from an aquifer than is replaced by recharge, the drawdown gradually reaches greater depths and the safe well yield is reduced. Under prolonged pumping, the drawdown can get so low that the pump begins to suck air, which will damage it. To prevent this damage to the pump, water can be kept at a safe level by limiting the pump rate, lowering the pump depth, or operating the pump for shorter periods of time.

Ideally, wells should pump continuously with no permanent drawdowns. A more common practice is to pump wells that have a significant drawdown for only a few hours each day, allowing an extended period for the aquifer to recover. But even this is difficult, as the long-term capacity of an aquifer can be determined by short-term tests and study of the geology of the area. Rarely is a consultant paid to determine that sustainable water supplies are not available. The result is the potential for aquifer drawdown accompanied by aquifer mining and land subsidence. Confounding the problem is that many aquifer systems cross political boundaries, so careful regulation in one jurisdiction may not be supported by others.

US Geological Survey (USGS) Report 1323 by Reilly et al. (2009) outlines the current condition of groundwater in the United States. The report estimates that the pumpage of fresh groundwater in the United States is approximately 83 billion gallons (314 billion L) per day (Hutson and others 2004), which is about 8 percent of the estimated 1 trillion gallons per day of natural recharge to the nation's groundwater systems (Nace 1960). Though this small percentage may not sound like a serious issue, Reilly et al. found that the loss of groundwater supplies in many areas will be catastrophic, affecting economic viability of communities and potentially disrupting lives and ecological viability. Figure 5-6 combines regional water-level declines and local water-level declines for changes on a national scale and shows declines in water levels over the last 40 years throughout the United States. The Great Plains states, Texas, and the western states are particularly affected. The red regions indicate areas in excess of 500 square miles (130 km2) that

well yield
The rate of water withdrawal that a well can supply over a long period of time.

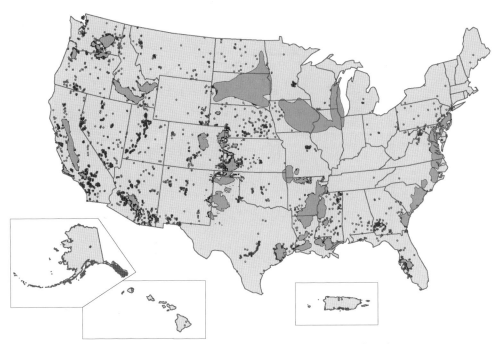

Figure 5-6 Regional and local water-level declines on a national scale

have water-level decline in excess of 40 ft (12 m) in at least one confined aquifer since predevelopment, or in excess of 25 ft (8 m) of decline in unconfined aquifers since predevelopment. Blue dots are wells in the USGS National Water Information System database where the measured water-level difference over time is equal to or greater than 40 ft (12 m). This decline would indicate that groundwater in these areas is not sustainable and therefore will become less available with time. Given the critical nature of this issue, Reilly et al. (2009) call for a coordinated nationwide effort to organize available information on changes in groundwater storage.

Bloetscher (2009) notes that drilling deeper is not a solution. Deeper waters tend to have poorer water quality, having been in contact with the rock formation longer and absorbed more dissolved minerals. Therefore, while a deep aquifer may be prolific, water obtained from a well that taps into it may not be desirable or potable without substantial amounts of treatment. In addition, most deeper aquifers are confined and therefore do not recharge significantly locally. The withdrawal of water may appear to be a permanent loss of the resource in the long term. For example, portions of the Black Creek aquifer in eastern North and South Carolina were virtually depleted by pumpage because there is no local recharge. As a result, the aquifer was mined, exceeding its safe yield, and the large utilities converted to surface water. Likewise, most of the aquifers in the western United States have minimal potential for recharge. In parts of the western plains states and Great Basin, the aquifers have dropped hundreds of feet (meters). With an average of 13–18 in. (33–46 cm) per year of rainfall and high evaporation rates throughout the summer, there is little potential that the aquifer will be recharged (Bloetscher and Muniz 2008).

The current evaluation suggests the likelihood of conflicts over water supplies in the near future. To reduce this potential, laws must be enacted that resolve water rights and water quality issues. In the absence of negotiated settlements between the parties in conflict over water rights or withdrawal rights, these cases often go to court and are not likely to be quickly decided there.

Identifying critical natural capital requires a systematic analysis and evaluation of whether environmental resources are being used sustainably, the extent of any sustainability gaps, the economic and environmental pressures, and public policies aimed at improving ecological systems. Ekins (2003) suggests criteria that can be used:

- Maintenance of human health to avoid negative health impacts
- Avoidance of loss of ecological function
- Economic sustainability—maintenance of economic activities on a basis that does not deplete the resource

Specific Capacity

One of the most important concepts in well operation and testing is **specific capacity**, which is a measure of well yield per unit of drawdown. It can be calculated as follows:

$$\text{specific capacity} = \text{well yield} \div \text{drawdown}$$

For example, if the well yield is 200 gpm (757 L/min) and the drawdown is measured to be 25 ft (7.6 m), the specific capacity is

$$200 \text{ gpm} \div 25 \text{ ft (or } 757 \text{ L/min} \div 7.6 \text{ m)} = \text{specific capacity}$$

$$\text{specific capacity} = 8 \text{ gpm per 1 ft (or 30 L/min per 0.3 m) of drawdown}$$

The calculation is simple and should be made frequently in the monitoring of well operation. A sudden drop in specific capacity indicates trouble such as pump wear, screen plugging, or other problems that can be serious. These problems should be identified and corrected as soon as possible.

Types of Wells

Wells are generally classified according to their type of construction as follows:

- Dug wells
- Bored wells
- Driven wells
- Jetted wells
- Drilled wells

Dug Wells

A dug well can furnish large quantities of water from shallow groundwater sources. Dug wells are uncommon because of the cost to install them and the potential for contamination of the shallow aquifers and the wells themselves. Small-diameter wells can be constructed manually with pick and shovel; larger wells are constructed with machinery such as a clamshell bucket if the soil conditions are suitable. Figure 5-7 illustrates a typical dug well installation.

If the exposed soil will stand without support, it may not be necessary to line the excavation until the water table is reached. Precast or cast-in-place concrete liners, commonly called curbs, are used to seal the shaft. The liners in contact with

specific capacity
A well's pumping rate divided by the drawdown.

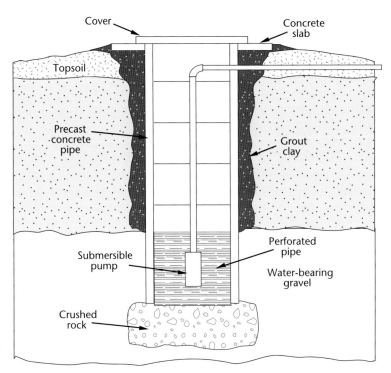

Figure 5-7 Construction of a dug well

the water-bearing layers are perforated to allow water to enter. If the aquifer is sandy material, a layer of gravel is placed around the curb to act as a sand barrier.

Yield from a dug well increases with an increase in diameter, but the increase is not directly proportional. Dug wells serving a public water system may be 8–30 ft (2–9 m) in diameter and 20–40 ft (6–12 m) deep.

Most dug wells do not penetrate much below the water table because of the difficulty of excavating in the saturated soil. For this reason, a dug well may fail if the water level recedes during times of drought or if there is unusually heavy pumpage from the well.

The surface opening of a dug well is large, making protection from surface contamination difficult. For that reason, state regulatory agencies usually classify these wells as being vulnerable to contamination, and the wells must be treated as a surface water source. Disinfection and possibly filtration treatment will be required if the water source is to be used by a public water system.

Bored Wells

Wells can be constructed quickly by boring where the geologic formation types are suitable. The formation must be soft enough for an auger to penetrate yet firm enough so it will not cave in before a liner can be installed. The most suitable formations for bored wells are glacial till and alluvial valley deposits.

A bored well is constructed by driving an auger into the earth. Bored wells are limited to approximately 3 ft (1 m) in diameter and depths of 25–60 ft (8–18 m) under suitable conditions. As the auger penetrates, extensions are added to the drive shaft. A casing is forced into the hole as material is removed until the water-bearing strata are reached. Installing well screens or a perforated casing in the water-bearing sand and gravel layer completes the well.

Cement grout is used to surround the casing to prevent entrance of surface water, which could cause contamination. Bored wells are infrequently used for public water supplies.

Driven Wells

Driven wells are simple to install; however, they are practical only when the water-bearing formations are relatively close to the surface and no boulders or bedrock exist in the soil or other formations between the surface and the aquifer. These wells consist of a pointed well screen, called a drive point, and lengths of pipe attached to the point. The point has a steel tip that enables it to be pounded through some gravel or hardpan (a hard layer of cemented soil near the ground surface) to the water-bearing formation (Figure 5-8).

The diameter of the well pipe varies from as small as 1 in. (32 mm) up to 4 in. (107 mm). The maximum depth that can be achieved is generally 30–40 ft (9–12 m). This well type is not generally used for public water supply because of the potential for environmental contamination of shallow aquifers and because of the well's relatively small diameter—a single well cannot produce the quantity of water generally needed for public supply. However, a battery of points may be used for greater production, with several wells connected by a common header to a suction-type pump. A suction pump can be used only when the static water level is no deeper than about 15 ft (5 m).

A smaller-diameter pilot hole is usually drilled or driven before driving the well to make installation easier and help prevent damage to the well casing. This casing of durable pipe can be pounded into the earth or placed in a bored hole. The casing prevents water contamination if there should be leaky joints in the well pipe.

After the outer casing is in place, the inner casing with a perforated well point is inserted. The drive point is then driven into the water-bearing formation.

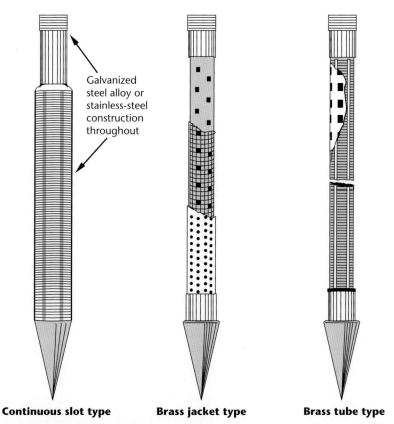

Galvanized
steel alloy or
stainless-steel
construction
throughout

Continuous slot type   **Brass jacket type**   **Brass tube type**

Figure 5-8 Different types of driven-well points

Source: *Manual of Individual Water Supply Systems.* 1982.

Jetted Wells

A jetting pipe, which is equipped with a cutting knife on the bottom, is used to construct jetted wells. Water is pumped down the pipe and out of the drill bit against the bottom of the hole. The high-pressure water jet at the bottom of the pipe, in coordination with the cutting knife, loosens and removes the soil beneath the pipe and allows it to advance downward.

The casing is usually sunk as the drilling progresses until it passes through the water-bearing formation. The well screen connected to a smaller-diameter pipe is then lowered into the casing, and the outer casing is withdrawn to expose the screen to the formation. These wells are generally suited to sandy formations and cannot be constructed by jetting through clay or hardpan or where there are boulders in the formation.

Drilled Wells

Drilled wells are the most commonly used well type for public water supplies because they can be installed in almost any situation. They can be constructed to extreme depths with small or large well diameters (up to 4 ft [1.5 m] or possibly larger). They are also the most common type of well drilled for oil extraction.

A drilled well is constructed using a drilling rig and casing. The rig makes the hole, and casing is placed in the hole to prevent the walls from collapsing. Screens are installed when water-bearing formations are encountered at one or more levels. The more commonly used methods of drilling water supply wells are the following:

- Cable tool method
- Rotary hydraulic method
- Reverse-circulation rotary method
- California method
- Rotary air method
- Down-the-hole hammer method

Cable Tool Method

The percussion drilling method, commonly referred to as the cable tool method, has been used extensively for wells of all sizes and depths but has waned in popularity because faster and easier methods have been developed. There are many commercial varieties of cable tool rigs. The operating principle for all varieties is the same. They use a bit at the end of a cable that is repeatedly raised and dropped to fracture the soil material. The drilling tool has a clublike chisel edge that breaks the formation into small fragments. The reciprocating motion of the drilling tool mixes the loosened material into a sludgelike substance.

In each run of the drill, a depth of 3–6 ft (1–2 m) of the hole is drilled. The drill is then pulled from the hole, and a bailer is used to remove the sludge. The bailer consists of a section of casing 10–25 ft (3–8 m) long, slightly smaller in diameter than the drilled hole, and having a check valve in the bottom. A casing is forced into the hole as soon as it is necessary to prevent a cave-in of the walls.

As the drill operates, an operator continually adjusts the length of stroke and rapidity of blows based on experience and the feel of the vibrations. A skilled operator will be able to distinguish the hardness of the formation being drilled by the vibrations in the cable and can sense the passing of the drill from one formation to another. As drilling progresses, samples of the cuttings will be taken periodically to check on the type of formation being penetrated.

After drilling the well to the maximum desired depth, a screen is lowered inside the casing and held in place while the casing is pulled back to expose the screen (Figure 5-9). The top of the screen is then sealed against the casing by expanding a packer of neoprene rubber or lead. When a well reaches consolidated rock, the normal practice is to seat the casing firmly in the top of the rock (providing a secure seal where the casing meets the rock) and drill an open hole to the depth required to obtain the needed yield (Figure 5-10).

Rotary Hydraulic Method

In the rotary method of well drilling, the hole is made by spinning a cylinder-shaped bit on the bottom of multiple sections of drill pipe. The speed of rotation can be varied to achieve the best cutting effectiveness for different types of soil and rock.

Drilling fluid (typically a thin slurry of clay and water, also called drilling mud) is pumped down to the bit (Figure 5-11). The fluid flows out through holes in the bit, picks up loosened material, and carries it up the borehole to the surface. The circulating fluid also helps to cool the bit and keep the hole open during drilling. The fluid that flows to the surface overflows from the well and is routed by a ditch into a settling pit or tub, where the cuttings settle out. The fluid can then be reused.

Clay that is added to the drilling fluid will adhere to the sides of the hole and, together with the pressure exerted by the drilling fluid, prevents a cave-in of the

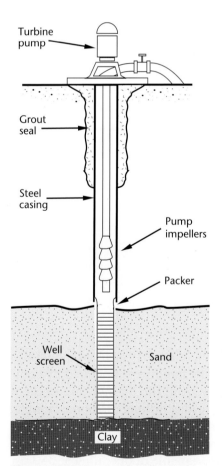

Figure 5-9 Exposed well screen

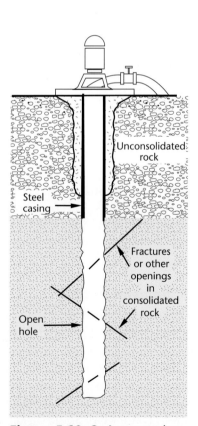

Figure 5-10 Casing seated at top of rock layer with an open hole underneath

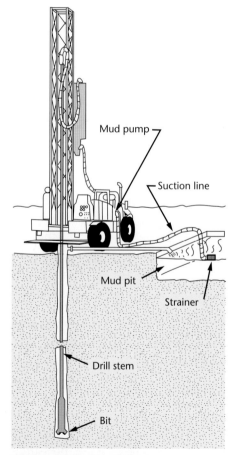

Figure 5-11 Circulation of drilling fluid in a direct rotary drilling rig

formation material. In some cases, native clay can be used; otherwise, prepared materials such as bentonite (a commercially available, highly expansive clay) or a special powdered substance is used. The drilling fluid is prepared in a pit near the drilling operation before it is pumped into the well. Its composition can be varied depending on the material that is being drilled through.

Reverse-Circulation Rotary Method

The reverse-circulation rotary method of drilling differs from the regular rotary method in that the drilling fluid is circulated in the opposite direction. The advantage is that because water is generally used as the drilling fluid, the method can be used where drilling additives are undesirable. This method is also particularly well suited for constructing gravel-packed wells, because the drilling fluid mixture used in the regular rotary method tends to plug the walls of the well.

Drilling fluid is forced down through the borehole and returns to the surface in the hollow drill pipe, carrying the cuttings with it. A pump with a capacity of 500 gpm (1,900 L/min) or more is required to keep the fluid moving at high velocity. If an abundant freshwater supply is available, the discharge can be diverted to waste and not recycled. Otherwise, the cuttings are allowed to settle in a large pit and the fluid is recirculated.

Both rotary methods can drill holes up to 5 ft (1.5 m) in diameter, and the drilling is usually faster than cable tool drilling.

California Method

The California method, also called the stovepipe method, was developed primarily for sinking wells in unconsolidated material such as alternating strata of clay, sand, and gravel. The process is similar to the cable tool method except that a special bucket is used as both bit and bailer. Each time the bit is dropped, some of the cuttings are trapped in the bailer. When the bailer is filled, it is raised to the surface and emptied.

The process also uses short lengths of sheet metal for casing. The casing is forced down by hydraulic jacks or driven by means of cable tools. After the casing is in place, it is perforated in place using special tools.

Rotary Air Method

The rotary air method is similar to the rotary hydraulic method except that the drilling fluid is air rather than a mixture of water and clay. The method is suitable only for drilling in consolidated rock. Most large drill rigs are equipped for both air and hydraulic drilling so that the method may be changed as varying strata are encountered.

Down-the-Hole Hammer Method

A method frequently chosen to drill wells into rock uses a pneumatic hammer unit that is attached to the end of the drill pipe. The hammer is operated by compressed air. The air also cleans the cuttings away from the bit and carries them to the surface. For most types of rock, this is the fastest drilling method available.

The drilling rig for this method must be furnished with a very large air compressor. Most standard rigs use 750–1,050 ft³/min (0.35–0.49 m³/sec) of air at a pressure of 250 psi (1,700 kPa). Some rigs are also capable of operating at 350 psi (2,400 kPa), which will advance the drill twice as fast as a standard rig. A drilling rig of this type is illustrated in Figure 5-12.

Figure 5-12 A truck-mounted drilling rig
Courtesy of Ingersoll-Rand Company.

Special Types of Wells

The names of several types of wells refer not to their method of construction, but to other characteristics. Two such types are discussed here:

- Radial wells
- Bedrock wells

Radial Wells

Radial wells are commonly used near the shore of a lake or near a river to obtain a large amount of relatively good-quality water from adjacent sand or gravel beds. Radial wells are also used in place of multiple vertical wells to obtain water from a relatively shallow aquifer or to obtain water from a surface body in such a way that the sediment underneath the river or lake acts as a filter. A radial well can be described as a dug well that has horizontal wells projecting outward from the bottom of the vertical central well (Figure 5-13). The central well, or caisson, serves as the water collector for the water produced by the horizontal screened wells.

Construction of a radial well begins by sinking the central caisson, which is generally 15–20 ft (5–6 m) in diameter. The caisson is made by stacking poured-in-place reinforced concrete rings, each about 8–10 ft (2–3 m) high. The first section is formed with a cutting edge to facilitate the caisson's settling within the excavation. As sediment is excavated from within the caisson, the concrete ring sinks into place. Additional sections are then added and the excavation progresses. When the desired depth is reached, a concrete plug is poured to make a floor.

Horizontal wells are then constructed through wall sleeves near the bottom of the water-bearing strata. The laterals may be constructed of slotted or perforated pipe, or they may have conventional well screens. Each horizontal well is constructed with a gate valve located inside the caisson to enable subsequent dewatering or to

radial well
A very wide, relatively shallow caisson that has horizontally drilled wells with screen points at the bottom. Radial wells are large producers.

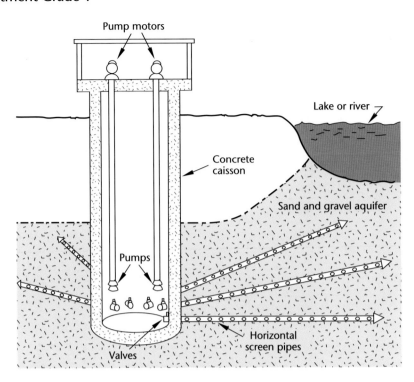

Figure 5-13 Details of a radial well

be closed if use of individual collector wells is discontinued. A superstructure is then erected on top of the caisson to house pumps, piping, and controls.

Bedrock Wells

Bedrock wells are drilled into the underlying bedrock. Water flows to the well through fractures in the bedrock rather than from a saturated layer.

Well Construction Procedures

Wells can be constructed using several procedures. The principal factors affecting the choice of construction method are how deep the well must be and whether the material around the well is gravel, clay, or rock. After a well has been constructed, it is usually necessary to specially treat the well to obtain optimum productivity and water quality. The last step in well construction is to run pumping tests to confirm the well's capacity.

Well Components

As discussed previously, most wells share certain common components. A few in particular merit a closer look as they relate to well construction:

- Well casings
- Gravel pack
- Well screens
- Grouting

Well Casings

A well casing is a lining for the drilled hole that maintains the opening from the land surface to the water-bearing formation. The casing also helps prevent surface water from contaminating the water being drawn from the well.

Materials commonly used for well casings include alloyed or unalloyed steel, fiberglass, and plastic. The principal factors determining the suitability of casing materials are the stress that will be placed on the casing during installation and the corrosiveness of the water and soil that will be in contact with the casing.

When a well is being drilled by the cable tool method, the casing is driven as soon as it becomes necessary to prevent the walls of the well from caving in. A drive shoe of hardened steel is attached to the lower end of the pipe, and a drive head is attached to the top of the pipe to withstand the hard blows of driving the casing into the ground. As the drilling progresses, the casing is continually pounded by the action of the drilling equipment.

Wells constructed using rotary methods are not usually cased until the well hole has been completed. A casing diameter smaller than the hole is used so that the casing does not have to be driven.

If additional protection from corrosion and surface water pollution is required, an outer casing is first installed and an inner casing is lowered into place. The space between them is filled with cement grout.

Gravel Pack

Gravel pack is used in formations composed of fine-grained soils having uniform grain size. As illustrated in Figure 5-14, a bed of gravel is installed around the

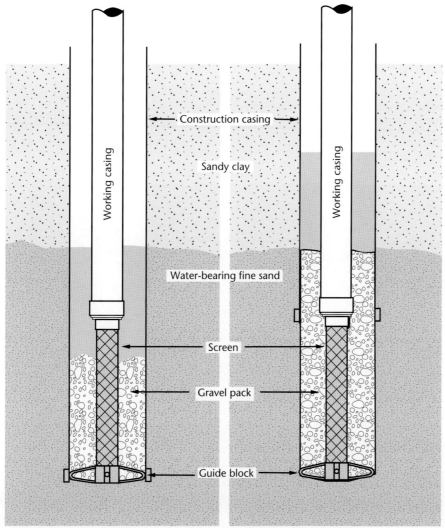

A. Gravel-wall well with casing in place   B. Completed gravel-wall well

Figure 5-14 Gravel-wall well construction

screen, which in effect gives greater surface area for the infiltration of water into the well, while effectively blocking the entrance of sand.

The most common construction method is to install a large-diameter casing into the water-bearing strata and then lower a small casing with a well screen into the hole. The area around the screen is then filled with gravel as the outer casing is withdrawn corresponding to the length of the screen. The gravel used must be clean, washed, and composed of well-rounded particles that are four to five times larger than the median size of the surrounding natural material. The size and gradation of the gravel are critical in effectively blocking the entrance of fine sand.

Well Screens

Wells completed in unconsolidated formations such as sand and gravel are usually equipped with screens (Figure 5-15). A properly sized screen allows the maximum amount of water from the aquifer to enter the well with a minimum of resistance, while blocking formation materials from passing into the well. Well screens are made from a variety of materials, including plastic, mild steel, red brass, bronze, and stainless steel. Types of well screens include sawn or slotted, wound, and bridged and louvered. The type of screen and material used depends on the type of soil, corrosivity of the water, cleaning and redevelopment methods, and other factors.

The size of a screen, or the slot number, is usually expressed in thousandths of an inch or in millimeters. The slot size is usually selected to permit some of the formation material to pass through it, depending on the uniformity of the grains. During development of the well, the fines pass through the screen while larger particles are held back, forming a graded natural-gravel barrier around the screen (Figure 5-16). The gravel pack is placed between the screen and the formation to help stabilize the formation materials.

The open area of the screen after the well has been developed must be carefully estimated because up to 50 percent of the screen slots may be plugged by

Figure 5-15 Properly designed well screen

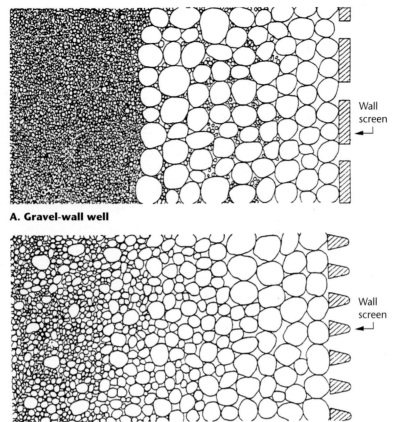

A. Gravel-wall well

B. Properly developed drilled well in natural formation

Figure 5-16 Coarse material used to hold fine sand away from a well screen

formation particles. After the slot size has been determined, either the screen length or diameter must be adjusted to provide the total required screen opening.

Information and specifications for screen selection are furnished in AWWA A100, *Standard for Water Wells* (latest edition).

Grouting

Wells are cemented, or grouted, for the following reasons:

- To seal the well from possible surface water pollution
- To seal out water from water-bearing strata of unsatisfactory quality
- To protect the casing against exterior corrosion
- To restrain unstable soil and rock formations

After a well is drilled and its casing installed, space is left along the length of the well between the casing and the formation material. This cavity must be sealed to prevent contaminants from getting down the well, either directly from the land surface or through formations with crevices connected to the surface (Figure 5-17). In formations that tend to cave in, such as sand, the cavity tends to seal itself eventually as the material shifts against the casing; in stable formations, such as solid rock, the cavity may remain indefinitely open if it is not filled.

When corrosion of the casing is likely, a well is usually drilled larger than the casing so that the extra space can be filled with grout. Grout typically contains bentonite and portland cement. Portland-cement grout is usually mixed in a ratio of about one bag of cement to 5.5 gal (21 L) of clean water. Special additives are often used to accelerate or retard the time of setting and provide other special

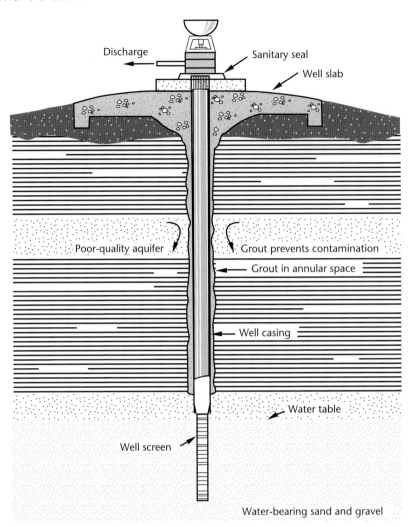

Figure 5-17 Sealed annular space that prevents contamination

properties to the grout. Bentonite clay is used because it expands, thereby filling the voids around the casing.

The grout must be placed in the annular space, starting at the bottom and progressing upward so that no gaps or voids exist in the seal. Different methods may be used to place the grout, depending on the size of the annular space, including a dump bailer, water-pressure driving, pumping, or a tremie pour. Grout must be placed in compliance with state regulations.

Pumping Tests

After a well is developed and the quality of water produced is satisfactory, pumping tests are performed. These practical tests are intended to confirm that the well will produce at its designed capacity. Most water supply well contracts specify the duration of the drawdown test that must be conducted to demonstrate the yield of the aquifer.

Many well acceptance tests are conducted with a temporary pump installed, usually powered by a gasoline or diesel engine. The test period for public water supply wells is generally at least 24 hours for a confined aquifer and 72 hours for an unconfined aquifer.

A means of measuring the flow rate of the pumped water must be provided. A commercial water meter, an orifice or weir, and periodic checking of the time required to fill a container of known volume are all methods of measuring flow rate.

The pumping rate must be held constant during the test period, and the depth to the water level in the well must periodically be measured. Drawdown is usually measured frequently (often at 1-minute intervals) during the first hour or so of the test and is then measured at gradually longer intervals (often up to 10-minute intervals) as the test period progresses.

Sanitary Considerations

Whenever possible, wells should be developed from formations that are deep enough to protect the water from surface contamination. Where a shallow groundwater source must be used, surface water contamination can be reduced if an impervious surface is created over the ground surface surrounding the well. One method is to place a 2-ft (0.6-m) layer of clay having a radius of about 50 ft (15 m) around the well. Filling the space between the casing and the hole with cement grout prevents contamination of wells by surface water flowing along the exterior of the casing. A concrete cap or platform should then be put in place around the well and built high enough to prevent floodwater from entering the well. The construction methods for wells are detailed by state regulatory agencies and, in some cases, by local jurisdictions as well. The well driller must follow the requirements, and the installation must be approved before the well is certified for use.

It is almost impossible to completely avoid contamination of the soil, tools, aquifer, casing, and screen during construction, so the water from the well, even after development, is likely to be contaminated. Extended pumping will usually rid the well of contamination, but disinfection with a chlorine solution is often quicker and more desirable.

A well is typically disinfected by the addition of sufficient chlorine to give a concentration of 50 mg/L. The pump can then be started and stopped to surge the disinfectant into and out of the aquifer, throughout the length of the well, and through the pump components. It is difficult to disinfect gravel packing by this procedure, so powdered or tablet calcium hypochlorite is usually added when the gravel is being placed.

For more details and specific procedures, refer to AWWA C654, *Standard for Disinfection of Wells* (latest edition).

Aquifer Performance

The sustained use of a well depends on the performance of the aquifer as a whole. Aquifer parameters also define how pumping in one well will affect other wells. These parameters are generally obtained via the pumping tests performed after well construction is complete. To measure changes in an aquifer during the pumping tests, small-diameter test wells called observation wells are installed. There is no set number of observation wells that should be used. One well positioned near an operating well is sometimes sufficient, but several may be required under different circumstances.

Aquifer Evaluation

The evaluation of an aquifer requires precise knowledge of the location of observation wells. The distances measured between the well being tested and the observation wells—and between the observation wells themselves—should be established carefully. The water level in each observation well is periodically measured relative to an elevation reference point, or benchmark.

One method of measuring the water depth in a test well is to use a steel tape graduated in tenths and hundredths of a foot (or metric units), with a weight attached (Figure 5-18A). The tape is chalked and lowered into the well until the weight reaches the bottom. When the tape is withdrawn, the water depth is indicated by the wetted position on the tape. Electronic depth-measuring devices are also available. They include a probe that is lowered into the well to activate a signal when water is contacted (Figure 5-18B).

Another way of measuring water depth, effectively used for many years for fixed installations, is the air-pressure tube method (Figure 5-18C). A small-diameter tube is suspended in the well beneath the water level, and the exact distance from the bottom of the tube to the ground surface is known. The top of the tube is fitted with a pressure gauge and a source of compressed air. Determining the water depth involves forcing air into the tube until it bubbles from the submerged end of the tube. The pressure gauge is then read, and the submerged length of tube can be calculated from the pressure required to displace the column of water in the tube.

 WATCH THE VIDEO
Water Wells/Groundwater (www.awwa.org/wsovideoclips)

Evaluating Performance

Aquifer performance can be evaluated by three methods:

- Drawdown
- Recovery
- Specific-capacity

In the drawdown method, the production well is pumped and water levels are periodically observed in two or more observation wells. The data are plotted

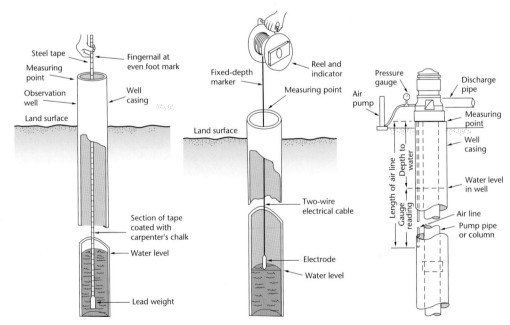

A. Chalked steel tape method   **B. Electronic measurement**   **C. Air-pressure tube method**

Figure 5-18 Methods of measuring water level depth in wells

and can be analyzed by various methods to relate drawdown in feet (or meters) to time measured in hours or days at a specific pump rate.

The recovery method involves measuring the change in water level in an observation well after the pumping has been stopped.

The specific-capacity method involves a relatively short test. As discussed earlier, specific capacity is the well yield per unit of drawdown. It does not indicate aquifer performance as completely as the other tests. However, it is especially valuable for evaluating well production after a period of time and for making comparisons with the data from when the well was new.

Well Operation and Maintenance

When a well is in service, it is important to maintain and monitor records for any performance changes that might indicate future problems. Data from the following tests should be recorded regularly for each well:

- Static water level after the pump has been idle for a period of time
- Pumping water level
- Drawdown
- Well production
- Well yield
- Time required for recovery after pumping
- Specific capacity

Conditions for these tests should be the same each month so that direct comparisons can be made.

Regular maintenance of all the structures, equipment, and accessories is important to provide long-term, trouble-free service. Wells can fail if the casing or screen collapses or corrodes through. Perhaps the most common operational problem for wells is the plugging of the screen. The causes of screen plugging can be mechanical, chemical, or bacteriological. It is usually best to get professional assistance to correct the problem. If the screen is accidentally damaged, repair can be extremely expensive; the entire well may have to be replaced.

Periodically, bacteriological samples should be collected directly from each well and tested. If there are indications of contamination, periodic disinfection of a well may be necessary to prevent growth of nuisance bacteria that can lead to production problems.

Well Abandonment

When test holes and production wells are no longer useful, their equipment should be dismantled and their shafts sealed before they are abandoned. Proper preparation of a test hole or well for abandonment will accomplish the following:

- Eliminate a physical hazard
- Prevent groundwater contamination
- Conserve the aquifer
- Prevent mixing of desirable and undesirable water between aquifers

The basic objective governing the proper sealing of abandoned wells is the restoration of the geologic and hydrologic conditions that existed before the well was constructed. Each well that is abandoned should be considered unique. The methods used should be those that will give the best results at that location. Recovery of pumps, casings, screens, and other hardware is best performed by the firm that installed the well. The well construction company is also likely to be the best firm to complete the abandonment procedures properly.

Springs and Infiltration Galleries

Springs and infiltration galleries are both types of conduits between groundwater and surface water. While it is important to recognize their hydrologic importance, they are not typically used as the water source for a public water supply because it is difficult to predict their reliability and more effort is required to protect them from contamination.

Springs

Springs occur where groundwater exits the ground surface (i.e., where the groundwater surface and ground surface intersect) and are typically found at the base of a hill. Artesian springs occur where water from a confined aquifer is under enough pressure to flow to the surface through fractures in the rock or soil. Springs generally take the form of free-flowing water from fractures in an exposed bedrock surface or embankment or as seeps in soil embankments.

Springs are difficult to protect from contamination because they are generally closely connected to surface water infiltration and because the water intake is at the ground surface. This is in contrast to deep wells, which are not as readily influenced by surface water and which have pumps with intakes at depths below where animals or humans can easily access. When a water supply intake is placed at a spring, it should be enclosed in a tamper-proof, vermin-proof concrete box, and the site should have diversion channels that route surface drainage around the area. Furthermore, the protective structure should be designed to prevent clogging by sediment, debris, or ice. Drains should be installed to prevent stagnation during times of low flow, and access ways should be built to allow for periodic inspection and cleanout. Operational and structural controls should be in place to keep chemicals a safe distance away from the spring and outside the spring's recharge area. Regulatory requirements for treatment and periodic chemical analysis should be determined. They tend to be more stringent and more costly for springs than for well sources.

Flow rates from springs are often strongly influenced by the time of year and the amount of recent precipitation. Drought conditions or climate changes that reduce precipitation over an extended time may significantly reduce the rate of flow from a spring. So before a spring is depended on for water supply, adequate observations should be made to ensure that the spring is as reliable as it needs to be.

Infiltration Galleries

infiltration gallery
A subsurface structure to receive water filtered through a streambed.

The purpose of an infiltration gallery is usually to collect water from a surface water source at a point where the water can flow down through a filter material, such as several feet or meters of sand or gravel, to remove most of the particulate

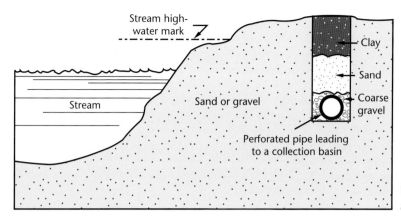

Figure 5-19 Example of an infiltration gallery

matter. It is generally more costly to install infiltration galleries than surface water intakes, and they are used when the cost for primary treatment and infiltration of the surface water justifies the additional effort.

As illustrated in Figure 5-19, a typical infiltration gallery installation involves the construction of a trench that is parallel to a streambed and about 10 ft (3 m) beyond the high-water mark. Perforated or open joint pipe is placed in the trench in a bed of gravel and then covered with a layer of coarse sand. The pipe and gravel can be wrapped with a geotextile filter fabric for additional filtration and to prevent silt clogging of the gravel pack.

The upper part of the trench is filled with fairly impermeable material to reduce entry of surface water. The collection pipes terminate in a concrete basin from which water is pumped. Although the water collected in an infiltration gallery may be of much better quality than the surface source, it will not necessarily be free of all turbidity (cloudiness) or pathogenic (disease-causing) organisms. The water is therefore generally treated in compliance with state and federal requirements for surface water.

Study Questions

1. The most frequent in-situ well treatment is the application of a(n)
   a. chemical to adjust the pH of well water that is either too acidic or too alkaline.
   b. phosphate inhibitor to prevent well pump corrosion.
   c. oxidant to reduce iron bacteria.
   d. coagulant for high-turbidity well water.

2. Which of the following is usually used to disinfect the gravel packing of a groundwater well?
   a. Chlorine dioxide
   b. Powder of calcium hypochlorite tablet
   c. Sodium hypochlorite
   d. Chloramines

3. Which of the following is the most common well operational problem?
   a. Plugging of the pump with sediment
   b. Pump failure
   c. Plugging of the well screen
   d. Corrosion of the well's metal parts

4. Which of the following is the last step in well construction?
   a. Placement of the well seal
   b. Disinfection
   c. Installation of the pump
   d. Pump test to confirm capacity

5. Which gas occurs mainly in groundwater, is heavier than air, and is odoriferous?
   a. Hydrogen sulfide
   b. Carbon dioxide
   c. Radon
   d. Methane

6. Disinfection of water wells with free chlorine requires exposure for _____ at a concentration of _____.
   a. 6–12 hours; 25 mg/L
   b. 12–24 hours; 25 mg/L
   c. 12–24 hours; 50 mg/L
   d. 24–48 hours; 100 mg/L

7. The percussion drilling method, commonly referred to as the cable tool method, has been used extensively for wells of all sizes and depths but has waned in popularity because
   a. of the geological damage caused by this method.
   b. faster and easier methods have been developed.
   c. wells are no longer deep enough to necessitate this method.
   d. this method releases harmful by-products into the surrounding ground.

8. What water quality problems are prevalent in groundwater?

9. What is a well casing?

10. What is the term for the level of the water surface in the well when no water is being taken from the aquifer?

11. What term refers to the rate of water withdrawal that a well can supply over a long period of time?

12. Which type of wells are commonly used near the shore of a lake or near a river to obtain a large amount of relatively good-quality water from adjacent sand or gravel beds?

Chapter 6
Surface Water Source Treatment

Surface Water Sources

Surface water is the term used to describe water on the land surface. The water may be flowing, as in streams and rivers, or quiescent, as in lakes, reservoirs, and ponds. Surface water is produced by runoff of precipitation and natural groundwater seepage. In this book, surface water is defined as all water open to the atmosphere and subject to surface runoff. That definition distinguishes surface water from both groundwater and ocean water.

Most large population centers in the United States are supplied by surface water sources. Although groundwater is used as a water supply source in rural areas and by most small communities, it is rare for sufficient groundwater to be available to serve large cities. Many large cities, such as those around the Great Lakes and along many major rivers, have thrived because of the availability of fresh water. In the arid Southwest, water may be routed great distances to a city from other areas through canals or pipelines.

Surface Runoff

Patterns of surface runoff are described in terms of land areas that drain rainfall and melting snow to a certain point in a river or stream. Those land areas may be called drainage areas, drainage basins, catchments, or watersheds. Each watershed is bounded by relatively high ground called a divide, which separates it from other watersheds.

Groundwater from springs and seeps also contributes flow to most streams. This is often referred to as base flow. If the adjacent water table is at a level higher than the water surface of the stream, water from the water table will flow to the stream (Figure 6-1). If the water table is at a level lower than the water surface of the stream, the stream will recharge the groundwater. The pattern of flowing to or from the stream can vary according to seasonal fluctuation of the water table. Many streams would dry up shortly after a rain if it were not for groundwater flow.

Influences on Runoff

The following principal factors affect how rapidly surface water runs off the land:

- Rainfall intensity
- Rainfall duration
- Soil composition

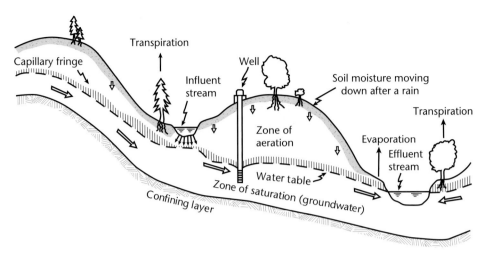

Figure 6-1 Groundwater and stream interaction
Adapted from Linsley et al. 1999.

- Soil moisture
- Ground slope
- Vegetation cover
- Human influences

Rainfall Intensity In a typical storm event, the intensity of rainfall is low at first, and the initial rainfall soaks into, or infiltrates, the ground (provided the ground has not been paved over or built upon). As rainfall intensity increases and the ground becomes wetter, however, the rate at which the rain falls will eventually exceed the rate at which the ground can absorb it, and runoff will be generated.

Rainfall Duration The amount of runoff increases with rainfall duration for two reasons:

1. As the soil gets wetter, its capacity to absorb more rain decreases.
2. After runoff begins, a portion of each additional increment of rainfall is converted to runoff.

Soil Composition The composition of the surface soil also significantly influences how much runoff is produced. Coarse sand, for example, has large void spaces that allow water to pass through readily, so even a high-intensity rainfall on sand may result in little runoff. In contrast, even light rainfall on relatively impervious soils, such as those that contain a lot of clay, tends to result in a relatively large amount of runoff. Clay soils not only have small void spaces, but the soil swells when wet. This expansion closes the void spaces, further reducing the infiltration rate and resulting in greater surface runoff.

Soil Moisture If soil is already wet from a previous rain, surface runoff occurs sooner than if the soil were dry. Consequently, the amount of existing soil moisture has an effect on surface runoff. If the ground is frozen, it is essentially impervious, and runoff from rain or melting snow may approach 100 percent.

Note that although the increase in soil saturation means a sharp decrease in its capacity to absorb water (i.e., its infiltration rate), the saturation of a soil does not mean it has altogether lost its capacity to absorb water. Depending on the soil composition, a saturated soil's infiltration rate can still be significant.

Ground Slope   Where land is relatively flat, runoff tends to spread out and soak into the ground more easily. Where land is sloped more steeply, however, runoff more readily collects in rivulets and flows downstream, resulting in a relatively high rate of runoff.

Vegetation Cover   Vegetation plays an important role in limiting runoff. One way it affects runoff is through the process of interception. As discussed in Chapter 4, interception refers to the collection or disruption of rainfall by vegetation or aboveground structures before it can reach the ground.

Vegetation also influences runoff through its impact on surface conditions and soil composition. At the surface, decaying organic litter such as leaves, branches, and pine needles readily absorbs water and helps move it into the ground. Vegetation and organic litter also act as a cover to protect soil from getting compacted or crusted over. The physical interception of rainfall by vegetation prevents raindrops from dislodging fine soil that can clog open channels at the soil surface or be transported downstream as sediment. Vegetative cover also reduces evaporation of soil moisture.

Decaying vegetative matter on top of the soil eventually becomes part of the soil. Soil that is high in such organic matter can absorb relatively large amounts of water while maintaining many openings through which water can pass to the soil layers below.

Human Influences   Human activities can have a dramatic effect on rates and amounts of surface runoff. The impervious surfaces of buildings and of streets and other paved areas greatly increase the amount of runoff and the peak flow rates that occur during a storm. Drainage structures such as gutters, ditches, and canals have conventionally been designed to convey water efficiently downstream, diminishing the opportunity for water to soak into the ground and percolate to groundwater, where it can slowly supply the base flow of nearby streams. In general, increasing amounts of imperviousness in a drainage area result in flashy streams that are more likely to flood during storm events but become drier in between storms.

Stormwater detention facilities can help keep rates of runoff from becoming excessive immediately downstream, but they cannot reduce the total volume of runoff coming from upstream. Some states and local jurisdictions have passed stormwater management laws requiring that infiltration devices be used to lessen the effects of increased runoff from urbanization. A few jurisdictions are encouraging the use of site development techniques that reduce the amount of runoff generated. These development techniques are often referred to as sustainable urban drainage systems (SUDS), water-sensitive urban design (WSUD), low-impact development (LID), and environmental site design (ESD).

Natural Watercourses

Surface runoff naturally flows along the path of least resistance. All of the water within a watershed flows toward one primary natural watercourse unless it is diverted by a constructed conveyance such as a canal or pipeline or it flows back into the ground to become groundwater.

Typical natural watercourses include brooks, creeks, streams, washes, arroyos, and rivers. Watercourses may flow continuously, occasionally, or intermittently, depending on the frequency of rainfall, the availability of snowmelt, and the rate at which groundwater contributes to the base flow of the watercourse.

- *Perennial streams.* Natural watercourses that flow continuously at all times of the year are called perennial streams. They are generally supplied by a combination of surface runoff, springs, groundwater seepage, and possibly snowmelt.
- *Ephemeral streams.* Streams that flow only occasionally are called ephemeral streams (Figure 6-2). These streams usually flow only during and shortly after a rain and are supplied only by surface runoff.
- *Intermittent streams.* The frequency of flow in intermittent streams falls somewhere between perennial and ephemeral. The streams flow when groundwater levels are high, and they are dry at other times. Depending on the amounts of rainfall and snowmelt and the resulting groundwater levels, intermittent streams may flow for weeks or months at a time and then remain dry for a while.

 WATCH THE VIDEO
Water Sources and Issues (www.awwa.org/wsovideoclips)

Constructed Conveyances

Many facilities are constructed to hasten the flow of surface water or to divert it in a direction other than the one in which it would flow under natural conditions. Ditches, channels, canals, aqueducts, conduits, tunnels, and pipelines are all examples of constructed conveyances. In many cases, constructed conveyances are used to divert water from its natural watershed into another watershed where it is needed (referred to as inter-basin transfer).

Many local conveyances are constructed to prevent water from ponding in areas where it would impede agricultural or urban development. Other examples of constructed conveyances include canals provided for boat access or shipping,

Figure 6-2 Bed of an ephemeral stream

aqueducts to provide irrigation water to arid regions, and pipelines to bring potable water to areas that have an insufficient natural supply.

Of course, manipulating the course of water is effective only if the water can be properly controlled in its new location, which brings us to the discussion of water storage.

Water Storage

Water can be stored by natural features, artificial impoundments, or deliberately recharging natural aquifers.

Natural Storage

Natural lakes are often used as a source for public water supply. Natural lakes occur most often in glaciated regions. Large lakes such as the Great Lakes of North America were formed by the movement of massive lobes of ice that left deep, wide valleys after the glaciers receded. The melting of large ice blocks that had been earlier stranded by the receding glaciers formed the smaller lakes (called *kettles*) in that region.

Generally, a lake must be relatively isolated from human activities to have good water quality. Lakes having a watershed with heavy agricultural activity, industrial operations, or urban development are often highly polluted.

If a lake located some distance from a community is being considered for use, it must be decided whether it is better to treat the water at the source and then pipe the finished water to the community or to pipe the raw water to the community and treat it there. Because of the considerable cost of piping water over long distances, an engineering analysis of all the alternatives must be made.

Impoundments

Impoundments, for the purposes of this discussion, refer to any significant accumulation of water in a basin surrounded by land. The basin can be a natural formation, such as a pond or lake, or a reservoir constructed by carving out a basin or by building a dam across a stream valley. The impoundment is designed to serve some specific water need and can range from a small basin constructed by farmers for watering livestock to a massive reservoir that stores water for public water systems and recreational uses.

Although there is evidence of dam construction as far back as 4000 BCE (Nile River), dams were not widely used until the mid-1800s. Dams were first used primarily for water supply and to harness river flow for mills. In glaciated regions, dams and perimeter berms have been used to increase the depth and storage capacity of kettle lakes.

With the development of modern construction equipment and techniques, dams have become a common way of creating a large reservoir. They are usually built where damming a valley stream or river can form the reservoir. The deeper and narrower the valley, the more economical it is to construct the dam. Dams can be made of earth, rock, or concrete.

Off-stream reservoirs can be constructed next to major rivers to add storage to a water system. Water can be pumped from the river to the reservoir during high-flow periods, then withdrawn for water supply during low-flow periods. This type of impoundment is commonly referred to as a pumped-storage reservoir and can involve constructing a dam across the stream of a small tributary, thereby avoiding many of the adverse environmental and navigational effects of building a dam on a major river.

impoundment
A pond, lake, or reservoir constructed by carving out a basin or building a dam across a stream valley.

Types of Dams Dams are classified by what they are made of and how they resist the pressure forces imposed on them. The four general types of dams are gravity, arch, buttress, and embankment (Figure 6-3). The first three types are typically constructed of concrete; embankment dams are constructed either of earth-fill or rock-fill. A gravity dam resists both sliding and overturning by its own weight. In a buttress dam, which is a type of gravity dam, buttresses support reinforced concrete slabs, and the impounded water's weight is used to help resist sliding and overturning. In contrast, an arch dam resists movement by transferring the thrust of water pressure laterally to the rock walls of a canyon.

Dams constructed of earth and rock, called embankment dams, are the most common. Although the concept of an embankment dam seems simple, such a dam must be carefully engineered to resist the forces of the reservoir water and prevent damage or failure due to seepage or undermining.

A cross section of a typical earth dam and intake tower is shown in Figure 6-4. An embankment dam may be constructed mostly of sandy or rocky soils if they are locally available, but there must be an inner core of impermeable

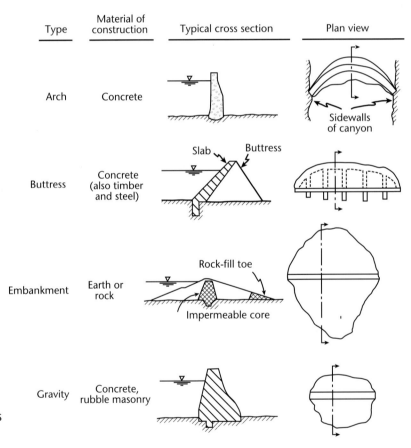

Figure 6-3 Types of dams
Adapted from Linsley et al. 1999.

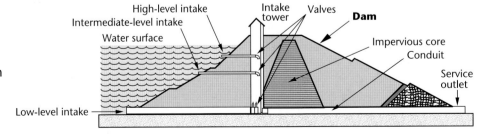

Figure 6-4 Cross section of dam and intake tower for impounded surface water supply

material to ensure watertightness. Earth dams often require an internal drainage system (using sand and gravel) to reduce water pressure in the dam, which in turn helps prevent soils from shifting or becoming soft because of the presence of water.

Rock-fill dams are another type of embankment dam. Rock-fill dams use a broad range of rock sizes to provide stability; watertightness is provided by building a reinforced concrete slab on the upstream face of the dam.

Dam Design   Subsurface conditions are among the most important to consider in dam construction. The natural substrate on which the dam is constructed must have sufficient strength and be impermeable enough that the dam will not fail because of undermining by water. Subsurface conditions are investigated using core borings. If necessary, unsafe material must be removed and replaced with suitable material before the dam is constructed.

To keep construction costs to a minimum, a dam should be built with locally available materials to the extent possible. An earth dam is typically used where there is an abundance of fill material and where bedrock is very deep. A concrete dam is often used where fill is scarce and/or bedrock is shallow.

Some small reservoirs have sufficient capacity to hold all the water that flows into them, so no outlet is necessary. However, because most dams are constructed across a stream or river, they are expected to overflow at least occasionally, especially during flood conditions. Spillways must be provided to ensure that excess water is conveyed downstream safely and does not rise to the point of overtopping and eroding the dam. If a dam is overtopped, the entire structure can be severely damaged or destroyed, depending on the construction of the dam and the degree of overtopping.

For most spillways, water simply flows freely over the spillway crest when the pool rises above that level. The spillway crest typically defines what is called the normal pool condition of the reservoir. Figure 6-5 shows a concrete chute spillway on the abutment of an earth dam. Other spillways consist of gates that must be raised to allow water to flow through the dam (Figure 6-6).

To ensure public safety, dams for water supply should be designed to withstand at least a 100-year flood event, defined as the rate of flow that has a 1 percent chance of being equaled or exceeded at that location in any given year. However, if failure of the dam could cause loss of life to people downstream, it

Figure 6-5 Yellow Creek Dam. Intake structure is to the left of the dam, and chute spillway is to the right of the dam.

Figure 6-6 Chute spillway on a concrete dam

should be designed for a larger flood. In many states, such dams must be designed to pass the probable maximum flood, which can be up to five times the size of a 100-year flood. Nearly all states have safety regulations that pertain to dam design and construction.

Dam Maintenance Most of the larger dams in the United States have been constructed with federal funds and remain under federal ownership. Others are owned by the state or local jurisdiction or solely by a water utility.

When a dam is owned by a water utility, the system operator may have responsibility for dam maintenance. The structure must be inspected periodically and maintained to prevent failure. Failure of a dam can result in loss of a water source, destruction of downstream property, and injury or loss of life among the people living and working in that area. Water-control structures such as mechanical spillways and slide gates require periodic maintenance to keep them in good working order and to prevent failure.

Detailed records should be kept carefully of all inspections and work done on dams and water-control structures. Most states have specific inspection procedures and reporting requirements. Any inspection and maintenance procedures should be documented in an operation and maintenance manual.

The National Inventory of Dams (NID), maintained by the US Army Corps of Engineers, now lists approximately 75,000 dams in the United States. Because of the number of dams already built and the economic and environmental considerations of new projects, the rate of construction of new dams has declined. Some existing dams have even been destroyed because it has become more desirable to have a free-flowing river where the dam was built.

Groundwater Recharge

A few attempts have been made to provide water storage underground by **recharging** depleted groundwater aquifers with surface water. One way to accomplish this is to excavate large basins that collect water and allow it to infiltrate into the subsurface. Direct injection of water into the subsurface is another approach.

The use of underground storage presents some technical challenges. If untreated surface water is to be injected into the soil, care must be taken not to pollute the aquifer. In addition, turbidity in the injected water, which is caused by fine suspended particles, will gradually plug the injection zone in the target formation(s). So to ensure that the storage system will continue to function as needed, the injection water must generally be treated to drinking water quality before it is stored. Because aquifers are not sealed off from the rest of the natural environment, losses can occur, and the volume of water pumped into the aquifer cannot always be fully recovered.

The use of underground storage creates important political and economic issues as well. It is not uncommon for the construction of new surface reservoirs to face opposition for a variety of environmental reasons. In some cases, projects may have been approved by local regulatory agencies but are then disapproved by regional, state, or federal agencies. When storage of large quantities of water is necessary but the creation of new surface impoundments is unacceptable, the options will be either to pipe water for long distances from an available reservoir or to store water in local aquifers. All injection of fluids into the ground (including water that has been treated to drinking water quality) is subject to federal and state approval under the rules of the federal Underground Injection Control (UIC) Program.

recharge

The addition of water to the groundwater supply from precipitation and by infiltration from surface streams, lakes, reservoirs, and snowmelt.

Intake Structures

Water is drawn into a water supply system from a surface impoundment or stream through an **intake structure**. Types of intake structures include simple surface intakes, submerged intakes, movable intakes, multiple-port intakes, pump intakes, and infiltration galleries.

Surface Intakes

A simple surface intake consists of a small concrete structure situated near the bank of a river or lake. When a slide gate or stop log is removed from the opening, water spills through the intake into a canal, ditch, or pipeline, which then carries the water to a treatment plant. Larger intake structures may be built with a bar screen and have mechanical devices for removing accumulated trash from the screen.

The principal disadvantage of using a surface intake on a river or reservoir is that the water quality is not usually as good there as it is at greater depths. The water may be warmer in summer, may have ice on the surface in winter, and may have algae, leaves, logs, and other floating debris at the surface at certain times of the year. The elevation of the water in the lake or stream may fluctuate substantially; therefore, the intake must be designed and located so that it will draw water under all conditions.

Submerged Intakes

Submerged intakes draw water from below the surface. The best water quality in most lakes and streams can usually be obtained in deep water. Intakes should not be located directly on the bottom or they will draw in silt and sand; therefore, they are often raised a short distance above the bottom. Submerged intakes have the advantages of presenting no surface obstruction to navigation and being less likely to be damaged by floating debris and ice. Many designs are used for submerged intakes; one typical type is illustrated in Figure 6-7. In some instances, screens with very fine openings are used to prevent fish from being drawn into the intake (Figure 6-8).

Many surface water treatment plants that normally draw water from a submerged intake also have an emergency surface intake (also called a shore intake). In the event of some kind of clogging or other failure of the submerged intake, the surface intake can be activated to furnish water of usable quality while repairs are made.

> **intake structure**
> A structure or device placed in a surface water source to permit the withdrawal of water from that source.

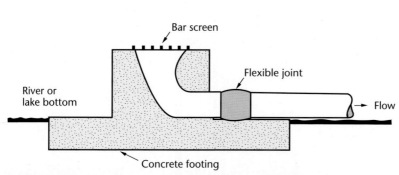

Figure 6-7 Schematic of a typical submerged intake

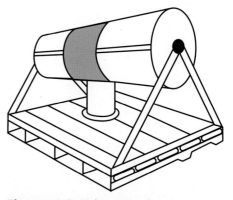

Figure 6-8 Fish screen for a submerged intake

Movable Intakes

Water quality at different depths can vary with the season depending on the degree to which the source lake or reservoir is subject to stratification and turnover during the year. During the summer months, warm water that is near the surface tends to stay near the surface because it remains less dense than the water below. If it contains sufficient nutrients, algae growth that taints the water may occur. In that case, water drawn from deeper levels is generally more likely to be of higher quality.

Near the bottom of the lake or reservoir, however, a different kind of water quality problem may occur. At that depth, low oxygen levels may result in conditions that tend to dissolve nutrients and metals that would otherwise remain in the bottom sediment. In that case, it is more desirable to draw water from above that lowest zone.

Finding the depth at which the best water quality is found is complicated by the phenomenon of turnover, which may occur once or twice a year as water temperatures change and the speed of wind at the surface changes. During turnover, the layers of water mix from top to bottom.

To ensure that the raw water that supplies the public system is withdrawn from a depth where the highest water quality is expected, movable intakes are frequently used. The use of movable intakes is generally advantageous in lakes and streams where the water levels vary greatly or there are other reasons for varying the depth at which water is withdrawn. Movable intakes are also used where good foundation is lacking or where other conditions prevent the construction of a more substantial structure.

Multiple-Port Intakes

Intake structures that have multiple inlet ports are also used in locations where the water level or water quality varies (Figure 6-9). By opening and closing valves, the operator can withdraw or mix water from several different depths to compensate for changing water elevation, to avoid ice cover, or to select the depth from which the best-quality water can be withdrawn.

Pump Intakes

Pump intakes are used where it is not possible to construct a facility that will allow water to flow from the source by gravity alone. One design, illustrated in Figure 6-10,

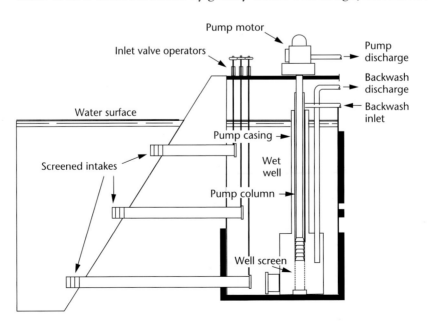

Figure 6-9 Intake structure with multiple inlet ports

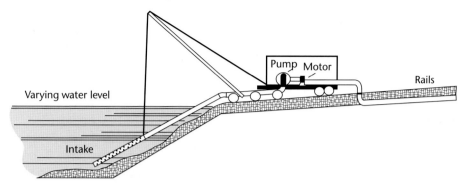

Figure 6-10 Movable pump intake

has an intake pump and suction piping mounted on a dolly that runs on tracks. As the water level rises or falls, sections of discharge piping are removed or added and the railcar is moved accordingly.

Infiltration Galleries

An infiltration gallery is a type of intake that is usually located next to a lake or river where it can pick up seepage from the surrounding sediment. A buried intake (instead of an open intake) can similarly be located in the bottom of a lake or stream, but it can be used only if the bottom sediment is porous enough and has the proper gradation to provide a reasonable flow rate. There must also be enough wave action or flow across the bottom to prevent the accumulation of fines, which would plug the sediment surface.

Where the proper conditions are present for installing an infiltration system, infiltration galleries usually provide water of much better quality than water taken directly from the source because the natural straining action of the sediment eliminates debris and reduces turbidity. Infiltration galleries also have the advantages of not freezing or icing over, and they are not as vulnerable to damage.

Surface Water Source Considerations

The development of a surface water source for use by a public water supply requires careful study of the quantity and quality of water available and of the expected rates of water demand.

Quantity of Water Available

The prime consideration in selecting a water source is that the supply must reliably furnish the quantity of water required. The flow in any watercourse fluctuates in relation to the amount of rainfall and runoff that occurs, so it is crucial to know that a sufficient amount of water will be available for withdrawal during low-flow or drought conditions.

Community water needs are normally the greatest during the warm months of summer and early fall, and this is usually the period when natural streamflow is the lowest. To compensate for this problem and ensure water supply reliability, reservoirs can be constructed to store water during periods of excess supply. The stored water can then be tapped during periods when natural streamflow is deficient.

Safe yield is a concept that describes the availability of water through a critical dry period. It is calculated based on the size of the impoundment, the area of the watershed, and the desired level of reliability. In simple terms, the safe yield represents the maximum rate at which water can be withdrawn continuously over a long period of time, including during very dry periods. For example, without storage, the safe yield of a stream is simply the amount of water that can be withdrawn during a period of lowest flow. In many states, the safe yield of a direct stream withdrawal for public water supply is the "1Q30," or the lowest one-day flow that occurs on average once every 30 years.

Safe yield from a natural water source can be increased by adding storage to the water supply system. If a stream has a high enough flow in the winter or other season to replenish water in an impoundment, the amount of water available for withdrawal during dry seasons can be greatly increased.

Many interrelated factors must be considered when calculating the safe yield of a public water supply. In addition to rainfall and streamflow considerations, allowances must also be made for other uses for agricultural irrigation or by other water systems. The amount of instream flow required to sustain downstream habitat for fish and other aquatic organisms is also an issue that must not be overlooked.

Water Quality

Although it is technically possible to treat water of just about any quality to make it suitable for a public water supply, it is often not economically practical to do so. In some situations, it may be more cost effective to pipe water a considerable distance from a remote, good-quality supply than to treat poor-quality water that is available locally. In some parts of the United States, for example, it is less expensive for some coastal cities to transport fresh water from sources hundreds of miles away than to desalt the ocean water nearby. Elsewhere in the world, however, desalinization must be used because the amount of available fresh water is not sufficient.

The economic concerns associated with drawing on a limited water resource to provide adequate water where several communities need it are often complex. Costs are influenced by the supply and demand among all the parties that have an interest in using the water. Political and legal considerations, such as who has the rights to the water, also come into play. The costs of the energy needed to operate the treatment plant may fluctuate considerably over the life of the plant.

As water treatment technology becomes more efficient, however, the cost of treating poor-quality sources decreases, making treatment a more attractive option for some communities.

The following are some of the principal quality factors that must be considered in evaluating the suitability of a water source for use:

- Excessive turbidity
- Microbiological contamination
- Chemical or radiological contamination
- Undesirable taste, odor, or color
- Presence of algae growth
- Water temperature

The influences of factors on water use and treatability are covered next.

Surface-Supply Operating Problems

Surface water sources present several physical, chemical, and biological challenges that can be troublesome for the water system operator.

Stream Contamination

The quality of water taken from streams and rivers is influenced by all upstream water use and land use. The quality of water in major rivers that are used for navigation and by industries can decrease suddenly because of spills from barges, leaks from tank facilities, broken pipelines, accidental industrial spills, and overflows from combined and sanitary sewers. Utilities that draw water from particularly vulnerable sources depend on warning systems to give advance notice when pollutants are approaching their intake. Some streams also have occasional periods when water quality is especially poor as a result of natural causes, such as heavy spring runoff. Drought conditions can greatly diminish water quality because pollutants in the water (e.g., from wastewater effluent) are less diluted.

Any water system that is vulnerable to episodes of poor-quality water should construct adequate storage facilities. These facilities are then used when the intake is shut down due to poor-quality water at the intake point.

Lake Contamination

Lakes and reservoirs are also vulnerable to natural and human contamination. One problem encountered by some water systems using reservoirs in agricultural areas is the occasional occurrence of nitrate levels exceeding state and federal standards. High nitrate concentrations are caused by runoff from farmlands in the drainage basin, and they may persist for several months each year. High sediment loads carrying phosphorus, a common nutrient, are also a problem in agricultural basins and those undergoing urbanization.

Excessive growth of algae and aquatic weeds in reservoirs is quite common, particularly in warmer climates. High levels of nutrients in the water usually cause this, and the problem can be minimized by proper treatment and land use management.

Invasive aquatic species can present another threat. In the Great Lakes, the zebra mussel, which was brought by international shipping vessels, is notorious for the problems it can cause. This organism grows profusely in intake structures and can quickly choke off the flow of water if it is not controlled. Another mussel, the quagga, causes similar problems. Unfortunately, these organisms are gradually being transported to other surface water impoundments by boats and birds. They will probably become established as permanent nuisance organisms in most waters of North America.

Icing

Operators in cold-weather areas often face additional operational challenges presented by frazil ice or anchor ice. When surface water is almost at the freezing point and is rapidly being cooled, small, disk-shaped frazil ice crystals form and are distributed throughout the water mass. When the frazil crystals are carried to the depth of a water intake, they may adhere to the intake screen and quickly build up to a solid plug across the opening.

Anchor ice is different in that it is composed of sheetlike crystals that adhere to and grow on submerged objects. Although experience varies at different locations, most systems experience ice blocking only at night. The following conditions are generally favorable to ice crystal formation:

- Clear skies at night (because there will be high heat loss by radiation)
- Air temperature of less than 19.4°F (−7°C)
- Daytime water temperature not greater than 32.4°F (0.2°C)
- Winds greater than 10 mph (16 kph) at the water surface

A falling water level in the intake well usually indicates icing of an intake. When icing is noticed, it is generally best to stop using the intake immediately, because the blockage will only get worse. If sufficient storage is available or another intake can be used, the easiest method of ridding the intake of ice is just to wait; the ice will float off within a few hours.

Water utilities that frequently experience icing have tried providing the intake with piping to backflush the line with settled water or blowing the line with compressed air or steam. If more than one intake is available, alternating intakes allow any accumulated ice to melt and float away from the intake opening.

Ice formation at inlet structures can be minimized by using very widely spaced screening, or no screen at all, and by constructing the intake pipe and structures of nonferrous materials such as fiberglass. Some intake designs keep the entrance velocity very low by using large bell-shaped structures or several inlets.

Stream source intakes are not ordinarily deep enough to allow water to be taken from a depth beneath the supercooled level near the surface. Consequently, multiple intake points and use of heating elements may be necessary to prevent icing.

Evaporation and Seepage

Surface water reservoirs naturally lose water to evaporation and seepage. Rates of evaporation loss can range from less than 2 ft (0.6 m) per year in the northern part of the United States to more than 6 ft (2 m) in the southwestern United States. To minimize evaporation losses from the surface of a reservoir, deep and narrow canyons are preferred over shallower impoundments. Seepage losses occur through the bottom and sides of the impoundment and can vary greatly depending on local soil type, geology, and the elevation of the lake surface relative to the surrounding groundwater table. These losses cannot economically be controlled in large reservoirs, so the reservoirs are generally designed to be larger than required to compensate for these losses.

In small, excavated reservoirs, seepage can be controlled by lining the impoundment with compacted clay or a synthetic liner. Evaporation can also be controlled by covering a reservoir with floating plastic sheets (Figure 6-11) or by applying a thin layer of a liquid chemical to the surface.

Figure 6-11 Reservoir cover installed on Garvey Reservoir at Monterey Park Metropolitan Water District of Los Angeles, California
Courtesy of Burke Environmental Products, a Division of Burke Industries, Inc.

Siltation

All streams carry sediment. The sediment settles out when the velocity of the water drops, as it does while the water is entering an impoundment. The rate of reservoir **siltation** is generally a function of both the type of soil in the watershed and how well the land is protected by vegetation and management practices. In some locations, siltation is so rapid that most of the capacity of a reservoir can be lost within a few years after it is constructed.

The problem of siltation can never be completely solved, but through better land use management, it can be minimized. Enforcement of regulations governing good practice in farming, logging, road construction, and other operations that disturb the land will help reduce the amount of sediment entering tributary streams.

Creation of artificial wetlands for small streams or at the upper ends of a reservoir can also help reduce siltation. Wetlands reduce the stream's velocity and thereby cause the bulk of the sediment load to settle in the wetlands before the water flows into the impoundment. Water quality in the reservoir is also improved, because many nutrients that adhere to sediment are trapped by the wetlands and are prevented from entering the reservoir.

When the capacity of a reservoir has been decreased by siltation, there are three general solutions: the silt can be removed by dredging, the reservoir can be drained and the silt excavated, or a new reservoir can be constructed. Draining and excavating are only an option when the water system has other water sources available, and constructing a new reservoir is only possible if the necessary additional land is available. A cost analysis of the available options must be made to decide how best to restore the lost reservoir capacity.

Treatment of Water at the Source

The treatment applied to raw water to make it safe and palatable for public use is typically performed in a treatment plant, where the process can easily be applied, controlled, and closely monitored. There are a few circumstances in which it is more economical or practical, and sometimes even necessary, to provide treatment at the source (in situ treatment).

In Situ Treatment

The addition of chemicals to a well should be considered carefully. If similar results can be obtained by treating the water after it leaves the well, that approach may be better because treatment can usually be controlled more easily. Consideration must also be given to any adverse effects that added chemicals may have in terms of disintegrating or clogging the well pump and piping.

The most frequently used in-well treatment is the application of an oxidant to wells that have an infestation of iron bacteria. A weak chlorine solution or other oxidant fed at a point near the pump can help reduce the red color in the water caused by iron bacteria. In situ control of iron can also be accomplished by feeding polyphosphate into the well to sequester the iron before it has a chance to oxidize. Additional details of iron and manganese control are discussed in Chapter 12.

In-well chemical application may also be justified when the pH of the groundwater is such that damage may be done to the pump and piping unless immediate pH correction is made.

If in situ treatment is considered, recommendations concerning its advantages, disadvantages, and usage procedures should be obtained from well installation

siltation
The accumulation of silt (small soil particles between 0.00016 and 0.0024 in. [0.004 and 0.061 mm] in diameter) in an impoundment.

firms and chemical suppliers. Final approval should be obtained from the state before the treatment begins.

Aquatic Plant Control

Excessive growth of aquatic plants can cause problems for the operation of a surface water treatment plant. However, it is important to remember that these aquatic plants are normal inhabitants of the aquatic environment and have a definite role in maintaining the ecological balance in lakes, ponds, and streams. For example, algae help purify the water by adding oxygen during the process of photosynthesis. Algae and rooted aquatic plants, in moderate amounts, are essential in the food chains of fish and waterfowl.

In addition, aquatic plants remove nutrients from the water that would otherwise be available for the growth of algae. Therefore, overcontrol of aquatic plants may result in algae problems more serious than the plant problem.

The problems encountered at water treatment facilities from aquatic plants usually arise from the overproduction of a few types of plants at certain times of the year. The goal of a well-planned control program is to control aquatic plants only to the extent necessary to prevent water quality and treatment problems.

Aquatic plants are classified into the following categories based on their growth form and location in the water:

- Algae
- Emergent plants
- Floating aquatic plants
- Submerged aquatic plants

The latter three plant types are referred to collectively as rooted aquatic plants.

The taste, odor, color, and mechanical problems caused by aquatic plants can usually be treated or dealt with in a treatment plant if necessary. However, it is usually much easier, less expensive, and more effective to control the growth in the source water.

Algae

Algae are primitive plants that have no true leaves, stems, or root systems and reproduce by means of spores, cell division, or fragmentation. About 17,500 species of algae have been identified, and there are probably many more. The four major groups of algae of interest in water treatment are blue-green algae (now known as cyanobacteria), green algae, diatoms, and pigmented flagellates.

Problems Associated With Algae   Heavy concentrations of algae may cause the following operational problems in a water system:

- Taste, odor, and color
- Toxicity
- Filter clogging
- Slime accumulation on structures
- Corrosion of structures
- Interference with other treatment processes
- Formation of trihalomethanes when the water is chlorinated

Table 6-1 lists the problems caused by various types of algae that are experienced by water suppliers.

Table 6-1 Problems caused by algae in water supplies

Problem and Algae	Color of Water	Algae Group
Slime-Producing Algae		
Anacystis (Aphanocapsa, Gloeocapsa)		Blue-green
Batrachospermum		Red
Chaetophora		Green
Cymbella		Diatom
Euglena sanguinea var. furcata		Flagellate
Euglena velata		Flagellate
Gloeotrichia		Blue-green
Gomphonema		Diatom
Oscillatoria		Blue-green
Palmella		Green
Phormidium		Blue-green
Spirogyra		Green
Tetraspora		Green
Algae Causing Coloration of Water		
Anacystis	Blue-green	Blue-green
Ceratium	Rusty brown	Flagellate
Chlamydomonas	Green	Flagellate
Chlorella	Green	Green
Cosmarium	Green	Green
Euglena orientalis	Red	Flagellate
Euglena rubra	Red	Flagellate
Euglena sanguinea	Red	Flagellate
Oscillatoria prolifica	Purple	Blue-green
Oscillatoria rubescens	Red	Blue-green
Algae Causing Corrosion of Concrete		
Anacystis (Chroococcus)		Blue-green
Chaetophora		Green
Diatoma		Diatom
Euglena		Flagellate
Phormidium		Blue-green
Phytoconis (Protococcus)		Green
Algae Causing Corrosion of Steel		
Oscillatoria		Blue-green
Algae Persistent in Distribution Systems		
Anacystis		Blue-green
Asterionella		Diatom
Chlorella		Green
Chlorococcum		Green
Closterium		Green
Coelastrum		Green

(continued)

Table 6-1 Problems caused by algae in water supplies (continued)

Problem and Algae	Color of Water	Algae Group
Cosmarium		Green
Cyclotella		Diatom
Dinobryon		Flagellate
Elaktothrix gelatinosa		Green
Epithemia		Diatom
Euglena		Flagellate
Gomphosphaeria aponina		Blue-green
Scenedesmus		Green
Synedra		Diatom
Algae Interfering With Coagulation		
Anabaena		Blue-green
Asterionella		Diatom
Euglena		Flagellate
Gomphosphaeria		Blue-green
Synedra		Diatom
Algae Causing Natural Softening of Water		
Anabaena		Blue-green
Aphanizomenon		Blue-green
Cosmarium		Green
Scenedesmus		Green
Synedra		Diatom
Toxic Marine Algae		
Caulerpa serrulata		Green
Egregia laevigata		Brown
Gelidium cartilagineum var. robustum		Red
Gonyaulax catenella		Dinoflagellate
Gonyaulax polyedra		Dinoflagellate
Gonyaulax tamarensis		Dinoflagellate
Gymnodinium brevis		Dinoflagellate
Gymnodinium veneficum		Dinoflagellate
Hesperophycus harveyanus		Brown
Hornellia marina		Flagellate
Lyngbya aestuarii		Blue-green
Lyngbya majuscula		Blue-green
Macrocystis pyrifera		Brown
Pelvetia fastigiata		Brown
Prymnesium parvum		Flagellate
Pyrodinium phoneus		Dinoflagellate
Trichodesmium erythraeum		Blue-green

Table 6-1 Problems caused by algae in water supplies (continued)

Problem and Algae	Color of Water	Algae Group
Toxic Freshwater Algae		
Anabaena		Blue-green
Anabaena circinalis		Blue-green
Anabaena flos-aquae		Blue-green
Anabaena lemmermanni		Blue-green
Anacystis (Microcystis)		Blue-green
Anacystis cyanea (Microcystis aeruginosa)		Blue-green
Anacystis cyanea (Microcystis flosaquae)		Blue-green
Anacystis cyanea (Microcystis toxica)		Blue-green
Aphanizomenon flos-aquae		Blue-green
Gloeotrichia echinulata		Blue-green
Gomphosphaeria laeustris (Coelosphaerium kuetzingianum)		Blue-green
Lyngbya contorta		Blue-green
Nodularia spumigena		Blue-green
Parasitic Aquatic Algae		
Oodinium limneticum		Dinoflagellate
Oodinium ocellatum		Dinoflagellate

Note: Blue-green algae is now known as cyanobacteria.

Source: *Algae in Water Supplies*. 1962. US Public Health Service.

Taste, Odor, and Color   Although the exact mechanism of taste-and-odor production by algae is not completely understood, the problems are probably caused by certain complex organic compounds that are by-products of their life cycle. The tastes caused by the presence of algae have been categorized as sweet, bitter, and sour. Algae-caused tongue sensations are categorized as oily or slick, metallic or dry, and harsh or astringent. Odors are frequently described as musty, earthy, fishy, grassy, hay-like, or septic. Color can be caused by algal by-products and is usually an indicator that taste-and-odor problems will also occur. Colors range from yellow-green to green, blue-green, red, and brown.

Toxicity   Several types of freshwater algae are somewhat toxic (poisonous). Effects on humans from various toxic algae include skin irritation, promotion of hay fever allergies, and outbreaks of gastrointestinal illness. Blooms of blue-green algae (cyanobacteria) on ponds have also been known to cause fish kills when oxygen levels were depleted and livestock poisoning. The threat posed by toxins from cyanobacteria to water supplies has increased worldwide during the past 30 years. Health problems attributed to the presence of such toxins in drinking water have been reported in a number of countries, including Australia, Brazil, China, England, South Africa, and the United States.

Filter Clogging   Algae can shorten filter runs by forming a mat on the filter's surface. This is known as "blinding the filter." Filters must then be backwashed more frequently to restore their filtering capacity, which adds to the treatment plant's operating costs. Diatoms are usually the primary group associated with this problem.

Slimes Slimes come from the layer that surrounds the algal cell. The slime from algae can form a slimy, slippery layer that is unsightly, has a bad odor, and can be dangerous if it accumulates on walking surfaces. Because most algae require sunlight to grow, slime that accumulates in dark portions of treatment plants and distribution systems is not caused by algae but is usually caused by bacteria.

Corrosion Algae may contribute to the corrosion of concrete and metal structures, either directly on surfaces where they grow or indirectly by changing the water physically or chemically. Algae are not usually the direct cause of corrosion of iron or steel pipes because most algae cannot grow without light.

Interference With Other Treatment Processes As algae grow and die, they may cause changes in the water's pH, alkalinity, hardness, level of dissolved oxygen, and concentration of organic matter. These changes can interfere with normal treatment processes—for example, by increasing the chlorine demand and chemical dosages necessary for adequate coagulation. Inadequate control of algae may also require the use of carbon adsorption treatment to reduce taste, odor, or color to acceptable levels.

Trihalomethane (THM) Formation Free chlorine will react with certain organic substances in the water to produce THMs (see Chapter 11 for more details). The chlorination of water that has a high concentration of natural organic matter derived from algae may produce particularly high levels of THMs.

Algae Control Before any algae control procedures are attempted, the operator should establish a routine program of collecting raw-water samples at least once a week and then counting the numbers of the different types of algae in each sample. Based on this information, a decision can be made concerning the best time to initiate algae control procedures.

Several biological and chemical methods have been evaluated for algae control in large water bodies. For drinking water supplies, copper sulfate, potassium permanganate, and powdered activated carbon are commonly used to control algae. Use of pond covers is yet another effective method of controlling algae.

Copper Sulfate The concentration of copper sulfate pentahydrate ($CuSO_4 \bullet 5H_2O$) or "bluestone" needed for effective control of algae is influenced by the species and amount of algae, and the alkalinity, pH, temperature, suspended solids, and organic content of the water. All of these factors are influenced by the action level of 1.3 mg/L of copper at the consumer's tap as established by the US Environmental Protection Agency (USEPA).

Not all algae are effectively killed by copper sulfate. The problem-causing algae must be accurately identified. Table 6-2 summarizes the effectiveness of copper sulfate against various types of algae.

The effectiveness of copper sulfate treatment also depends on its ability to dissolve in water, which in turn depends on pH and alkalinity. The required dosage therefore depends on the chemical characteristics of the water to be treated. The best and most lasting control will result if the water has a total alkalinity less than or equal to approximately 50 mg/L as calcium carbonate ($CaCO_3$) and a pH between 8 and 9.

The following suggested dosages for copper sulfate are general recommendations only and may not be the best dosages for every situation:

- Bodies of water with a total methyl orange alkalinity equal to or greater than 50 mg/L as $CaCO_3$ are usually treated at a dosage of about 1 mg/L, calculated for the volume of water in the upper 2 ft (0.6 m) of the lake, regardless of

Table 6-2 Relative toxicity of copper sulfate to algae

Group	Very Susceptible	Susceptible	Resistant	Very Resistant
Blue-green	*Anabaena, Anacystis, Gomphospharia, Rivularia*	*Cylindrospermum, Oscillatoria, Plectonema*	*Lyngbya, Phormidium, Nostoc*	*Calothrix, Symploca*
Green	*Hydrodictyon, Oedogonium, Rhizoclonium, Ulothrix*	*Botryococcus, Cladophora, Oscillatoria Enteromorpha, Gloeocystis, Microspora, Phytoconis, Tribonema, Zygnema*	*Characium, Chlorococum, Clorella, Coccomyxa, Crucigenia, Desmidium, Draparnaldia, Golenkinia, Mesotaenium, Oocystis, Palmella, Pediastrum, Staurastrum, Stigeoclnium, Tetraedron*	*Ankistrodesmus, Chara, Coelastrum, Dictyosphaeium, Elakatothrix, Kirchneriella, Nitella, Pithophora, Scenesdesmus Testrastrum*
Diatoms	*Asterionella, Cyclotella, Fragilaria, Melosira*	*Gomphonema, Navicula, Nitzschia, Stephanodiscus, Synedra, Tabellaria*	*Achnanthes, Cymbella, Neidium*	
Flagellates	*Dinobryon, Synura, Uroglenopsis, Volvox*	*Ceratium, Cryptomonas, Euglena, Glenodinium, Mallomonas*	*Chlamydomonas, Peridinium, Haematococcus*	*Eudorina, Pandorina*

Source: *Algae and Water Pollution.* 1977. USEPA.

the lake's depth. This converts to about 5.4 lb (2.4 kg) of commercial copper sulfate per acre of surface area. The 2-ft (0.6-m) depth has been determined as the effective range of surface application of copper sulfate in those waters. The chemical tends to precipitate below this application depth.

- For water bodies having a total methyl orange alkalinity that is less than 50 mg/L as $CaCO_3$, a dosage of 0.3 mg/L is recommended. This dosage is based on the total lake volume and converts to about 0.9 lb (0.4 kg) of commercial copper sulfate per acre-foot of volume.

The minimum copper sulfate dosage depends on the alkalinity of the water; the maximum safe dosage depends on the toxic effect on aquatic animal life. A safe dosage for most fish is 0.5 mg/L; however, trout are very sensitive and can be killed by dosages greater than 0.14 mg/L. The state department of game and fish must be consulted to determine if any special precautions are required.

The simplest way to apply copper sulfate to control algae in small lakes, ponds, or reservoirs is to drag burlap bags of the chemical behind a motorboat. The boat is guided in a zigzag course for overlapping coverage over the water, as shown in Figures 6-12 and 6-13. Lakes are also sometimes treated by power spray application from the shore (Figure 6-14) or from a motorboat.

The effect of the copper sulfate treatment on algae populations can be noticed soon after the chemical has been added. Within a few minutes, the color of the water will change from dark green to grayish-white. At no time are all the algae in the lake entirely eliminated, but the water should be visibly free of cells for two or three days following a complete application.

Proper treatment ensures that most of the algae will be eliminated, and a long time will pass before the algae can again create problems. The frequency

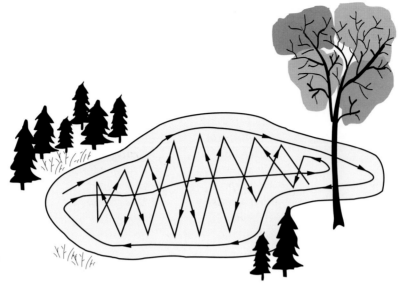

Figure 6-12 Path taken for copper sulfate application to small water bodies

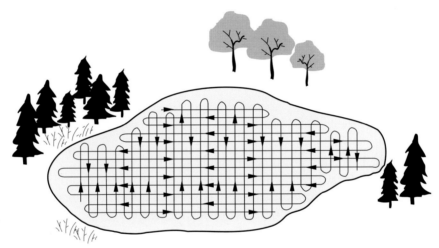

Figure 6-13 Path taken for copper sulfate application to large water bodies

Figure 6-14 Power spray application of chelated copper algaecide

Courtesy of Applied Biochemists, Inc., Milwaukee, Wisconsin.

of treatment depends on local climate and the amount of nutrients in the water. Warm temperatures, plentiful sunlight, and a high nutrient concentration all tend to encourage a rapid regrowth of algae. In general, one to three complete treatment applications per season should be sufficient. The actual length of time between applications can best be determined by obtaining periodic algae counts.

It is *extremely important* to note that copper sulfate, or any other active chemical used to control aquatic organisms in bodies of water, is classed as a pesticide and is therefore regulated by USEPA under the Federal Insecticide, Fungicide, and Rodenticide Act (FIFRA). Under this law, each package sold must be specifically labeled, and the product must be used in accordance with the label directions. For example, the current USEPA regulations require that only a portion of a body of water be treated at one time, and a time delay of 10 to 14 days is required before treating the remainder of the water. The waiting period allows for decomposition and oxygen levels to return to normal, thereby reducing stress or death to aquatic animals.

Many states also require a special permit for algae control. Operators should carefully check that all local, state, and federal requirements are met before undertaking an algae control program. Failure to comply with regulations could result in a fine or liability for damages if the chemical application has an adverse effect on wildlife or the environment as a result of improper application.

 WATCH THE VIDEO
Algae/Copper Sulfide/T&O Study (www.awwa.org/wsovideoclips)

Potassium Permanganate   Control of algae in reservoirs has also been accomplished by applying potassium permanganate. Although experience using it is limited, potassium permanganate has worked successfully to control algae conditions when copper sulfate has not worked well. One theory for its success is that iron is essential for the formation of chlorophyll in plants; if the iron in the water is oxidized and precipitated by the permanganate, the iron deficiency will retard the growth of the algae.

Permanganate can be applied to the water using the same technique used with copper sulfate: towing a burlap sack containing the chemical through the water. This method is appropriate only for small reservoirs because the sack will quickly be disintegrated by the permanganate. Larger reservoirs have been treated by feeding the crystals into a wooden hopper, with a screened bottom, hung over the side of a boat (Figures 6-15 and 6-16).

Figure 6-15 Crew preparing to feed permanganate for algae control
Courtesy of *Public Works Magazine*.

Figure 6-16 Boat equipped with a wooden hopper for applying permanganate
Courtesy of *Public Works Magazine*.

Permanganate is a strong oxidizer, so persons working with the chemical should wear rubber gloves and clothing and use caution in handling it.

Powdered Activated Carbon   Powdered activated carbon (PAC) can also be used to control algae. This is not a form of chemical treatment because it operates by a physical rather than a chemical process. The activated carbon forms a black blanket over the water, cutting off sunlight, which is vital for algae growth. However, a large amount is needed to block the sun effectively, and powdered carbon is messy and difficult to handle from a boat. PAC can also be added manually or by a chemical feeder as the water enters the treatment plant, to adsorb algal by-products responsible for taste-and-odor problems.

Pond Covers   A pond cover can be used to control algae growth in smaller bodies, such as presedimentation impoundments. Covers greatly reduce the amount of sunlight available to the algae for photosynthesis. The cover shown in Figure 6-17 is made of a synthetic rubber fabric that floats on the surface of the water. The fabric must be specifically approved for contact with potable water. Although floating covers effectively control algae, they can interfere with normal dewatering and cleaning operations.

Rooted Aquatic Plants

Rooted aquatic plants are different from algae in that they are plants with defined leaves, stems, and root systems.

Types of Rooted Aquatic Plants   They can be classified as

- emergent plants,
- floating plants, and
- submerged plants.

These three types of rooted aquatic plants are illustrated in Figure 6-18.

Emergent Plants   Emergent plants grow in shallow water on or near the shoreline. They root in the bottom mud and can extend well above the water surface. Cattails, water willows, and rushes are familiar examples. Figure 6-19 shows emergent plants surrounding a lake.

Figure 6-17 A floating cover helps control algae growth

Photo courtesy of JPS Elastomerics Corp.

Figure 6-18 Types of rooted aquatic plants

Courtesy of Applied Biochemists, Inc., Milwaukee, Wisconsin.

Figure 6-19 Emergent plants around a lake

Courtesy of Applied Biochemists, Inc., Milwaukee, Wisconsin.

Floating Plants   Plants that have leaves floating on the surface of the water can be either free floating or rooted in the bottom mud. Sometimes they are mixed with emergent plants. The most common example of the rooted types of these plants is water lilies. Duckweed and similar plants are free floating.

Submerged Plants   Submerged plants grow entirely underwater and are rooted in the bottom mud. The depth to which they will grow is limited primarily by the depth of sunlight penetration. The clearer the water, the taller the plants are likely to grow. Coontail and bladderwort are examples of submerged plants.

Effects of Aquatic Plants   Aquatic plants can cause the same problems—color, tastes, and odors—for water system operations and treatment as algae. In addition, floating plants can clog intakes and pumps. Rooted aquatic vegetation can also serve as a habitat (breeding area) for disease-causing and nuisance insects, which can create problems for both operators and nearby residents.

However, aquatic plants do serve many beneficial functions. They provide shelter and attachment surfaces for small organisms, they provide spawning and schooling areas for fish, and they produce dissolved oxygen. They also consume and temporarily store nutrients, such as phosphorus, that could otherwise support the growth of algae.

Control of Rooted Aquatic Plants   Procedures to control rooted aquatic plants should begin whenever the plants start to cause operational control problems at the treatment plant or add color, taste, or odor to the raw water.

The three methods for controlling rooted aquatic plants in lakes, reservoirs, and other surface water are

- physical treatment,
- biological treatment, and
- chemical treatment.

Physical Methods   Methods for physically controlling the growth of aquatic plants include the following:

- *Harvesting.* Methods used for harvesting depend on the extent and amount of control desired. The technique employed can vary from hand-pulling or hand-cutting and raking to using power-driven harvesting machines.
- *Dewatering.* Completely or partially draining a body of water is known as dewatering. It can be effective in killing aquatic plants. It is most practical if the plant problem is in a small impoundment, such as a presedimentation basin. It may not be practical if the plants are in a major lake or reservoir. During the dewatering process, the water level is lowered and the impoundment is allowed to dry. If the lake bottom is stable enough to support heavy equipment, a scraper or front-end loader is used to clear away the dried plant material; otherwise, the dewatered area is left exposed for a period of time (several months) until the plants' root systems dehydrate.
- *Dredging.* A clamshell crane, dragline, or hydraulic dredge can be used to control aquatic plants because dredging the bottom mud removes any plants that are growing there. In addition, dredging the near-shore areas of a water body increases the water depth, thereby decreasing the area of suitable habitat for the plants.
- *Shading.* Two methods of shading (i.e., limiting the amount of sunlight reaching the bottom of a water body) have been used for controlling aquatic

plant growth. One method raises the turbidity of the water by adding clay to form a colloidal suspension. This allows less sunlight penetration into the water and thereby reduces the amount of growth. Shading can also be accomplished by placing sheets of black plastic on the lake bottom. This effectively shades areas of the bottom from the sun and reduces plant growth.

■ *Lining.* Ponds can be lined with a synthetic rubber material to prevent the growth of rooted aquatic plants. The lining also prevents water loss caused by seepage through the bottom of the pond (Figure 6-20).

Biological Methods Biological controls using specific species of crayfish, snails, fish, and insects have proved extremely effective for control of rooted aquatic plants. However, the state department of game and fish must be contacted before such a program is instituted to determine if they allow the species to be introduced to the water body.

Chemical Methods Chemical control of aquatic plants by the use of herbicides should be undertaken only when the problem becomes unmanageable by other means. A registered professional should be obtained for this service.

Suggested Records for Algae and Plant Control Programs

An important part of an algae and aquatic plant control program is keeping good records. Data for threshold odor test results and for any complaints of tastes and odors registered by consumers should be recorded daily. When chemical treatment is performed, records should also include the following:

■ The reason for pretreating, such as taste-and-odor problems or filter clogging
■ Type of algae or plant treated
■ Manufacturer/supplier of chemicals
■ Algae count or estimated plant coverage
■ Chemical used, concentration, and dosage
■ Date of pretreatment

Figure 6-20 Pond lining to control algae growth
Photo courtesy of JPS Elastomerics Corp.

- Length of time since last treatment
- Weather conditions
- Other water conditions, such as temperature, pH, and alkalinity
- Method of application
- Names of personnel involved
- Results of pretreatment, such as taste and odor following final treatment or filter conditions

These types of records can be used to solve similar problems in the future. With good records, the operator will be able to reproduce previous results and, as a result, save considerable time. Residual algae counts or estimates of plant coverage can serve as reliable guides in deciding when the next treatment will be needed.

Destratification of Reservoirs

Stratification of the water in lakes and reservoirs occurs when a warm layer of water overlies a colder layer. In temperate zones, stratification occurs during the spring and summer when the air temperature is higher than the water temperature. Water has its greatest density at 39°F (4°C), so the colder water sinks to the bottom and the lighter, warm water stays at the surface.

The Effects of Stratification

Stratification occurs when there are three water layers with different temperatures. The upper, warmer layer is called the **epilimnion**; the lower layer is the **hypolimnion**; and the temperature transition zone in between is the **thermocline**. In the hypolimnion, the water is stagnant and frequently becomes anaerobic (completely void of oxygen). The decomposition of matter under anaerobic conditions can result in a reduction in pH and the production of hydrogen sulfide gas, which can cause taste-and-odor problems in finished water. In addition, the hydrogen sulfide may reduce iron and manganese in the soil of the lake's bottom to a soluble form that may then have to be removed in the treatment plant to avoid complaints of rusty water by customers.

While the water is stratified, acceptable water quality can often be obtained from the epilimnion because it is mixed by the wind. However, when the upper layer cools later in the year and its density becomes the same as the bottom water, destratification occurs—or, as this process is often expressed, the lake *turns over*. When this happens, water quality can be extremely bad for a number of days. An intense storm over a reservoir can occasionally generate enough energy to mix the water in a stratified reservoir, which can also result in poor water quality.

In colder climates, lakes may become stratified because the ice-covered upper layer is lighter than deeper, warmer water. In this case the lower layer, or even the entire lake, may become anaerobic. Figure 6-21 shows conditions in a stratified lake at the spring and fall turnovers and destratification using compressed air.

Methods of Destratification

Destratification of a lake is often accomplished by pumping compressed air through a hose to the low point on the lake bottom and releasing it through a diffuser. The rising air bubbles add air to the water and also serve to bring the cold water up from the bottom. Destratification is also successfully done in lakes by using an electrically driven floating aerator that is moored over the deep part of the lake.

The destratification equipment must start operating in early spring, when the average air temperature is higher than the water temperature, and continue until

---

stratification

The separation of water in lakes and reservoirs such that a warm layer of water overlies a colder layer.

epilimnion

The upper, warmer layer of water in a stratified lake.

hypolimnion

The lower layer of water in a stratified lake. The water temperature is near 39.2°F (4°C), at which water attains its maximum density.

thermocline

The temperature transition zone in a stratified lake, located between the epilimnion and the hypolimnion.

destratification

Use of a method to prevent a lake or reservoir from becoming stratified. Typically consists of releasing diffused compressed air at a low point on the lake bottom.

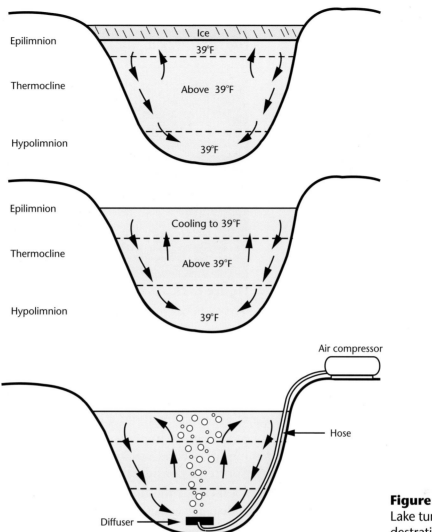

Figure 6-21
Lake turnover and destratification

late fall. In addition to eliminating the problems caused by anaerobic bottom water, destratification of lakes often reduces the growth of objectionable algae.

Asiatic Clams and Zebra Mussels

The Asiatic clam (*Corbicula fluminea*) was introduced to the United States from Southeast Asia in 1938 and has become a significant pest in almost every river system south of 40 degrees latitude. If not controlled, the clams can infest raw-water intake pipelines and treatment facilities, resulting in a reduction in flow capacities and a clogging of mechanical equipment.

The zebra mussel (*Dreissena polymorpha*) is a freshwater shellfish that grows to about 1.5 in. (3.8 cm) long (Figures 6-22 and 6-23). These mussels invaded the Great Lakes in the late 1980s, having first been found in Lake St. Clair in 1988. After a 10-year period of unfettered growth in the Great Lakes, their numbers have stabilized or diminished somewhat, but the mussels have found their way into inland water supplies. The mussel is native to the Black and Caspian Seas and is thought to have been brought over from Europe in the ballast water of a freighter around 1985. The zebra mussel population is spreading to most waters of North America.

Figure 6-22 An adult zebra mussel
Courtesy of Fred Snyder, Ohio Sea Grant.

Figure 6-23 An accumulation of zebra mussels
Courtesy of Fred Snyder, Ohio Sea Grant.

There are several reasons why the zebra mussel multiplies and spreads so rapidly:

- A female zebra mussel may release 30,000 to 40,000 eggs in a single season, and a mussel's life span is about 4 or 5 years.
- The larvae (veligers) that develop after the external fertilization of the eggs are free-swimming for several weeks before they attach themselves; thus, they can be transported a considerable distance by water currents.
- They commonly adhere to the bottom of boats, so the adults are readily moved around to disperse eggs throughout a body of water.
- Adult mussels can survive out of the water for several days, so they are liable to be transferred from one body of water to another on the bottom of a transported boat.

The proliferation of zebra mussels in a lake can have great ecological consequences. The mussels obtain their food by filtering algae and other matter that passes by. The volume of water filtered by one mussel may be small, but the number of mussels can be so great that it is estimated that the entire population may be able to completely filter the volume of a large lake once every 11 days. The consequence is that the food source is taken away from other filter-feeding organisms, such as native mussels and fish. In addition, there is an increased deposition of organic material on the lake bottom and a destruction of fish-spawning areas.

The mussels attach themselves to virtually any hard surface, such as rocks and pilings. They particularly favor water intake structures and the interior of water intake pipes because they can filter the flowing water. The buildup of mussel shells can completely block an intake screen, and it can greatly decrease flow through a pipe as a result of the increased roughness of the pipe surface. In extreme cases, the interior diameter of an intake pipe can be materially reduced.

Another problem is that a sudden die-off of mussels near an intake can cause serious taste-and-odor problems and an increase in oxidant demand. As the material decays, it can release the large amounts of toxins it has absorbed. It has also been reported that clumps of older shells can break off and block intake screens.

Control of Asiatic Clams and Zebra Mussels

Asiatic clams and zebra mussels have a few predators, but they are relatively insignificant for controlling the growth of these pests in US waters. Once Asiatic clams and zebra mussels have attached themselves to a structure and grown to adult size, they are relatively difficult to kill. They can sense adverse conditions and close up in their shells for a period of time. The common way to kill the adults is to feed chemicals that will destroy them continuously for several days at a time. If contaminated structures can be dewatered for several days, this may be a useful and effective weapon against the organisms. When adults are killed, it is likely that offensive tastes and odors will be created. In addition, the shells of the dead mussels continue to adhere to the intake or pipe and must be removed mechanically. It reportedly requires a water pressure of at least 80 psi (550 kPa) to dislodge shells that have accumulated on intake screens.

Because ridding structures of the adults is so difficult, initiating treatment prior to invasion is advisable. Zebra mussels breed only when the water temperature is above about 53.6°F (12°C) (which is about June through October in the central United States), so control measures need to be practiced only during the reproductive season, if desired.

Application of low-voltage electric current to a metallic pipeline has been tried and is reported to discourage attachment, but it also accelerates corrosion of the pipe. Another control method is to backflush the intake periodically with a high concentration of chlorine or some other oxidant. Only larvae will be killed by a short dose, so the treatment must be done often enough to kill them before they develop protective shells.

A control method used by many systems in the United States is to feed a control chemical at the intake. The equipment for this is difficult and expensive to install in intakes that are a long distance from shore, but it seems to be one of the best alternatives. Chemicals that have been used include chlorine, potassium permanganate, copper sulfate, or one of several biocides that are approved for addition to potable water. The most common chemical used in Europe is chlorine; however, the concern in the United States over generating excessive levels of THMs makes it necessary to consider other alternatives.

Any North American water system installing new intakes should consider installing control methods for Asiatic clams and zebra mussels, even if they are not currently a threat in the area. It appears that the mussels will eventually invade most surface waters, and the cost of installing control equipment during original construction is much lower than it would be later.

Study Questions

1. Where land is _____, runoff tends to spread out and soak into the ground more easily.
   a. steep
   b. relatively flat
   c. V-shaped
   d. hilly

2. Streams that flow only occasionally, usually only during and shortly after a rain, are called
   a. intermittent streams.
   b. perennial streams.
   c. natural streams.
   d. ephemeral streams.

3. To limit construction costs, a dam should be built
   a. with locally available materials to the extent possible.
   b. only in the summer months, when there is less chance of weather-related problems.
   c. on land that has little property value.
   d. with the cheapest possible construction materials.

4. Which of the following plant types grow in shallow water on or near the shoreline, rooting in the bottom mud and sometimes extending well above the water surface?
   a. Submerged plants
   b. Emergent plants
   c. Amphibious plants
   d. Floating plants

5. What are the main causes of algae blooms?

6. What are the concerns when using a direct river intake for the water supply to a drinking water treatment plant?

7. What are the most common methods of algae control in lakes and reservoirs?

8. What are the water quality problems caused by impoundment stratification?

9. What are some invasive species that require monitoring and treatment?

10. What type of intake is usually located next to a lake or river where it can pick up seepage from the surrounding sediment?

Chapter 7
Treatment Plant Pretreatment

Preliminary treatment, also known as pretreatment, is typically used when a water source contains large quantities of sticks, aquatic plants, leaves, or other floating debris as well as gravel, sand, or other gritty substances. If not removed, this material can jam equipment, damage pumps and piping, and greatly add to the loading on the normal treatment processes. Preliminary treatment is also used when the raw water contains unusually heavy concentrations of sediment. In some cases, preliminary treatment can reduce the amounts of chemicals needed in the main treatment plant. The following preliminary treatment processes are discussed in this chapter:

- Screening
- Presedimentation
- Microstraining

Screening

The first pretreatment provided in most surface water treatment systems is **screening**. Coarse screens located on an intake structure are usually called *trash racks* or *debris racks*. Their function is to prevent clogging of the intake by removing sticks, logs, and other large debris in a river, lake, or reservoir. Finer screens may then be used at the point where the water enters the treatment system to remove smaller debris that has passed the trash racks.

The two basic types of screens used by water systems are bar screens and wire-mesh screens. Both types are available in models that are manually cleaned or automatically cleaned by mechanical equipment.

Bar Screens

Bar screens are made of straight steel bars, welded at both ends to two horizontal steel members. The screens are usually ranked by the open distance between bars as follows:

- Fine: spacing of $\frac{1}{16}$ to $\frac{1}{2}$ in. (1.5–13 mm)
- Medium: spacing of $\frac{1}{2}$ to 1 in. (13–25 mm)
- Coarse: spacing of $1\frac{1}{4}$ to 4 in. (32–100 mm)

screening

A pretreatment method that uses coarse screens to remove large debris from the water to prevent clogging of pipes or channels to the treatment plant.

bar screens

A series of straight steel bars, welded at their ends to horizontal steel beams, forming a grid. Bar screens are placed on intakes or in waterways to remove large debris.

A bar screen assembly is installed in a waterway at an angle of about 60 to 80 degrees from the horizontal (Figure 7-1).

This angle is important, particularly in manually cleaned bar screens. The slope makes it convenient to rake debris up the screen and onto the concrete operating platform for drainage and eventual disposal. The slope also helps keep the screen from clogging between cleanings. As debris stacks up against the screen, the passing water lifts and pushes it up the slope, leaving the submerged part of the screen open and clear.

Small treatment plants that receive only small amounts of debris usually have manually cleaned bar screens at the raw-water intake. Automatically cleaned screens are used at plants receiving large amounts of debris and at any plant or intake structure where it is not practical or convenient to reach the screen for cleaning.

Automatically cleaned bar screens are available in a variety of styles. The bar screen shown in Figure 7-1 is equipped with an automatic rake, which is a horizontal piece of metal that moves up the face of the screen. It is pulled by a continuous chain-and-sprocket drive attached at both ends of the rake. Figure 7-2 is a side view of an automatically cleaned bar screen. Note how the rakes move up past the screen, dump the debris (known as screenings) into the collecting hopper, and then return into the water to repeat the cycle.

Wire-Mesh Screens

Wire-mesh screens, commonly referred to as *traveling water screens*, are made of fabric woven from stainless steel or other corrosion-resistant, wire-like materials (Figure 7-3). The fabric may have openings as wide as ⅜ in. (10 mm) or as narrow as ⅟₆₀ in. (0.4 mm).

wire-mesh screen
A screen made of a wire fabric attached to a metal frame. The screen is usually equipped with a motor so that it can move continuously through the water and be automatically cleaned with a water spray. It is used to remove finer debris from the water than the bar screen is able to remove.

Figure 7-1 Bar screen assembly installed in a waterway
Courtesy of US Filter Envirex Products.

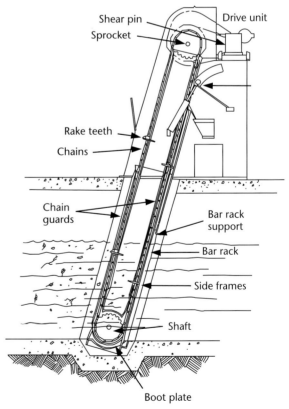

Figure 7-2 Side view of an automatically cleaned bar screen
Courtesy of US Filter Envirex Products.

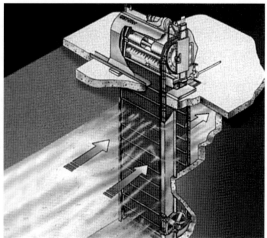

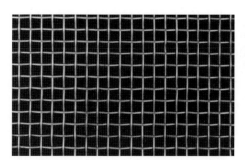

Figure 7-3 Wire-mesh screen material
Courtesy of FMC Corporation, MHS Division.

Figure 7-4 Automatically cleaned wire-mesh screen
Courtesy of US Filter Envirex Products.

Screens can be cleaned manually if they do not require frequent cleaning. Screen segments can be lifted out of the water and cleaned with a brush or hose. However, because debris can accumulate quickly on wire mesh, automatically and continuously cleaned wire-mesh screens are usually favored over manually cleaned units. Figure 7-4 shows an automatically cleaned wire-mesh screen. It is mounted vertically in the water and moves continuously, while spray nozzles located in the head terminal are used to wash away the screenings. The screenings and wash water then fall away from the screen and are conveyed to the disposal area.

Maintenance of Screening Equipment

Clogging and corrosion are the principal problems associated with screening. To prevent these problems, routine cleaning and inspection are required.

Manually cleaned screens must be checked and cleaned frequently. The frequency of inspections depends on weather conditions and the type of watershed. The largest amount of debris is usually encountered during autumn, when trees lose their foliage. Large amounts of debris may also be deposited on screens during the spring and rainy seasons, when high water transports debris, leaves, and branches along riverbanks. Heavily wooded watersheds will usually produce a very heavy loading of debris at certain times of the year.

Automatic screening devices should not be neglected. Routine inspection of the units is essential. The mechanical and electrical systems are usually equipped with protection devices designed to shut down operation in case of emergency or jamming. A mechanical protection device is incorporated into the unit (see Figure 7-2); if a piece of debris becomes jammed between the screen and the rake, a shear pin is designed to break and disconnect the motor.

Electrical protection devices include circuit breakers that automatically shut down the system when there is an electrical malfunction or the motor is overloaded. If possible, an alarm should be provided to alert the plant operator of any malfunction of the screening equipment. If there is no alarm system, visual inspection must be made more frequently to check for possible clogging or equipment failure.

The constant wetting and drying of the screen equipment create ideal conditions for accelerated corrosion. Screening equipment should therefore be inspected at least monthly for signs of corrosion. A stock of replacement parts should be available so that repairs can be made promptly in the event of equipment failure.

Suggested Records for Screening Equipment

Records should be kept of the type and quantity of screened material that is removed. Reference to these records will help identify an appropriate schedule of inspection and cleaning frequency. The records may also help identify activities in the watershed that are causing excessive amounts of debris. An investigation can then be made to see if there is any way to reduce the amount of debris reaching the water intake.

Complete, up-to-date operating records should include the following:

- Date of inspection
- Amount of material removed from screens (in cubic feet or cubic meters)
- Notations regarding unusual or unexpected types of debris or water conditions

Maintenance records, which identify the type and location of equipment, should include a list of required spare parts, a checklist of spare parts on hand, and the date and description of maintenance performed.

Presedimentation

Silt and other gritty material are present to some extent in most surface water supplies. In many sources, this material is particularly extensive after storms or heavy rains that stir up the water. Presedimentation is a pretreatment process used to remove gravel, sand, and silt from the raw water before it enters the main treatment facility. Sand and gravel must be removed because they could jam equipment and wear down pump impellers and other moving parts. In addition, reducing the heavy silt loading of river water can greatly reduce the load on the coagulation and sedimentation facilities. A well-designed presedimentation system can remove up to 60 percent of the settleable material.

Sand is also a problem in groundwater supplies. Sand can typically be prevented from entering wells through the use of proper grouting, screening, and well development. If sand is getting into a well through a broken screen, for instance, it will quickly damage the pump impellers. And if it is pumped into the distribution system, it can eventually block the water mains and could be quite expensive to remove. Sand pumping by some wells cannot be avoided, so sand traps or other removal equipment must be installed to remove the sand before the water enters the distribution system.

The three types of presedimentation systems are

- presedimentation impoundments,
- sand traps,
- mechanical sand-and-grit removal devices.

Presedimentation Impoundments

Impoundments are commonly used for river supplies that have a heavy loading of silt. An impoundment can be a simple earthen reservoir or a concrete structure. The storage capacity can range from one day to several months of actual aquatic

---

presedimentation
A preliminary treatment process used to remove gravel, sand, and other gritty material from the raw water before it enters the main treatment plant. This is usually done without the use of coagulating chemicals.

plant use. Although presedimentation impoundments may be constructed for the primary purpose of allowing sediment to settle out of the water, they also serve other functions.

An important extra benefit of an impoundment is that it stores raw water that can be used if, for some reason, it is undesirable to draw water from the source. For example, there might be a toxic chemical spill upstream on a river or a particularly bad taste or odor problem in the source water.

A major problem with impoundments is that water held for an extended period may develop an excessive growth of algae or aquatic plants. Chlorine cannot normally be used for controlling the aquatic plants because it will generate excessive trihalomethanes (THMs), but the use of other chemicals may be possible. Research is continuing on by-product formation from the use of alternative oxidants. Growth of rooted plants can be controlled by lining the impoundment, and algae growth can be controlled by installing a cover over the impoundment.

It is usually best to have two or more impoundments. Individual basins can then be taken out of service one at a time to control aquatic life by using chemicals or dewatering the impoundment for a short time.

Sand Traps

A **sand trap** is a depression in the bottom of a structure—for example, the bottom of a wet well (Figure 7-5). Because the wet well is much larger than the inlet pipe, the water slows down as it enters, and the suspended sand and gritty material settle to the bottom. A baffle is usually installed in sand traps to prevent short-circuiting and to direct the incoming flow downward.

A drain valve installed at the bottom of the wet well is used to periodically flush out the accumulated sand. Sand traps must be cleaned manually and have relatively small holding capacity, so they are best suited for raw water that contains relatively little sand and grit (less than 100 mg/L).

Mechanical Sand-and-Grit Removal Devices

Mechanical devices are typically used when the raw water contains large amounts of suspended solids. A centrifugal sand-and-grit removal device, often called a **cyclone degritter**, is illustrated in Figure 7-6. As sand-laden water enters the

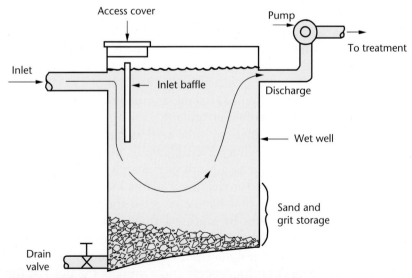

Figure 7-5 Sand trap at the bottom of a wet well

sand trap
An enlargement of a conduit carrying raw water that allows the water velocity to slow down so that sand and other grit can settle.

cyclone degritter
A centrifugal sand-and-grit removal device.

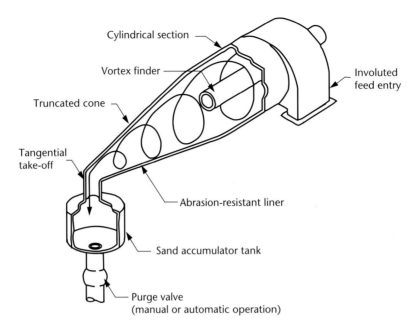

Figure 7-6 Centrifugal sand-and-grit removal device

unit, it begins to travel in a spiral path inside the cylindrical section. Centrifugal force several times the force of gravity develops and throws the sand particles toward the cylinder wall. The sand particles then move in a spiral toward the small end of the cone, where they are discharged, along with some water, into the sand accumulator tank. The clean water leaves the unit through the vortex finder with almost all sand removed.

Figure 7-7 illustrates the simplicity of a typical cyclone installation. These devices have no moving parts, so they require relatively little maintenance even though they handle relatively abrasive material.

Plate and Tube Settlers

Several types of shallow-depth settling units are designed to achieve settling of suspended solids much more rapidly than in open basins (see Chapter 9 for more detail). Several water systems that use very turbid water sources have, in recent years, installed plate or tube settlers to improve the presedimentation process. These devices provide elevated surfaces on which solids can settle, rather than fall to the basin's bottom.

In the past, these systems used large open basins to decrease the solids loading of the water before it entered the plant, but these basins typically have problems. If the water is held for long periods of time, algae will grow. Chlorine cannot be used to control the algae because it will increase the level of THMs. If coagulants are added to the raw water to enhance settling, additional processing of the sludge may be required to deal with residual coagulant.

Systems that have installed plate or tube settlers have found that the solids loading of the water is quickly reduced with little or no chemical addition. The installation also occupies as little as a tenth of the area of a typical open basin, which is an additional advantage for treatment plants located in congested areas.

There are still other utilities that have converted their old presedimentation basins into solids removal devices by adding Lamella plates and coagulants. A municipal water treatment facility in Cincinnati, Ohio, is once such utility. They report that the use of alum and polymer prior to the Lamella plates can be very effective as a primary sedimentation process and eliminate the need of further coagulant chemical addition in the water treatment plant. The old presedimentation

Figure 7-7 Typical cyclone separator installation

Courtesy of LAKOS Filtration Systems, Claude Laval Corp.

basins were difficult to clean, so each year the units had to be removed from service and cleaned manually. With the retrofit of the Lamella plates, Cincinnati installed continuous sludge removal equipment to eliminate the annual cleaning of the presedimentation basins. An additional benefit of nutrient removal is gained, which can help control the growth of algae in the clearer water.

Operation and Maintenance of Presedimentation Systems

To ensure successful removal of sand and grit, presedimentation systems must be tested regularly and cleaned routinely. Influent and effluent samples must be collected and tested for settleable solids.

The frequency of sampling and testing varies from plant to plant, depending on the amount of sand and gritty material in the raw water. During peak flow periods, sampling and testing may be required daily because of the rapidly increasing sand and grit loads; at other times, weekly or even monthly testing may be adequate.

All presedimentation systems should be cleaned routinely to prevent the water flowing through the removal system from mixing the grit and sand back into suspension and carrying it into the treatment plant or water distribution system. Deposits can also become anaerobic (lacking free oxygen), resulting in taste-and-odor problems.

Where the accumulation of settleable solids in the presedimentation basin is inevitable, utilities typically treat some of the solids in the water treatment plant and dredge the rest. The amounts that are treated compared to those that are dredged depend on many factors, but at a minimum the utility must characterize the quality of the solids and determine the amount that needs to be removed. A wet-well type of sand trap is cleaned by allowing accumulations to discharge through a drain line. An access cover is provided so that the wet well can be hosed down during the draining.

Cyclone separators are cleaned automatically and continuously. The operator must periodically check that the sand-and-grit discharge storage bin or hopper is emptied and that the material is properly disposed of.

To clean a presedimentation impoundment, it must be completely drained and dried. The accumulated material can then be removed by scrapers, dozers, or front-end loaders. If the impoundment has a floating cover, the cover must be carefully rolled out of the way of the cleaning equipment.

Suggested Record Keeping for Presedimentation Systems

Detailed record keeping is important. Information about the type of grit and the amount removed by presedimentation helps to determine the frequency of sampling and testing. It also provides a record of the time of year when sand and grit are expected to be a problem.

Records are also necessary for monitoring the continued efficiency of sand-and-grit removal. A gradual decrease in removal efficiency may signal the need to clean accumulated deposits or perform other maintenance work. Detailed records for presedimentation should cover

- date of sampling and testing;
- the amount of suspended solids in the raw water, in milligrams per liter, or milliliters per liter if a settleability test is used;
- the amount of suspended solids in presedimentation effluent; and
- cleaning date, time required, and estimated quantity of removed material.

Records of the nature and quantity of sediment can be kept if samples of the sediment are obtained through core sampling. Figure 7-8A shows contractors for the Northern Kentucky Water District (NKWD) in the process of taking core samples at five locations from the North Reservoir that will be analyzed for total solids, specific gravity, and depth. Figure 7-8B shows a core sample extracted from one of those locations. The extracted materials can be subjected to several kinds of physical and chemical tests that provide useful information the utility needs for making a decision on disposal methods. Table 7-1 shows some of the analysis results of the core samples taken from the North Reservoir of NKWD.

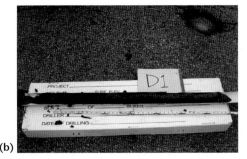

(a) (b)

Figure 7-8 (a) Personnel on reservoir collecting core samples of sediment. (b) Close-up of the extraction at sample site D1.

Courtesy Northern Kentucky Water District.

Table 7-1 Analysis results of core samples taken from North Reservoir of NKWD

Sample Location	Length of Core, in. (cm)	Percent Solids	Specific Gravity	Gradation Analysis: % sand, % silt, % clay
B1	32 (81)	36.4	2.612	11, 43, 46
D1	35 (89)	37.0	2.442	8, 51, 41
F1	36 (91)	40.1	2.566	10, 49, 41
F2	36 (91)	37.3	2.610	4, 48, 48
H1	36 (91)	33.6	2.546	1, 48, 51

Microstraining

A **microstrainer** (Figure 7-9) is a very fine screen used primarily to remove algae, other aquatic organisms, and small debris that can clog treatment plant filters.

Process Equipment

The most common type of microstraining unit consists of a rotating drum lined with finely woven material, such as stainless-steel wire fabric. One commonly used fabric has about 160,000 openings per square inch (250 openings per square millimeter), which is about the same as tightly woven clothing fabric. Other fabrics may have larger or smaller openings.

The microstrainer drum rotates slowly, usually 4 to 7 revolutions per minute (rpm), as water enters the inside of the drum and flows outward through the fabric. Algae and other aquatic organisms deposited on the inside of the fabric form a mat of debris, which adheres to the fabric and rotates up to the backwash hood area. At the top of the rotating drum, high-pressure (25–50 psi, or 172–345 kPa) jets spray the back side of the fabric, causing the matted debris to break away. The debris and backwash water fall by gravity into a debris trough inside the drum and flow either directly to a disposal point or to a pond or tank that separates the debris from the water.

Advantages and Disadvantages

A major advantage of microstrainers is the improvement they make in the operation of sand filters. They normally remove from 50 to 90 percent of the filter-clogging material from the water, depending on the type of algae present. Because the load on sand filters is reduced, the filters can be operated for a longer time without backwashing. This saves backwash water and increases the amount of filtered water available to the water system.

Although there are definite advantages to using microstrainers in certain situations, there are also limitations. Straining removes only relatively coarse particles

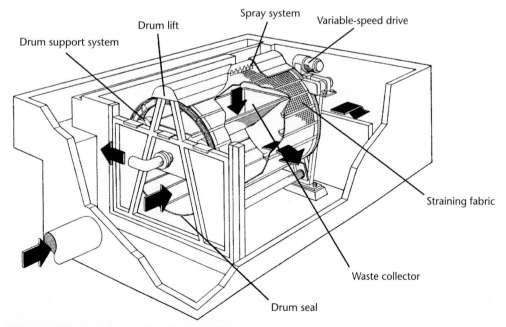

Figure 7-9 Fine-screened microstrainer
Courtesy of US Filter/Permutit.

> **microstrainer**
> A rotating drum lined with a finely woven material, such as stainless steel. Microstrainers are used to remove algae and small debris before they enter the treatment plant.

from the water. Microstrainers cannot remove all algae, and they do not remove bacteria, viruses, *Cryptosporidium*, *Giardia lamblia*, or most suspended matter that contributes to turbidity. Even eggs of tiny aquatic animals can pass through the fabric. In addition, microstrainers have no effect on the removal of dissolved substances, such as inorganic and organic chemicals. Therefore, microstrainers should not be considered or used as a substitute for coagulation, flocculation, and filtration.

Although microstrainers are made to resist corrosion, the constant wet–dry conditions under which they operate cause them to require quite a bit of maintenance. This includes painting, lubrication, replacement of worn parts, and fabric repair and replacement.

Finally, it is recommended that chlorine not be added before the water enters a microstrainer for the following reasons:

- Live algae are easier to clean off the mesh than dead algae.
- If there is soluble iron in the raw water, it may oxidize to ferric hydroxide on the mesh, which will form a sticky, jellylike coating.
- Chlorine reaction with algae may accentuate tastes and odors.
- The amount of chlorine required (chlorine demand) will be lower if applied after the microstrainer.
- Free chlorine may corrode the mesh.

Preoxidation

The addition of an oxidant compound (such as ozone or hypochlorite) to source water is called **preoxidation**. This same practice combined with filtration or membrane filtration is prefiltration oxidation.

The mechanism of preoxidation's effect on conventional water treatment plant operations is not clear, as each surface water's chemistry is different. Results have shown improved flocculation, sedimentation, and filtration.

Compliance with maximum contaminant levels for disinfection by-products as promulgated by the Stage 1 and Stage 2 Disinfectants/Disinfection By-Products Rule may affect the concentration of oxidants used in both source water and prefiltration oxidants. The by-products of ozonation must also be considered.

If preozonation improves coagulation, cost savings may result because of lower dosages of coagulant chemicals that are required. Unit processes, such as flocculation and sedimentation, may be eliminated or reduced in scale, also resulting in cost savings. More research on the ozonation process may further advance its effectiveness.

Study Questions

1. Which of the following is a principal problem associated with preliminary treatment screening?
   a. Broken screens
   b. Excessive downtime due to numerous shear pins being broken
   c. Clogging
   d. Chain comes out of foot sprocket

preoxidation
Source water oxidation with hypochlorite or ozone.

2. Bar screen assemblies are installed in a waterway at a(n) _____ angle from the horizontal.
   a. 40- to 60-degree
   b. 60- to 80-degree
   c. 80- to 90-degree
   d. 90- to 120-degree

3. Which of the following is *not* a term used to rank the distance between bars in a bar screen?
   a. Fine
   b. Medium
   c. Coarse
   d. Wide

4. _____ is a pretreatment process used to remove gravel, sand, and silt from the raw water before it enters the main treatment facility.
   a. Screening
   b. Presedimentation
   c. Preoxidation
   d. Microstraining

5. What is the opening size for medium-ranked fixed screens or bar screens?

6. What is the first pretreatment provided in most surface water treatment systems?

7. What details are included in complete, up-to-date operating records for screening equipment?

8. What is a microstrainer?

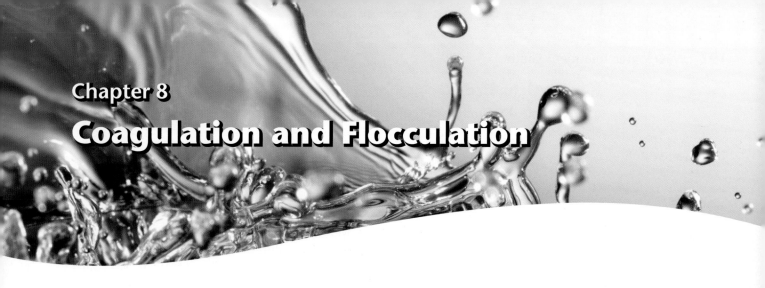

Chapter 8
Coagulation and Flocculation

The large particles of suspended matter in raw water can be removed by allowing them to settle out in a presedimentation basin. However, there are smaller particles in almost all surface water and some groundwater that will not settle out within a reasonable time without some help to accelerate the process. The common term for this suspended matter is **nonsettleable solids**, which usually consist of a combination of biological organisms, bacteria, viruses, protozoans, color-causing particles, organic matter, and inorganic solids. The term applied to all suspended matter in water is **turbidity**.

Not only is visible turbidity in drinking water objectionable to customers, but harmful bacteria, viruses, and protozoans (such as *Giardia lamblia*, *Cryptosporidium*, and amoebas) are likely to be present. These pathogens may be protected from contact with the disinfectant by the suspended matter, so disinfection of surface water without removing its turbidity cannot produce consistently safe water.

The treatment most frequently used to remove turbidity is known as **conventional treatment**. This is a combination of the following steps:

1. **Coagulation**: adding and rapidly mixing chemical coagulants into the raw water.
2. **Flocculation**: slowly mixing the chemicals with the water to assist in building up particles of **floc**.
3. *Sedimentation*: allowing the floc to settle out of the water.
4. *Filtration*: removing almost all of the suspended matter that remains by passing the water through filters.

Process Description

In the coagulation and flocculation processes, nonsettleable solids are converted into large and heavier settleable solids by physical–chemical changes brought about by adding and mixing coagulant chemicals into the raw water. The settleable solids can then be removed by the sedimentation and filtration processes. Nonsettleable solids resist settling for the following two reasons:

1. Particle size
2. Natural forces between particles

nonsettleable solids
Finely divided solids, such as bacteria and fine clay particles, that will stay suspended in water for long periods of time.

turbidity
A physical characteristic of water making the water appear cloudy. The condition is caused by the presence of suspended matter.

conventional treatment
A term that describes the treatment process used by most US surface water systems, consisting of the steps of coagulation, flocculation, sedimentation, and filtration.

coagulation
The water treatment process that causes very small suspended particles to attract one another and form larger particles. This is accomplished by the addition of a chemical, called a coagulant, that neutralizes the electrostatic charges on the particles that cause them to repel each other.

Particle Size

Untreated, natural water contains the following three types of nonsettleable solids:

1. Suspended solids
2. Colloidal solids
3. Dissolved solids

Suspended Solids

The particles held in suspension by the natural action of flowing water are called suspended solids. The smallest suspended solids do not settle quickly and for purposes of water treatment are called *nonsettleable*. Denser and heavier suspended solids are referred to as settleable solids because they will settle unaided to the bottom of a sedimentation basin within 4 hours.

One reason that nonsettleable particles resist settling is their small size. Consider a particle of coarse sand in the shape of a cube, 1 mm per side; it would have a surface area of 6 mm², which is about the area of the head of a large pin. This particle could be expected to settle quickly, dropping about 1 ft (0.3 m) every 3 seconds. If this same particle were to be ground down by erosion to a particle that is only 0.000001 mm per side, the exposed surface area of all particles would be increased to 6 m², which is about the area of two pool tables. The increase in surface area greatly increases the drag forces that resist settling, and it would now take about 60 years for these tiny particles to settle the same 1-ft (0.3-m) distance from natural forces alone. The natural settling rates for small particles are listed in Table 8-1.

Colloidal Solids

Very fine silts, bacteria, color-causing particles, and viruses that do not settle in a reasonable time are called colloidal solids. Although individual colloidal solids cannot be seen with the naked eye, their combined effect is often seen as color or turbidity in water. These particles are small enough to pass through later treatment processes if not properly coagulated and flocculated.

Dissolved Solids

Any particles of organic or inorganic matter that are dissolved in water—such as salts, chemicals, or gases—are referred to as dissolved solids. A dissolved solid is

Table 8-1 Natural settling rates for small particles

Particle Diameter, mm	Representative Particle	Time Required to Settle in 1-ft (0.3-m) Depth
		Settleable
10	Gravel	0.3 seconds
1	Coarse sand	3 seconds
0.1	Fine sand	38 seconds
0.01	Silt	33 minutes
		Considered Nonsettleable
0.001	Bacteria	55 hours
0.0001	Color	230 days
0.00001	Colloidal particles	6.3 years
0.000001	Colloidal particles	63-year minimum

Source: *Water Quality and Treatment*. 3rd ed. 1971.

---

flocculation

The water treatment process, following coagulation, that uses gentle stirring to bring suspended particles together so that they will form larger, more settleable clumps called floc.

floc

Collections of smaller particles (such as silt, organic matter, and microorganisms) that have come together (agglomerated) into larger, more settleable particles as a result of the coagulation–flocculation process.

suspended solid

A solid organic and inorganic particle that is held in suspension by the action of flowing water.

settleable solid

A denser and heavier suspended solid that will settle unaided to the bottom of a sedimentation basin within 4 hours.

colloidal solid

Finely divided solid that will not settle out of water for very long periods of time unless the coagulation–flocculation process is used.

dissolved solid

Any material that is dissolved in water and can be recovered by evaporating the water after filtering the suspended material.

the size of a molecule and is invisible to the naked eye. Most of the trace metals and organic chemicals found in water are dissolved. They are nonsettleable and can cause public health or aesthetic problems, such as taste, odor, or color, if not removed. Unless converted to a precipitate by chemical or physical means, they cannot be removed from the water. The size ranges of the various types of solids are shown in Figure 8-1.

Natural Forces

Particles in water usually carry a negative electrical charge. Just as like poles of a magnet repel each other, there is a repelling force between any two particles of like charge. In water treatment, this natural repelling electrical force is called *zeta potential*. The force is strong enough to hold the very small, colloidal particles apart and keep them in suspension.

The *van der Waals force* is an attraction that exists between all particles in nature and tends to pull any two particles together. This attracting force acts opposite to the zeta potential. As long as the zeta potential is stronger than the van der Waals force, the particles will stay in suspension.

Effect of Coagulation and Flocculation

The coagulation–flocculation processes neutralize or reduce the zeta potential of nonsettleable solids, allowing the van der Waals force of attraction to begin pulling particles together. These particles are then able to gather into small groups of microfloc, as shown in Figure 8-2. Although these particles are larger than the original colloids, they are held together rather weakly. Individual particles are invisible to the naked eye and are still nonsettleable. However, the gentle stirring action created by the flocculation process brings the microfloc particles together to form large and relatively heavy floc particles (macrofloc), which can settle or be filtered. The jellylike floc particles are usually visible and will look like small tufts of cotton or snowflakes in the water.

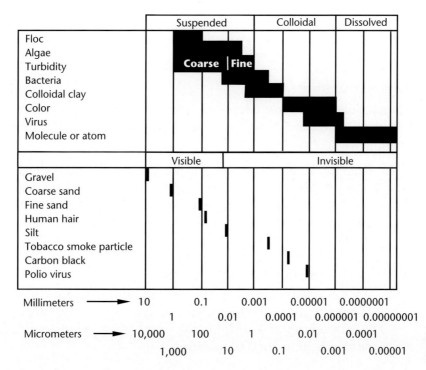

Figure 8-1 Size range of solids

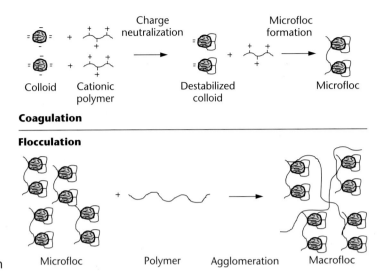

Figure 8-2 Microfloc and macrofloc formation

Coagulant Chemicals and Feed Equipment

There are two types of chemicals used in the coagulation process: coagulants and coagulant aids. The dosages of coagulants and coagulant aids must be closely monitored to ensure that effective coagulation is occurring. Tests for control of the coagulation and flocculation process are described later in this chapter.

Coagulants

The troublesome particles to be removed from water are usually negatively charged, and the coagulants used in water treatment normally consist of positively charged ions. The positive charges neutralize the negative charges and promote coagulation.

Some coagulants contain ions with more positive charges than others. Those consisting of trivalent ions, such as aluminum and iron, are 50 to 60 times more effective than chemicals with bivalent ions, such as calcium. They are 700 to 1,000 times more effective than coagulants with monovalent ions, such as sodium. (See Chapter 1 for a discussion of valences.)

Aluminum Sulfate (Alum)

Because alum is the most common coagulant used for water treatment, it is important to understand how it promotes floc formation and settling. The process is as follows:

1. Alum added to raw water reacts with the alkalinity naturally present to form jellylike floc particles of aluminum hydroxide, $Al(OH)_3$. A certain level of alkalinity is necessary for the reaction to occur. If not enough is naturally present, the alkalinity of the water must be increased. Alum will consume alkalinity in the ratio of 1 to 0.5; that is, 1 mg/L dry-basis alum will consume 0.5 mg/L alkalinity as $CaCO_3$. One mg/L dry-basis alum dosage will produce 0.26 mg/L **sludge**.

2. The positively charged trivalent aluminum ion neutralizes the negatively charged particles of color or turbidity. This occurs within 1 or 2 seconds after the chemical is added to the water, which is why rapid, thorough mixing is critical to good coagulation.

sludge
The accumulated solids separated from water during treatment.

3. Within a few seconds, the particles begin to attach to each other to form larger particles.

4. The floc that is first formed is made up of microfloc that still has a positive charge from the coagulant; the floc particles continue to neutralize negatively charged particles until they become neutral particles themselves. This is referred to as *charge neutralization*.

5. Finally, the microfloc particles begin to collide and stick together (agglomerate) to form larger, settleable floc particles.

Many physical and chemical factors can affect the success of a coagulant, including mixing conditions; pH, alkalinity, and turbidity levels; and water temperature. Alum works best in a pH range of 5.8 to 8.5. If it is used outside this range, the floc either does not form completely or it may form and then dissolve back into the water.

Aluminum Chlorohydrate (ACH)

ACH contains much more reactive aluminum than liquid alum, and so can usually be used in lower dosages. On a pound-for-pound basis, it produces more sludge than alum, but it can help to produce less sludge because of the lower dosages. Another benefit that is sometimes realized is that pH control is easier because less alkalinity is consumed when ACH is used instead of alum.

One mg/L ACH consumes 0.18 mg/L alkalinity as $CaCO_3$. One mg/L ACH will produce 0.35 mg/L sludge.

Iron Salts

Iron salts, such as ferric chloride and ferric sulfate, can operate effectively over a wider range of pH values than alum. However, they are quite corrosive and require special facilities for storage and handling.

Both alum and ferric sulfate are affected by the alkalinity of the raw water. If the alkalinity is not high enough, an effective floc will not form. If floc is not completely formed because of insufficient alkalinity or a pH value outside the optimal range, but the alkalinity or pH is later changed during treatment or in the system, the floc can reform in the distribution system. This will, of course, cause customer complaints and problems because of a buildup of sediment in the system piping.

Other Coagulant Chemicals

In general, if pH and alkalinity are at proper levels, coagulation can be improved by increases in turbidity, temperature, and mixing energy. Table 8-2 describes the commonly used coagulants. Other coagulant chemicals that are occasionally used for special conditions are aluminum ammonium sulfate and aluminum potassium sulfate. Table 8-3 gives typical dosage ratios for combinations of coagulants. In most cases, the secondary chemical is added to adjust the pH or otherwise enhance the effectiveness of the primary chemical. Table 8-4 shows the amounts of liquid alum needed to produce dry-basis dosage in mg/L at several flow rates.

It has also been found that the use of ozone as an initial disinfectant often improves coagulation. This has the effect of lowering the cost of coagulant chemicals, reducing sludge disposal costs, and lengthening filter runs.

Table 8-2 Common coagulation chemicals

Common Name	Chemical Formula	Comments
Aluminum sulfate	$Al_2(SO_4)_3 \cdot 14(H_2O)$	Most common coagulant in the United States; often used with cationic polymers
Aluminum chlorohydrate	$Al_2Cl(OH)_5$	May help to produce less sludge and less corrosivity
Ferric chloride	$FeCl_3$	May be more effective than alum in some applications
Ferric sulfate	$Fe_2(SO_4)_3$	Often used with lime softening
Ferrous sulfate	$Fe_2(SO_4)_3 \cdot 7H_2O$	Less pH-dependent than alum
Aluminum polymers	—	Include polyaluminum chloride and polyaluminum sulfates
Cationic polymers	—	Synthetic polyelectrolytes; large molecules
Sodium aluminate	$Na_2Al_2O_4$	Used with alum to improve coagulation
Sodium silicate	$Na_2O \cdot (SiO_2)_x$	x can range from 0.5 to 4.0; ingredient of activated silica coagulant aids

Source: Adapted from *Water Treatment Plant Design*. 1990.

Table 8-3 Coagulant combinations and ratios

Coagulants	Typical Dosage Ratio (First to Second Coagulant)
Aluminum sulfate + caustic soda	3:1
Aluminum sulfate + hydrated lime	3:1
Aluminum sulfate + sodium aluminate	4:3
Aluminum sulfate + sodium carbonate	1:1 to 2:1
Ferric sulfate + hydrated lime	5:2
Ferrous sulfate + hydrated lime	4:1
Ferrous sulfate + chlorine	8:1
Sodium aluminate + ferric chloride	1:1

Table 8-4 Required TOC removals based on source water alkalinity

TOC, mg/L	Alkalinity (mg/L CaCO₃)		
	0–60	>60–120	>120
2–4	35%	25%	15%
4–8	45%	35%	25%
>8	50%	40%	30%

Coagulant Aids

A coagulant aid is a chemical added during coagulation to achieve one or more of the following results:

- Improve coagulation
- Build stronger, more settleable floc
- Overcome the effect of temperature drops that slow coagulation
- Reduce the amount of coagulant needed
- Reduce the amount of sludge produced

The use of coagulant aids can significantly reduce the amount of alum used and, accordingly, the amount of sludge produced. Because alum sludge is difficult to dewater and dispose of, a reduction in sludge is often the prime consideration in the decision to use a coagulant aid. The three general types of coagulant aids are

1. activated silica,
2. weighting agents, and
3. polyelectrolytes.

Activated Silica

Activated silica has been used as a coagulant aid with alum since the late 1930s and remains in use today. Used in the proper dosage, activated silica will increase the rate of coagulation, reduce the coagulant dosage needed, and widen the pH range for effective coagulation. Activated silica must be prepared by the operator at the plant. The chemical actually delivered to the plant is sodium silicate, Na_2SiO_3. The operator "activates" the sodium silicate by adding an acid, typically hypochlorous acid, to reduce the alkalinity.

The chief advantage of using activated silica is that it strengthens the floc, making it less likely to break apart during sedimentation or filtration. In addition, the resulting floc is larger and denser and settles more quickly. Improved color removal and better floc formation at low temperatures can also result.

Activated silica is usually added after the coagulant, but adding it before can also be successful, especially with low-turbidity water. It should never be added directly with the alum because they react with each other.

A major disadvantage of using activated silica is the precise control required during the activation step to produce a solution that will not gel. Too much silica will actually slow the formation of floc and cause filter clogging.

Weighting Agents

When some natural materials are added to water, they form additional particles that enhance floc formation. Weighting agents are principally used to treat water high in color, low in turbidity, and low in mineral content. This type of water would otherwise produce small, slowly settling floc.

Bentonite clay is a common weighting agent. Dosages in the range of 10 to 50 mg/L usually produce rapidly settling floc. In water with low turbidity, the clay increases turbidity, which speeds formation of floc by increasing the number of chance collisions between particles. Powdered limestone and powdered silica can also be used as weighting agents.

Polyelectrolytes

Polyelectrolytes (also called *polymers*) have extremely large molecules that, when dissolved in water, produce highly charged ions. In general, compared with other coagulant aids, the required dosages of polyelectrolytes are extremely small.

The following are three basic polyelectrolyte classifications that may be either natural or synthetic materials:

1. Cationic polyelectrolytes
2. Anionic polyelectrolytes
3. Nonionic polyelectrolytes

Cationic Polyelectrolytes   Cationic polyelectrolytes are polymers that produce positively charged ions when dissolved in water. They are widely used because the suspended and colloidal solids commonly found in water are usually negatively

activated silica
A coagulant aid used to form a denser, stronger floc.

weighting agent
A material, such as bentonite, added to low-turbidity waters to provide additional particles for good floc formation.

polyelectrolyte
High–molecular weight, synthetic organic compound that forms ions when dissolved in water. Also called *polymer*.

charged. They can be used as the primary coagulant or as an aid to such coagulants as alum or ferric sulfate. For the most effective turbidity removal, the polymer is generally used in combination with a coagulant.

Advantages to using cationic polyelectrolytes include the following:

- The amount of coagulant can be reduced.
- The floc settles better.
- There is less sensitivity to pH.
- The flocculation of living organisms, such as bacteria and algae, is improved.

Anionic Polyelectrolytes   Anionic polyelectrolytes are polymers that dissolve to form negatively charged ions; they are used to remove positively charged solids. Anionic polyelectrolytes are used primarily with aluminum and iron coagulants. Advantages include increased floc size, improved settling, and generally stronger floc. They are not materially affected by pH, alkalinity, hardness, or turbidity.

Nonionic Polyelectrolytes   Nonionic polyelectrolytes are polymers having a balanced, or neutral, charge. Upon dissolving, they release both positively and negatively charged ions. Although nonionic polyelectrolytes must be added in larger doses than other types, they are less expensive.

Chemicals Used to Raise Alkalinity

Increasing the alkalinity of water often enhances the effect of coagulants. The chemicals principally used to increase alkalinity are lime, soda ash, caustic soda, and sodium bicarbonate.

Lime   Lime ($Ca(OH)_2$) is often used in conjunction with aluminum or ferrous sulfate to provide artificial alkalinity in water; in some waters, it may be used alone. It is used as either quicklime or hydrated lime.

Soda Ash, Caustic Soda, and Sodium Bicarbonate   Soda ash (Na_2CO_3), caustic soda (NaOH), and sodium bicarbonate ($NaHCO_3$) are also used to raise alkalinity in order to enhance the effectiveness of other coagulants. Although they are more expensive per unit weight than lime, they are often preferred because of easier feeding and handling. More information on feeding and handling lime, soda ash, and caustic soda is included in Chapter 16.

Approval of Coagulant Chemicals

All chemicals used in water treatment must be approved by a US or state regulatory agency as safe for addition to potable water. The label on any container must note that the product is acceptable and that application instructions provided by the supplier are followed.

 WATCH THE VIDEO
Coagulation and Flocculation (www.awwa.org/wsovideoclips)

Chemical Purchasing, Receiving, and Quality Control

Purchasing specifications for chemicals should contain requirements to ensure the correct chemical strength and grade is delivered. Special conditions added to bid and purchasing documents can ensure chemical reliability. Suppliers that sign these documents agree to the conditions allowing enforcement. The following are some suggestions of requirements for bid or purchasing documents:

1. *Adherence to standards.* Use only chemicals certified to NSF Standard 60 or equivalent for water treatment chemicals.

2. *Defined receiving hours.* Specify the hours and days of the week that shipments will be received at your facility.

3. *Certification of analysis.* Require a load-specific certificate of analysis.

4. *Wash-out verification.* If chemicals are shipped in a trailer or reusable container, specify that the trailer or container be dedicated for the use of water treatment chemicals and/or require a wash-out certificate to document that the contents of a previous load was thoroughly removed.

5. *Plant fill-line security.* Prohibit unloading until approved by plant personnel. It is also good practice to lock or secure all external fill lines to prevent unloading prior to completion of all quality control checks.

6. *Inspection prior to unloading.* Require inspection of chemical fill lines and equipment used to unload bulk shipments. Require that all openings to tankers be sealed with tamper-evident seals and that the driver be equipped and use proper safety equipment.

Chemical Storage and Handling

Coagulant chemicals are available both in dry granules or powder and in liquid form. Dry chemicals are available in various packaging sizes from 50-lb (23-kg) bags to drums. In bulk, they can be delivered by transport truck or railroad car.

Chemicals should always be stored in a dry area at a moderate and fairly uniform temperature. Most chemicals will harden and cake if exposed to moisture, so bags should be stored on pallets to allow air circulation beneath them. If possible, the storage area for dry chemicals should be located over the feed machines so that they can be dumped directly into feed hoppers. The types of equipment used to handle dry chemicals include hand trucks, overhead monorails, hoists, elevators, mechanical conveyors, and pneumatic conveyors.

Chemicals in liquid form are becoming increasingly popular, particularly at larger plants where it is practical to purchase chemicals in tank truck loads. Advantages of purchasing chemicals in liquid form include greatly simplified chemical storage, handling, and feeding; less dirt and mess in the plant; less required storage space; and reduced safety hazards.

Storage of chemicals should be carefully thought out and their condition monitored. Prolonged storage can adversely affect some chemicals. It is important to follow manufacturer (supplier) recommendations for proper storage. The strength and purity of some stored chemicals should be checked periodically to ensure that they remain viable.

WATCH THE VIDEO
Water Treatment Chemicals (www.awwa.org/wsovideoclips)

Chemical Feed Equipment

Coagulant chemicals can be fed in dry or liquid form.

Dry Chemical Feeders

There are two general types of dry chemical feeders: volumetric and gravimetric. Volumetric feeders measure out the chemical from the hopper to the mixing tank by volume per unit time. An example of this type of feeder is shown in Figure 8-3. Gravimetric feeders feed the chemical by weight, as illustrated in Figure 8-4. Volumetric feeders are generally less costly but are also less accurate than gravimetric ones. The types of dry feeding mechanisms include a rotating disk, an oscillating disk, a rotary gate, a belt, and a screw. The volume or weight of chemical to be fed may be set manually or adjusted automatically based on water flow rate, turbidity, zeta potential, or signal from a streaming current meter.

All chemicals must be in solution prior to mixing with the water to be treated. Most coagulants and coagulant aids dissolve with some difficulty, so it is necessary to provide good agitation and sufficient time for a solution to be formed as the dry chemical is added to water. Dry chemical feeders usually feed the chemical into a mixing tank where it is put into solution. In some instances, chemical solution water should be softened to avoid the creation of unwanted precipitates. Small quantities of chemicals can also be put into solution in batches using a small tank and mixer, as shown in Figure 8-5.

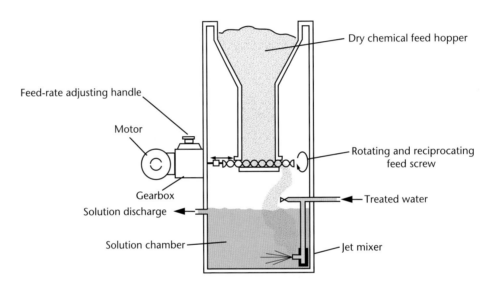

Figure 8-3 Volumetric feeder

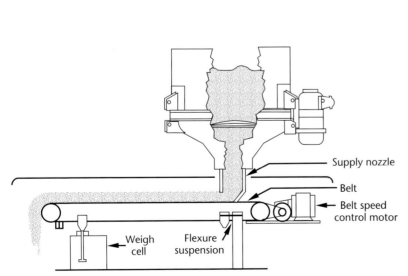

Figure 8-4 Gravimetric feeder

Figure 8-5 Solution mixer
Courtesy of Lightning.

Solution Feeders

Liquid coagulants and coagulant aids are fed by solution feeders. The feeders may draw directly from the liquid chemical storage tank or the chemical may be diluted in a smaller tank before it is fed, as illustrated in Figure 8-6.

The most common type of solution feeder is the metering pump. This is a positive-displacement pump that delivers a precise volume of solution with each stroke or rotation of the pumping mechanism. Figure 8-7 is a diagram of a typical metering pump. These pumps usually have variable-speed motors or drives, which can be manually adjusted or automatically controlled in response to a control signal.

Peristaltic pumps function by having a roller mechanism that squeezes a quantity of chemical through a loop of flexible hose. The advantages are their reasonable price and their capability of handling almost any nonflammable liquid. Their principal disadvantage is that the flexible tube must be periodically replaced.

Solution feeders may also be of the decanting type, consisting of a solution tank with a drawoff pipe that is lowered or raised at a controlled rate by

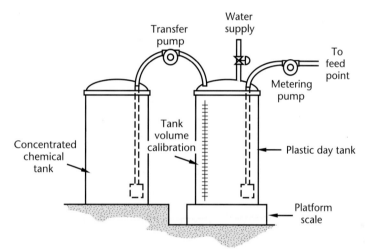

Figure 8-6 Chemical diluted in a day tank for feeding

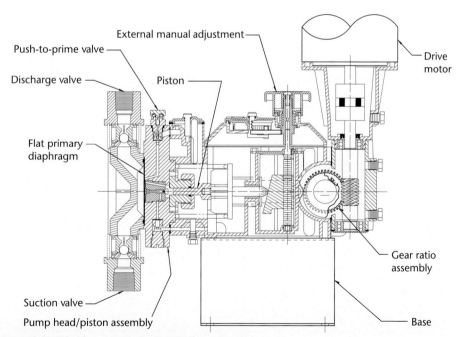

Figure 8-7 Diaphragm-type metering pump

Courtesy of Pulsafeeder, a unit of IDEX Corporation.

a variable-speed motor; a revolving dipper type, which rotates at a controllable speed; and a progressive cavity pump.

Rapid-Mix Facilities

Once coagulant chemicals have been added to raw water, it is essential to provide rapid agitation to distribute the coagulant evenly throughout the water. This is particularly true when alum or ferric salts are being used. The water must be briefly and violently agitated to encourage the greatest number of collisions between suspended particles.

The more common types of facilities used for **rapid mixing** (or flash mixing) are

- mechanical mixers,
- static mixers,
- pumps and conduits, and
- baffled chambers.

Mechanical Mixers

Mechanical mixers are widely used for rapid mixing because of their good control features. They are usually placed in a small chamber or tank and include the propeller, impeller, or turbine type. The detention time in these chambers is designed to be very short. Figures 8-8 and 8-9 are two designs for mechanical mixers in chambers.

Mechanical mixers can also be mounted directly into a pipeline; they are then referred to as *in-line mixers*. This type of unit provides good instantaneous mixing with little short-circuiting, costs much less than a conventional rapid-mixing installation, and still allows for adjustment to provide the correct amount of mixing energy. Figure 8-10 illustrates a typical in-line mixer. All in-line mixers must be located close to the flocculation chamber so that flocculation and settling will not occur within the pipeline.

Pipe Grids

Grid systems of perforated pipes are used to disperse the coagulant into the water being treated. These systems provide uniform distribution of coagulant but are susceptible to flow changes.

rapid mixing
The process of quickly mixing a chemical solution uniformly through the water.

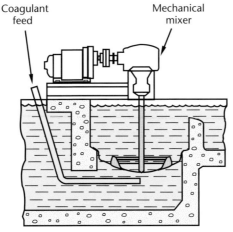

Figure 8-8 Mechanical mixing chamber—single-blade mixer

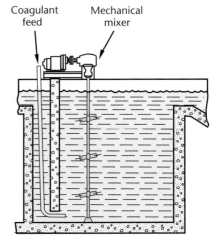

Figure 8-9 Mechanical mixing chamber—multiple-blade mixer

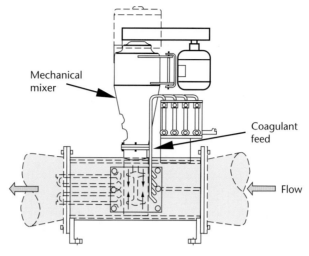

Figure 8-10 In-line mixer

Static Mixers

Static (or motionless) mixers produce turbulence and mixing using the fixed sloping vanes within the mixer, as illustrated in Figure 8-11. They are effective and economical to install and operate; however, head loss through a static mixer is significant. Another caution is that mixing efficiency is directly related to flow rate, so there is no way to adjust the mixing energy.

Pumps and Conduits

Coagulant chemicals can also be added to the suction side of a low-lift pump to use the turbulence in the pump as a mixing mechanism (Figure 8-12). The amount of mixing is determined by the speed of the pump, so the turbulence required for proper flash mixing may or may not be provided. If the turbulence is adequate, it can be used without investing in special equipment and without increasing the system head.

Disadvantages include the fact that there is little or no opportunity to adjust the operation to suit treatment needs and that coagulant may cause pump corrosion.

Baffled Chambers

The baffled chamber shown in Figure 8-13 provides turbulence to the water flowing over and under the baffles. The primary problem is that turbulence is determined by the rate of flow and normally cannot be controlled.

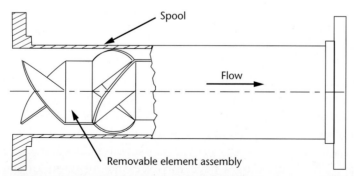

Figure 8-11 Section view of a static mixer
Source: *Water Quality and Treatment.* 5th ed. 1999.

> **static mixer**
> A device designed to produce turbulence and mixing of chemicals with water, by means of fixed sloping vanes within the unit, without the need for any application of power.

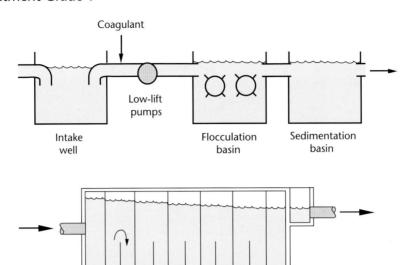

Figure 8-12 Low-lift pumps used for rapid mixing

Figure 8-13 Section view of a baffled chamber

Flocculation Facilities

Flocculation Basins

Flocculation follows coagulation and usually takes place in a chamber that provides a slow, gentle agitation of the water. In the flocculation stage, physical processes transform the smaller particles of floc formed by the rapid mix into larger aggregates of floc. The rate of aggregation is determined by the rate at which the particles collide. As the aggregates grow in size, they become more fragile, so the mixing force applied must not be so great as to cause the floc particles to break up or shear. Baffles are usually provided in the basin to slow down the water flow and reduce short-circuiting. Figure 8-14 illustrates various designs for mechanical flocculators.

In conventional water treatment plants, most flocculation basins are designed for tapered flocculation, which involves a reduction in velocity gradient as the water passes through the basin. This promotes the development of a readily settleable floc. In direct filtration plants, mixers are usually variable speed to accommodate energy changes based on changing water temperature, but energy across the basins is generally maintained equally to promote the formation of a pinpoint-sized floc. In direct filtration, the goal is not to form a settleable floc, but one that is filterable.

At least two basins should be provided so that one may be removed from service at a time. The units should also be designed for operation either in series or in parallel. The flow-through velocity should normally be between 0.5 and 1.5 ft/min (0.0025 and 0.0076 m/sec).

Like rapid mixers, flocculators are usually provided in multiple sets, and operators should keep the proper number of units in and/or out of service to provide the correct detention times (Figure 8-15). Flocculators are designed to provide 15 to 45 minutes of detention time. A common operational mistake is to keep too many units in service, thereby providing excessive flocculation time. This can break up fragile flocs, creating a need for excessive amounts of coagulant. It is not uncommon to see flocculators with large amounts of settled floc because the detention time was too long. This also creates a maintenance problem, as units

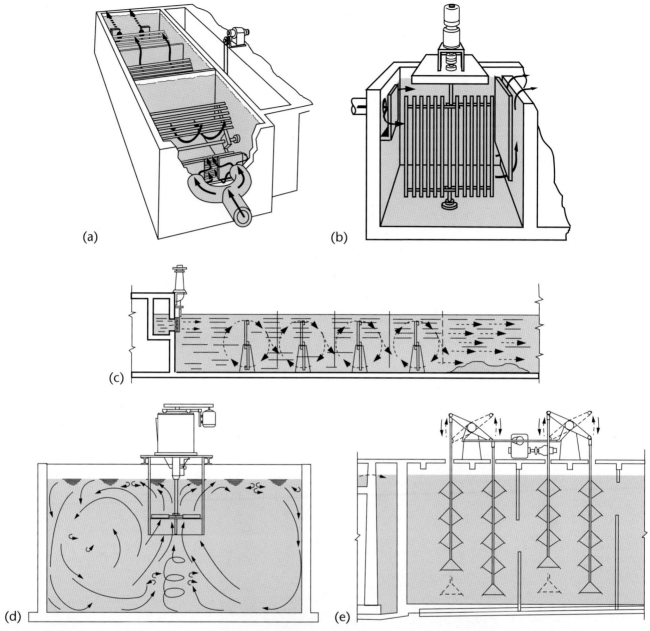

Figure 8-14 Various designs for mechanical flocculators. (a) Baffles and horizontal paddle-wheel flocculator. (b) Paddle-wheel flocculator, vertical type. (c) Propeller flocculator. (d) Turbine flocculator. (e) Walking-beam flocculator.

Courtesy of US Filter Envirex Products.

have to be cleaned more often. If they are not cleaned, short-circuiting occurs and the problem worsens.

In addition to operating the proper number of flocculators, operators must control the mixing energy imparted to the floc chambers. Control is designed into most modern flocculators so that an operator can choose the "tip speed," at least for the final stage. A good rule of thumb is that the tip speed of the final flocculator paddles should be about 1 ft/sec and operate in the range of 0.9 to 1.3 ft/sec most of the time (Figure 8-16). In colder water or when floc formation is heavy due to naturally occurring turbidity, a faster speed may be needed. The tip speed of the final paddle is determined using a stopwatch to measure the time it takes

Figure 8-15 Flocculators at Philadelphia Water Treatment Plant out of service for maintenance

Source: Philadelphia Water Department.

Figure 8-16 Flocculator drive at Philadelphia Water Treatment Plant used to control paddle speed

Source: Philadelphia Water Department.

for the paddle to make one revolution. If the distance from the center of the shaft to the end of the paddle is measured, the distance traveled in that one revolution can be calculated as $\pi \times D$, where D is the diameter of the circle, in feet, that the paddle makes when it revolves. D is calculated as 2 times the radius. The distance is divided by the time to obtain the tip speed, in feet per second. For example, if the final paddle in a flocculator revolves once every 55 seconds and the distance from the center of the shaft to the tip of the paddle (radius) is 11 ft, what is the tip speed? Distance traveled by the paddle is $\pi \times D$, or 3.14×22 ft, which is 69 ft; 69 ft divided by 55 seconds is 1.25 ft/sec.

Study Questions

1. Detention time in flocculation basins are usually designed to provide for
   a. 5–15 minutes.
   b. 15–45 minutes.
   c. 45–60 minutes.
   d. 60–90 minutes.

2. Alum works best in a pH range of
   a. less than 4.0.
   b. 4.0–5.5.
   c. 5.8–7.5.
   d. greater than 9.0.

3. Which statement is true concerning colloidal particles?
   a. Colloidal particles are so small that gravity has little effect on them.
   b. The zeta potential between colloidal particles is balanced by covalent bonding.
   c. Electrical phenomenon of colloidal particles predominate and control their behavior.
   d. The surface area of colloidal particles is very small compared to their mass.

4. Which natural electrical force keeps colloidal particles apart in water treatment?
   a. van der Waals forces
   b. Ionic forces
   c. Zeta potential
   d. Quantum forces

5. The zeta potential measures the number of excess _____ found on the surface of all particulate matter.
   a. electrons
   b. ions
   c. cations
   d. protons

6. Particles held in suspension by the natural action of flowing water are called
   a. settleable solids.
   b. sludge.
   c. suspended solids.
   d. dissolved solids.

7. In conventional water treatment plants, most flocculation basins are designed for
   a. immediate flocculation.
   b. tapered flocculation.
   c. intermittent flocculation.
   d. rapidly accelerating flocculation.

8. What is the van der Waals force?

9. Used in the proper dosage, what are the effects of activated silica?

10. What are the key virtues of mechanical mixers?

Chapter 9
Sedimentation and Clarifiers

Sand, grit, chemical precipitates, pollutants, floc, and other solids are kept in suspension in water as long as the water is flowing with sufficient velocity and turbulence. Sedimentation removes these solids by reducing the velocity and turbulence. Efficient solids removal by sedimentation greatly reduces the load on filtration and other treatment processes. Sedimentation basins should be designed and operated such that they apply a continually low-turbidity water to the filters regardless of the incoming raw-water turbidity.

Process Description

Sedimentation, which is also called *clarification*, is the removal of settleable solids by gravity. The process takes place in a rectangular, square, or round tank called a sedimentation (or settling) basin (or tank).

In the conventional water treatment process, sedimentation is typically used as a step between flocculation and filtration. Sedimentation is also used to remove the large amounts of chemical precipitates formed during the lime–soda ash softening process (see Chapter 16).

Performance goals for the sedimentation process should be instituted at treatment plants. Operators take samples of the influent and effluent water of the basin at regular intervals and calculate the percent removal of each contaminant or additive (e.g., chlorine) to determine the efficiency of this treatment process. When performance goals are not met, operator intervention is necessary. The following might represent a common goal for turbidity removal in a conventional water treatment plant sedimentation basin:

- Effluent turbidity of 1 nephelometric turbidity unit (ntu) or less when the 95th percentile raw-water turbidity is 10 ntu or less
- Effluent turbidity of 2 ntu or less when the 95th percentile raw-water turbidity is more than 10 ntu.

Basins designed for efficient sedimentation allow the water to flow very slowly, with a minimum of turbulence at the entry and exit points and with as little short-circuiting of flow as possible. Sludge, the residue of solids and water, accumulates at the bottom of the basin and must then be pumped out of the basin for disposal or reuse.

sedimentation
The water treatment process that involves reducing the velocity of water in basins so that the suspended material can settle out by gravity.

sedimentation basin
A basin or tank in which water is retained to allow settleable matter, such as floc, to settle by gravity. Also called a *settling basin*, *settling tank*, or *sedimentation tank*.

influent
Water flowing into a basin.

effluent
Water flowing from a basin.

Sedimentation Facilities

This section describes different types of sedimentation basins and their associated equipment and features.

Types of Basins

Although there are many variations in design, sedimentation basins can generally be classified as either rectangular or center-feed types. Figure 9-1 shows overhead views of the flow patterns in different types of sedimentation basins. Figure 9-1A shows a rectangular settling tank, and Figures 9-1B through 9-1E show circular and square tanks. The operating principles of these basins are described next.

Conventional Rectangular Basins

Rectangular basins are usually constructed of concrete or steel and designed so that the flow is parallel to the basin's length. This type of flow is called **rectilinear flow**. The basins must be designed to keep the flow distributed evenly across the width of the basin to minimize the formation of currents and eddies that would keep the suspended matter from settling. The basins are often constructed with a bottom that slopes slightly downward toward the inlet end to make sludge removal easier. Figure 9-2 shows uncovered rectangular sedimentation basins at a large treatment plant.

Conventional Center-Feed Basins

Basins can also be constructed as either round or square, so that the water flows radially from the center to the outside. This type of flow is called **radial flow**. It is important that these basins also be designed to keep the velocity and flow

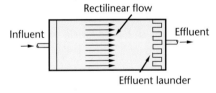

A. Rectangular settling tank, rectilinear flow

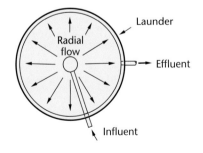

B. Center-feed settling tank, radial flow

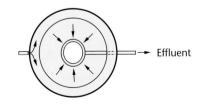

C. Peripheral-feed settling tank, radial flow

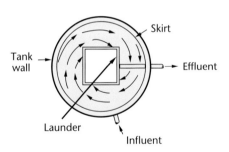

D. Peripheral-feed settling tank, spiral flow

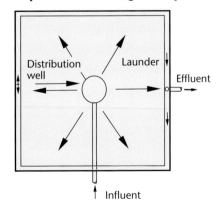

E. Square settling tank, radial flow

Figure 9-1 Overhead views of flow patterns in sedimentation basins

rectilinear flow
Uniform flow in a horizontal direction.

radial flow
Flow that moves across a basin from the center to the outside edges or vice versa.

Figure 9-2 Typical uncovered sedimentation basins

distribution as uniform as possible. Their bottoms are generally conical and slope downward toward the center of the basin to facilitate sludge removal.

Peripheral-Feed Basins Peripheral-feed basins are designed to feed incoming water from around the outer edge and collect it at the center. This type of basin also has radial flow. The design is otherwise similar to that of a center-feed basin.

Spiral-Flow Basins Spiral-flow basins have one or more points around the outer edge where water is admitted at an angle. This design causes the flow to circle around the basin and ultimately leave the basin at a center collector (launder).

Basin Zones

All basin types have four zones, each with its own function. As illustrated in Figure 9-3, these zones are as follows:

1. The *influent zone* decreases the velocity of the incoming water and distributes the flow evenly across the basin.
2. The *settling zone* provides the calm (quiescent) area necessary for the suspended material to settle.
3. The *effluent zone* provides a smooth transition from the settling zone to the effluent flow area. It is important that currents or eddies do not develop in this zone because they could stir up settled solids and carry them into the effluent.
4. The *sludge zone* receives the settled solids and keeps them separated from other particles in the settling zone.

These zones are not actually as well defined as Figure 9-3 illustrates. There is normally a varying gradation of one zone into another. The settling zone is particularly affected by the other three zones, based primarily on how the basin is designed and operated.

Parts of a Sedimentation Basin

Equipment used in conventional settling basins varies depending on the design and manufacturer. Figures 9-4 and 9-5 show the parts of typical rectangular and circular basins, respectively. The inlet distributes the influent evenly across (or

launder

A trough that collects the water flowing from a basin (effluent) and transports it to the effluent piping system.

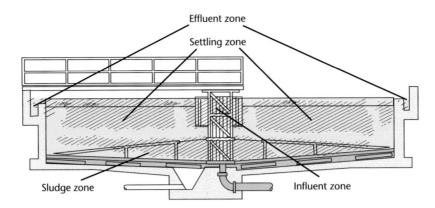

Figure 9-3 Zones in a sedimentation basin

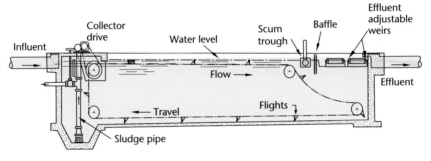

Figure 9-4 A typical rectangular sedimentation basin (with a continuous chain collector sludge removal system)

Courtesy of US Filter Envirex Products.

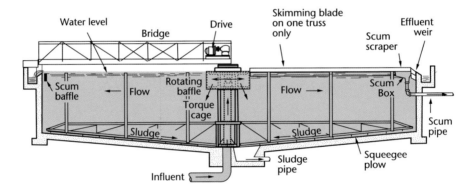

Figure 9-5 A typical circular sedimentation basin

Courtesy of US Filter Envirex Products.

around) the basin so the water will flow uniformly. A baffle installed downstream of the inlet reduces the velocity of the incoming water and helps produce calm, nonturbulent flow conditions for the settling zone. The water flows underneath the baffle and into the main part of the basin.

The effluent launder (also called the effluent trough) collects the settled water as it leaves the basin and channels it to the effluent pipeline, which carries the water to the next treatment process. Launders can be made of fiberglass or steel, or they may be cast concrete as a part of the tank.

The launder is equipped with an effluent (overflow) weir, which is a steel, plastic, or fiberglass plate designed to distribute the overflow evenly to all points of the launder. One of the most common types of effluent weirs is the V-notch, as illustrated in Figure 9-6. In some designs, launders can also receive the flow of water from beneath the water surface through holes in the launder wall.

Shallow-Depth Sedimentation

Shallow-depth sedimentation basins are designed to shorten the detention time required for sedimentation; this means the basins are smaller. Shallow basins and plate and tube settlers are two shallow-depth designs.

Figure 9-6 V-notch weir
Courtesy of Fisher Scientific.

Shallow Basins

Basins are occasionally designed to have a fairly shallow depth to reduce the time necessary for floc to settle to the bottom. Some rectangular sedimentation basins have two or three levels; the flow of water at the inlet to the basin divides into parallel flows, one over each level. These basins are designed on the principle that surface area is more important than depth. For shallow basins to work properly, it is important that coagulant doses and flash mixing be carefully controlled.

Plate and Tube Settlers

Several types of shallow-depth settling units are constructed of multiple, individual modules. These modules are either plates or tubes of fiberglass, steel, or other suitable material. They are spaced only a short distance apart and tilted at an angle with respect to horizontal (Figures 9-7 and 9-8). If the angle is greater than 50–60 degrees, they will be self-cleaning; in other words, the sediment will settle until it hits the plate or the tube bottom and will then slide to the bottom of the basin. An angle as small as 7 degrees is used when sludge is removed from the tubes or plates using periodic backflushing, possibly in conjunction with filter

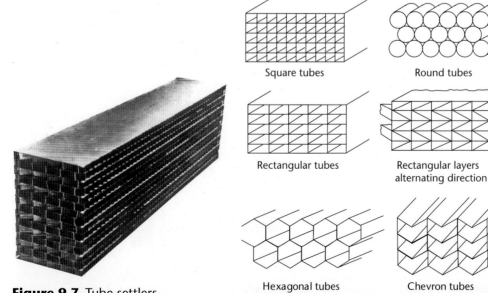

Figure 9-7 Tube settlers
Courtesy of Wheelabrator Engineered
Systems—Microfloc.

Figure 9-8 Various formats for tube modules
Courtesy of *Water Quality and Treatment.* 5th ed. 1999.

backwashing. A typical separation distance between the inclined surfaces of tube or plate settlers is 2 in. (50 mm); the inclined length is 3–6 ft (1–2 m).

The direction of flow through tube or plate settlers varies by the manufacturer's design. With countercurrent settling (Figure 9-9), the suspension is fed to the lower end and flows up the channels. If the angle of inclination is great enough, the solids slide down the surface, counter to the flow of the liquid. Concurrent settlers are designed so that the suspension is fed to the upper end and leaves at the bottom. In crossflow settlers, the flow is horizontal between the surfaces.

Tube and plate settlers are prefabricated in modules that can either be incorporated into new construction or be used to retrofit old basins so as to increase their settling efficiency. Their advantages include lightweight construction, structural rigidity, and the ability to settle a given flow rate in a much smaller basin size. As with all installations, however, the addition of tube or plate settlers to a treatment plant is not advisable unless a thorough engineering evaluation is made of the plant design to ensure they will operate properly. Figure 9-10 illustrates the installation of tube and plate settlers in rectangular and circular basins.

Another design for shallow-depth sedimentation uses inclined plates (Lamella® plates), as illustrated in Figure 9-11. This design incorporates parallel plates installed at a 45-degree angle. In this case, the water and sludge both flow downward. The clarified water is then returned to the top of the unit by small tubes.

Sludge Removal

As solids settle to the bottom of a sedimentation basin, a sludge layer develops. If this sludge is not removed before the layer gets too thick, the solids can become resuspended or tastes and odors can develop as a result of decomposing organic matter (Figure 9-12). Methods of removal are discussed in Chapter 17.

WATCH THE VIDEO
Sedimentation and Clarifiers (www.awwa.org/wsovideoclips)

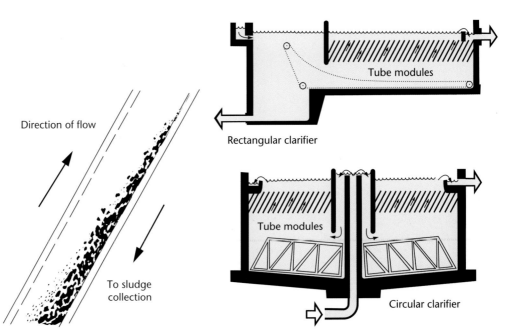

Figure 9-9 Countercurrent flow in tubes

Courtesy of Wheelabrator Engineered Systems—Microfloc.

Figure 9-10 Tube settlers installed in sedimentation basins

Courtesy of Wheelabrator Engineered Systems—Microfloc.

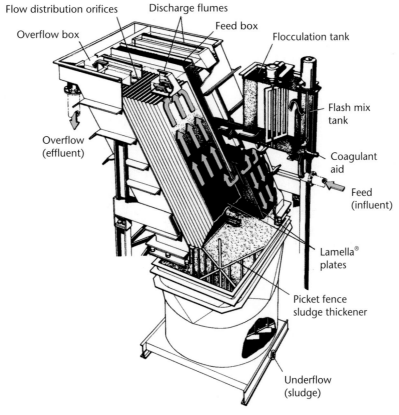

Flow distribution orifices
Discharge flumes
Overflow box
Feed box
Flocculation tank
Flash mix tank
Coagulant aid
Overflow (effluent)
Feed (influent)
Lamella® plates
Picket fence sludge thickener
Underflow (sludge)

Figure 9-11 Lamella® plates

Courtesy of Parkson Corporation.

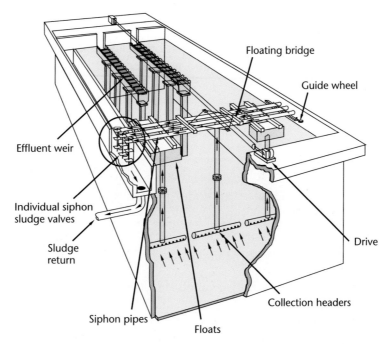

Floating bridge
Guide wheel
Effluent weir
Individual siphon sludge valves
Sludge return
Drive
Siphon pipes
Floats
Collection headers

(a)

Traveling bridge
Influent
Collecting
Bridge travel
Skimming
Scum trough
Skimming position
Sludge collection position
Sludge drawoff
Screw cross collector
Sludge hopper
Water level
Effluent

(b)

Figure 9-12 Two mechanical sludge removal systems used in rectangular basins. (a) Floating-bridge siphon collector. (b) Traveling-bridge collector.

Courtesy of F. B. Leopold Company, Inc.

Study Questions

1. Which device collects the settled water as it leaves the sedimentation basin?
   a. Effluent weir
   b. Effluent flow box
   c. Effluent baffle
   d. Effluent launder

2. In solids-contact basins with fairly constant water quality parameters, how often should the solids concentration be determined?
   a. At least once per week
   b. At least every other day
   c. At least once per month
   d. At least twice per day

3. The definition of *decant* is
   a. to draw off a liquid layer from a vessel of any size without disturbing any layer(s) above or below.
   b. to draw off the sediment at the bottom of a vessel of any size without disturbing the overlying liquid layer(s).
   c. to remove the precipitate at the bottom of any size of vessel.
   d. to draw off the liquid from a vessel of any size without stirring up bottom sediment.

4. How often should sedimentation basins with mechanical sludge removal equipment be drained and inspected?
   a. Twice a year
   b. Once a year
   c. Every other year
   d. Every 3 years

5. Which of the following is the most important reason to reduce turbidity?
   a. To reduce taste-and-odor problems
   b. To remove pathogens
   c. To reduce corrosion
   d. To determine the efficiency of coagulation and filtration

6. _____, which is also called *clarification*, is the removal of settleable solids by gravity.
   a. Sterilization
   b. Filtration
   c. Flocculation
   d. Sedimentation

7. Which area of a basin is designed to provide the calm (quiescent) area necessary for the suspended material to settle?

8. Which area of a basin is designed to receive the settled solids and keep them separated from other particles in the settling zone?

9. In shallow-depth settling units, at what angle must modules be slanted to be self-cleaning?

10. As solids settle to the bottom of a sedimentation basin, a layer of what develops?

Chapter 10
Filtration Fundamentals

The removal of suspended solids by **filtration** plays an important role both in the natural purification of groundwater and in the removal of naturally occurring and treatment-induced particulates in water in treatment plants. In the natural filtration process, most suspended material is removed from groundwater as the water percolates through the soil. It is therefore not usually necessary to filter groundwater. One exception is when the water must be treated for removal of hardness, iron, or manganese. In these instances, the water usually must be filtered to remove the chemical precipitates. Another exception relates to systems designated by the state as being "under the direct influence of surface water." These systems must provide filtration treatment.

Because surface water is subject to runoff and other sources of contamination, filtration is necessary to remove the suspended material for both aesthetic and public health reasons.

Process Description

The suspended material that must be removed from surface water can include floc from the coagulation, flocculation, and sedimentation processes; microorganisms; and precipitates. The material is collected and stored when water passes through a bed of granular material called **filter media**. The material is finally removed when the filter is backwashed. The common filter media are sand, anthracite coal, granular activated carbon, garnet sand, or some combination of these materials.

Performance goals for filters are set forth by the Interim Enhanced Surface Water Treatment Rule. The rule provides requirements for data collection and storage for each operating filter, as well as for reporting exceptions for any filter that does not perform in accordance with the turbidity values that are stated in the rule.

Turbidity Removal

Visible turbidity (the presence of suspended matter) in drinking water is usually objectionable to consumers, and its removal would be justified for aesthetic reasons alone. From a health and safety standpoint, however, there are good reasons to remove turbidity. The fine particles measured as turbidity can be harmful pathogens or can shelter contaminants from effective treatment. Thus, maintaining the lowest possible turbidity in finished water is important in protecting public health. This effort requires achieving turbidity levels that are far lower than can be seen by customers and that can be detected only with sensitive monitoring equipment.

Turbidity interferes with the disinfection process because the suspended particles shield microorganisms from the disinfectants. In addition, if not removed, the

filtration
The water treatment process involving the removal of suspended matter by passing the water through a porous medium, such as sand.

filter media
Granular material through which material is collected and stored when water passes through it.

Mechanical straining
Raw water

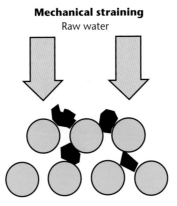

Adsorption
Raw water

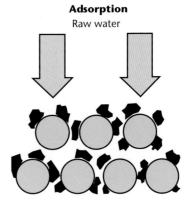

Figure 10-1 Filter media removal mechanisms

Large particles become lodged and cannot continue downward through the media.

Particles stick to the media and cannot continue downward through the media.

particles combine chemically with the disinfectant and leave less disinfectant to combat the microorganisms. If a sizable quantity of turbidity is allowed to enter the distribution system over a period of years, it can create tastes and odors and support bacterial growths.

The Filtration Process

The media through which water is passed in the filtration process are commonly thought of as a sieve or a microstrainer that traps suspended material between the grains of filter media. However, straining is only a minor part of the action that takes place because most suspended particles can easily pass through the spaces between the grains of the media.

As illustrated in Figure 10-1, filtration depends primarily on a combination of complex physical and chemical mechanisms, the most important being adsorption. As water passes through the filter bed, the suspended particles contact and adsorb (stick) onto the surface of the individual media grains or onto previously deposited material. The forces that attract and hold the particles to the grains are the same as those at work in coagulation and flocculation. In fact, some degree of flocculation and sedimentation occurs in the filter bed. This illustrates the importance of good chemical coagulation before filtration. Poor coagulation can cause operating problems for filters, as discussed later in this chapter.

Approaches to Filtration

Filters can be categorized as either gravity filters or pressure filters. For gravity filters, the force of gravity moves the water through the filter. For pressure filters, applied water pressure forces the water through the filter. Gravity filters are much more common, so they are discussed in more detail in this chapter.

Conventional Treatment

The combined processes of mixing, flocculation, sedimentation, and filtration shown in Figure 10-2 have formed the traditional water treatment plant design for many years. This approach is commonly called *conventional treatment*. This treatment has been found to provide effective removal of practically any range of raw-water turbidity.

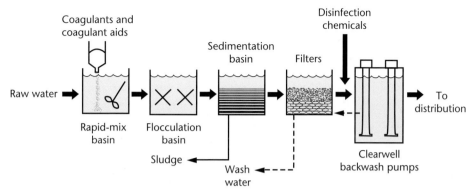

Figure 10-2 Conventional treatment plant

The success of this design is due primarily to the sedimentation step, which removes most of the suspended material before the water enters the filters. Proper control of sedimentation processes allows for an applied water to the filters that is *relatively constant* in turbidity value. After sedimentation, the water passing to the filters usually has a turbidity of 2–3 nephelometric turbidity units (ntu). For this reason, conventional treatment can be used regardless of raw-water turbidity and color levels. Historically, single-medium filters were used in the conventional process. However, essentially all new construction and plant conversions now use dual-media or multimedia filters to increase the process efficiency.

Direct Filtration

Water treatment plants using **direct filtration**, as shown in Figure 10-3, do not have a sedimentation step. This type of process is normally used to treat raw water that has average turbidities below 25 ntu and color below 25 units, but it has been successfully used for water with higher turbidity and color levels. The state regulatory authority should be consulted for its requirements on the use of direct filtration. Dual-media, multimedia, or deep-bed monomedium filters should always be used for direct filtration because they can remove more suspended solids before backwashing is needed than sand-only filters.

The major advantage of direct filtration is its lower construction cost compared with that of conventional plants. However, because of the short time span between coagulant addition and filtration, and the greater load applied to the filters, this type of system must be carefully monitored to avoid turbidity breakthrough into the finished water.

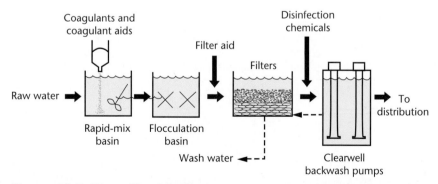

Figure 10-3 Direct filtration plant

direct filtration
A filtration method that includes coagulation, flocculation, and filtration but excludes sedimentation. Only applicable to raw water relatively low in turbidity because all suspended matter must be trapped by the filters.

Slow Sand Filtration

Slow sand filters were introduced in the United States in 1872. They were the first type of gravity filter used but are no longer very common. As shown in Figure 10-4, water is fed directly to the surface of slow sand filters without any chemicals being applied. Use of slow sand filters is typically limited to raw water having relatively low turbidity. The space required for slow sand filters is relatively large, so this process is usually limited to small water systems in more rural areas. Slow sand filters are discussed in more detail later in this chapter.

Diatomaceous Earth Filtration

In the diatomaceous earth (DE) filtration process, which uses pressure filtration, diatomaceous earth material must be fed to the filter unit to act as the filter medium (Figure 10-5). The process can be used only for water with low turbidity. DE filtration has a relatively low installation cost and minimal space requirements. Disadvantages include relatively high operating costs and the problem of disposing of the backwash sludge.

Package Treatment Plants

Package treatment plants are small, prefabricated units that have been designed and assembled at a factory and then shipped to the installation site. They have grown in popularity in recent years, primarily as a result of new technology that allows compact construction. Conventional treatment package systems typically include a coagulation–flocculation unit, a settling tank or a floc separation process, and a mixed-media gravity or pressure filter. A very small unit can be assembled and mounted on skids. The parts of larger installations are shipped as several units and piped together in the field (Figure 10-6). These treatment systems are often an economical solution for small utilities that must install filtration.

slow sand filtration

A filtration process that involves passing raw water through a bed of sand at low velocity, resulting in particulate removal by physical and biological mechanisms.

diatomaceous earth filter

A pressure filter using a medium made from diatoms. The water is forced through the diatomaceous earth by pumping.

package treatment plant

A small, prefabricated unit that has been designed and assembled at a factory and then shipped to the installation site.

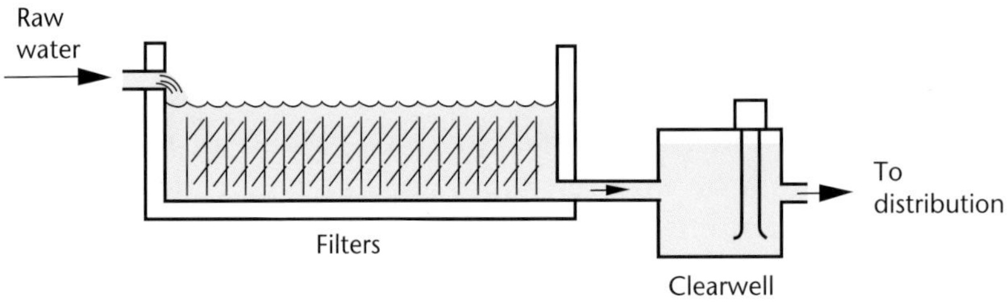

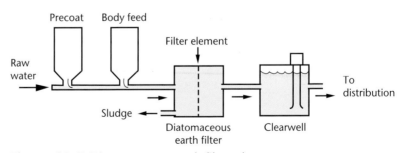

Figure 10-4 Slow sand filter plant

Figure 10-5 Diatomaceous earth filter plant

Figure 10-6 Typical package treatment plant
Courtesy of ONDEO Degremont.

Potential purchasers of these systems should be aware that some units require rather careful monitoring and control to produce good-quality water consistently. Although any filtration system requires a fair amount of monitoring, operators of very small plants do not ordinarily expect to spend much time "operating" the plant. Operators contemplating the installation of a package treatment plant should obtain assurance from the manufacturer that the system will consistently meet state and federal effluent standards. They should also obtain a realistic statement of the operation and maintenance labor that will be necessary to properly operate the facility. Pilot testing of the process is recommended before a package treatment plant is purchased.

The term *package treatment plant* can no longer be assumed to mean conventional treatment. Package treatment plants are now available to provide treatment by other methods, such as adsorption, aeration, or membrane technology.

Biological Treatment

Biological treatment of water uses microbes that are not harmful to humans to break down substances, such as biodegradable organic carbon. The use of biologically active sand or carbon filters produces water that is not conducive to microbial growth in the distribution system, is free of undesirable tastes and odors, and has a reduced chlorine demand.

Numerous installations in Europe have proved that biological treatment works effectively, but there has not been much interest in the United States. This is perhaps because, if the process is not properly designed and controlled, there is a risk of introducing pathogenic microorganisms or harmful by-products into the finished water. However, future federal restrictions on the level of disinfection by-products (DBPs) in drinking water could lead to interest in and development of biological treatment as an economical and effective method of minimizing DBPs.

Types of Gravity Filters

Filters can be classified based on several different features, including the filtration rate, types of filter media, or type of operation. For the purposes of this chapter, the following classifications will be used for gravity filters:

- Slow sand filters
- Rapid sand filters
- High-rate filters
- Deep-bed, monomedium filters

There are other variations in filter design, such as upflow and biflow filters. These have been used in only a few installations, however, so they are not discussed here. As detailed in Chapter 17, membrane processes are also being developed that can be used in place of a media filter to remove turbidity and microorganisms; they may see increasing use in the future. The characteristics of the principal types of gravity filters are summarized in Table 10-1.

Slow Sand Filters

As mentioned previously, slow sand filters were the first type of gravity filter used for water treatment. As shown in Figure 10-7, they typically consist of a layer of fine sand about 3.5 ft (1 m) thick, supported by about 1 ft (0.3 m) of graded

Table 10-1 Comparison of gravity filter characteristics

Characteristic	Slow Sand Filters	Conventional Rapid Sand Filters	High-Rate Filters
Filtration rate	0.05 gpm/ft^2 (0.1 m/hr)	2 gpm/ft^2 (5 m/hr)	3–8 gpm/ft^2 (7–18 m/hr)
Media	Sand	Sand	Sand and coal or sand, coal, and garnet
Media distribution	Unstratified	Stratified: coarse to fine	Stratified: coarse to fine
Filter runs	20–60 days	12–36 hours	12–36 hours
Loss of head	0.2 ft (0.1 m) initial to 4 ft (1.2 m) final	1 ft (0.3 m) initial to 8 or 9 ft (2.4–2.7 m) final	1 ft (0.3 m) initial to 8 or 9 ft (2.4–2.7 m) final
Amount of backwash water used	Backwash not used	2–4% of water filtered	6% of water filtered

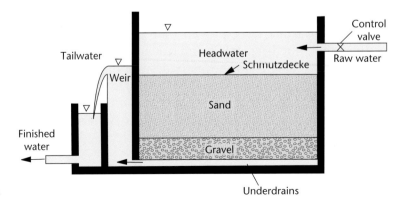

Figure 10-7 Schematic cross section of a slow sand filter

Courtesy of Barrett et al. 1991

gravel. The filtering action of the filters is dependent on fine sand and a sticky mat of suspended matter, called **schmutzdecke**, that forms on the sand surface.

The fine sand that is used has small voids that fill quickly, so slow sand filters are not normally used with waters that consistently have turbidities above 10 ntu. Chemical coagulation is not normally used to help form the schmutzdecke because it would just hasten the filling and clogging of the void spaces. Flow rates are kept quite low, with 0.05 gpm/ft^2 (0.1 m/hr) being about average. Consequently, it takes a filter 0.5–1 acre (0.20–0.40 ha) in size to process 1 mil gal (4 ML) of water per day.

Slow sand filters are not backwashed. Instead, they are cleaned by scraping about 1 in. (2 or 3 cm) of sand from the top. This can be done manually or with mechanical equipment. For small systems, the surface sand can be scraped off with shovels, but usually mechanical equipment is used to haul away the discarded sand. After several cleanings have reduced the sand depth to about 2 ft (0.6 m), new sand is added to bring the filter bed back to the original depth. After a filter has been cleaned, it may be necessary to filter to waste (i.e., treat the filtered water as wastewater) for as long as two days before a schmutzdecke forms that will effectively remove turbidity. Because a filter may be out of service for several days as a result of scraping and filtering to waste, it is necessary for a water system to have at least two filters to provide continuous service.

The advantages of slow sand filters include low construction, maintenance, and operating costs. Disadvantages include large land area requirements for large-capacity plants and the problem of filters freezing in northern locations unless they are covered. In recent years, there has been some resurgence in the use of slow sand filters because of more modern equipment and improved design criteria. The state regulatory agency should be consulted for advice if a utility is interested in constructing a slow sand filter system.

Conventional Rapid Sand Filters

Rapid sand filters can accommodate much higher filtration rates than slow sand filters because they use coarser sand. Instead of depending on the schmutzdecke for filtering action, the filters trap suspended matter through several inches (centimeters) or more of the depth of the filter sand. Rapid sand filters are designed so that they can be backwashed in order to be cleaned and restored for use. At least two filters must be provided so that one can remain in operation while the other is being backwashed. If there are only two filters, each must be capable of meeting plant design capacity.

High-Rate Filters

As shown in Table 10-1, higher-rate filters (i.e., dual-media and multimedia filters) can operate at rates up to four times higher than those of rapid sand filters. As illustrated in Figure 10-8, these filters use a combination of filter media, not just sand.

Dual-media filters usually have a bed of sand covered by a layer of granulated anthracite coal. Multimedia (mixed-media) filters use three or more types of media of varying coarseness and specific gravity (the weight of the material relative to the weight of water). The most common combination is garnet sand on the bottom layer, silica sand in the center, and coarse anthracite on the top.

In dual- and mixed-media filters, the coarsest material also has the lowest specific gravity, so it tends to stay at the top. The heaviest medium is also the finest, and it stays near the bottom. Some mixing of the layers does occur, but as illustrated in Figure 10-9, the media will approximately maintain their respective positions in the filter bed after backwashing. The effective size (ES) and the relationship of each medium's specific gravity to the other media's specific gravities

schmutzdecke
The layer of solids and biological growth that forms on top of a slow sand filter, allowing the filter to remove turbidity effectively without chemical coagulation.

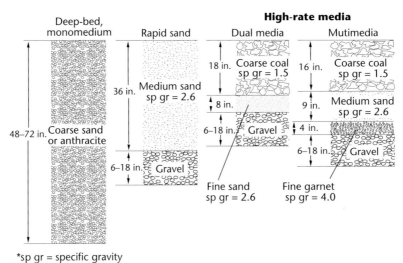

Figure 10-8 Comparison of deep-bed, rapid sand, and high-rate filter media

*sp gr = specific gravity

Figure 10-9 Mixing of filter media: left, as laid; right, after backwash

Courtesy of US Filter-Microfloc® Products.

are extremely important, and for that reason, operators should not add extra material to a filter without careful consideration.

In operation, the coarse layer on top removes most of the suspended particles. The particles that do pass through this layer are removed by finer media below. As a result, most of the filter bed is used to remove suspended particles. This system allows for longer filter runs and higher filtration rates when compared to a conventional sand filter, which traps most suspended matter near the sand surface. As a result, head loss does not build up as quickly as with a rapid sand filter.

Multimedia filters are now used almost exclusively because they can greatly increase a treatment plant's capacity while maintaining excellent water quality. The types of filter media used depend on many factors, including general raw-water quality, variations in water quality, and type of chemical treatment.

Pilot tests using different types of media are usually conducted to determine which media combination performs best for a particular water source.

Deep-Bed, Monomedium Filters

Deep-bed filters use a single filter medium—sand or anthracite—from 48 to 72 in. (1.2 to 1.8 m) deep. The bed must be deeper than a conventional filter because the medium is coarser. These filters are washed by the relatively gentle concurrent upflow of air and water. This wash causes the medium to be cleaned and mixed, but little or no stratification by size occurs. Monomedium filters can be operated at higher rates than dual-media filters and are well suited for use with direct filtration. They may be difficult to backwash thoroughly because particles trapped in the lower layers have to travel a long way before they are washed out during backwash.

WATCH THE VIDEO
Filtration and Filtration Processes (www.awwa.org/wsovideoclips)

Study Questions

1. When a filter is ripening,
   a. it is in need of a backwash.
   b. turbidity is just starting to break through.
   c. it is becoming more efficient in particle removal.
   d. it is beginning to grow algae in the filter bed, walls, and troughs.

2. Virgin greensand can be regenerated by soaking the filter bed for several hours in a solution of chlorine containing
   a. 50 mg/L Cl_2.
   b. 75 mg/L Cl_2.
   c. 100 mg/L Cl_2.
   d. 200 mg/L Cl_2.

3. Which role does the action of straining of suspended particles play during filtration?
   a. Minor
   b. Fair
   c. Good
   d. Major

4. The turbidity of settled water before it is applied to the filters (post-sedimentation process) should always be kept below
   a. 1–2 ntu.
   b. 2–4 ntu.
   c. 5 ntu.
   d. 8–10 ntu.

5. The combined processes of mixing, flocculation, sedimentation, and filtration are commonly called
   a. gravity filtration.
   b. minimum treatment.
   c. direct filtration.
   d. conventional treatment.

6. Performance goals for filters are set forth by which regulation?

7. In water treatment plants using direct filtration, which step of conventional treatment is not included?

8. What term refers to small, prefabricated units that have been designed and assembled at a factory and then shipped to the installation site?

9. What are three advantages of slow sand filters?

Chapter 11
Disinfection

Disinfection is the treatment process used to destroy or inactivate disease-causing (pathogenic) organisms, such as viruses, bacteria, fungi, or protozoa. Diseases caused by pathogenic organisms in water are called **waterborne diseases**; the more common ones are summarized in Table 11-1. The consequences of waterborne disease range from mild illness to death.

Disinfection should not be confused with sterilization. Sterilization is the destruction of *all* living microorganisms. To sterilize drinking water completely would require the application of much higher doses of chemical disinfectants, which would greatly increase operating costs. These larger doses of chemicals would create tastes that, in most cases, would be very objectionable to the public. Excessive application of disinfectants to some waters can generate excessive levels of unwanted disinfection by-products (DBPs).

disinfection
The water treatment process that kills disease-causing organisms in water, usually by the addition of chlorine.

waterborne disease
A disease caused by a waterborne organism or toxic substance.

Table 11-1 Common waterborne diseases

Waterborne Disease	Causative Organism	Source of Organism in Water	Symptom
Gastroenteritis	*Salmonella* (bacteria)	Animal or human feces	Acute diarrhea and vomiting
Typhoid	*Salmonella typhosa* (bacterium)	Human feces	Inflamed intestine, enlarged spleen, high temperature—fatal
Dysentery	*Shigella* (bacteria)	Human feces	Diarrhea—rarely fatal
Cholera	*Vibrio comma* (bacteria)	Human feces	Vomiting, severe diarrhea, rapid dehydration, mineral loss—high mortality
Infectious hepatitis	Virus	Human feces, shellfish grown in polluted waters	Yellowed skin, enlarged liver, abdominal pain—low mortality, lasts up to 4 months
Amoebic dysentery	*Entamoeba histolytica* (protozoan)	Human feces	Mild diarrhea, chronic dysentery
Giardiasis	*Giardia lamblia* (protozoan)	Animal or human feces	Diarrhea, cramps, nausea, and general weakness—not fatal, lasts 1 week to 30 weeks
Cryptosporidiosis	*Cryptosporidium* (protozoa)	Human and animal feces	Acute diarrhea, abdominal pain, vomiting, low-grade fever
Legionellosis	*Legionella pneumophila* and related bacteria		Acute respiratory illness

Destroying Pathogens in Water

Most pathogens are accustomed to living in the temperatures and conditions found in the bodies of humans and warm-blooded animals. In general, they do not survive outside of this environment, but there are some significant exceptions. Of those that do not survive for very long, significant numbers can still survive in water long enough to cause sickness, or even death, if ingested. In addition, certain viruses and protozoa that form cysts can survive for surprisingly long periods, even under adverse conditions. Some pathogenic organisms also tend to be somewhat resistant to disinfection processes, so disinfection alone cannot always be assumed to ensure safe drinking water.

Some pathogens can be destroyed by simply storing water in open tanks for extended periods of time. Some pathogens are removed by sedimentation in those tanks, and others experience natural die-off. This is not usually a practical treatment method because of the large investment required for the storage facilities. In addition, other nuisance organisms, such as algae, can actually multiply in the water while it is stored.

A significant number of pathogens are removed during coagulation, flocculation, sedimentation, and filtration. As a result, these processes are normally required in addition to disinfection if the source water turbidity and pathogen loading are significant. Table 11-2 lists the percentage of pathogen reduction from various treatment processes.

Detecting Pathogens in Water

Relatively simple, inexpensive tests are available for detecting the presence of coliform bacteria in water. The presence of these bacteria may indicate the presence of actual pathogens. All public water systems are required by federal and state regulations to collect representative samples from the distribution system periodically for coliform analysis. (Coliform sampling is discussed in Chapter 1.)

However, these tests indicate only the likelihood that water is contaminated by feces from a warm-blooded animal. They do not indicate the presence of specific, harmful organisms. Unfortunately, no tests are simple and inexpensive enough to be used routinely for indicating the presence or absence of pathogens, including *Giardia*, viruses, *Legionella*, and *Cryptosporidium*.

This inability to conduct routine tests for the presence of specific disease-causing microorganisms has been recognized in the federal Surface Water Treatment Rule (SWTR), which is discussed later in this chapter. In essence, the

Table 11-2 Pathogen reduction from various treatment processes

Unit Process	Reduction
Storage*	Significant amounts
Sedimentation*	0–99%
Coagulation*	Significant amounts
Filtration*	0–99%
Chlorination	99%

*These methods do not, in themselves, provide adequate pathogen reduction. However, their use prior to disinfection may significantly lower the costs associated with disinfection.

rule requires a "treatment technique" for all systems using surface water sources. The technique must consist of one or more methods of treatment that will ensure almost complete removal or inactivation of the most resistant pathogenic organisms presently known to be a threat to public health. In other words, establishing a maximum contaminant level (MCL) for pathogenic organisms is not practical because of the lack of practical tests for their presence, so compliance with regulations is based on properly operating the treatment process.

Disinfection Methods

Although chlorination is the most common disinfection method, other methods are available and can be used in various situations. The three general types of disinfection are

1. heat treatment,
2. ultraviolet radiation treatment, and
3. chemical treatment.

Heat Treatment

A method of disinfection first discovered many years ago is to boil the water. It is still a good emergency procedure for small quantities of water. When contamination of a public water supply is suspected, a "boil order" should be issued to the public, suggesting that all water for consumption be boiled before use until there is further notice that the water is proved safe. Campers should also take the precaution of boiling water from surface sources or other sources not known to be safe.

For proper disinfection, the water should be maintained at a rolling boil for at least 5 minutes to ensure inactivation of the most resistant organisms. A longer boiling time should be used at higher altitudes because water boils at a lower temperature. Boiling is obviously not well suited for large-scale use because of the high cost of energy required.

Ultraviolet Radiation Treatment

Applied in the correct dosage, ultraviolet (UV) light is a powerful water disinfectant capable of inactivating pathogenic microorganisms, including *Cryptosporidium* and *Giardia*. When used as part of a multiple-barrier system, UV technology can play a key role in providing safe drinking water while generating minimal, if any, DBPs. The Long-Term 2 Enhanced Surface Water Treatment Rule (LT2ESWTR) has specified that UV disinfection is an "upper bin" technology and can provide 2- to 3-log inactivation of *Cryptosporidium*. Typically, filtered surface waters and high-transmittance groundwaters are candidates for UV disinfection.

The inactivation of microorganisms by UV radiation is essentially an instantaneous process (low detention times), which relies on photochemical changes brought about when UV radiation is absorbed by the genetic material of the cell (deoxyribonucleic acid, or DNA, and ribonucleic acid, or RNA), making the organism incapable of infection. The wavelengths for optimum effectiveness correspond to the maximum absorption spectrum for nucleic acids—i.e., between 250 and 265 nanometers (nm). Germicidal UV radiation is usually considered between the wavelengths of 200 and 280 nm.

Because UV radiation leaves no residual, chlorination or chloramination is still required, but in much lower doses. Multiple-barrier systems incorporating UV and chlorination are effective in disinfecting both virus and *Cryptosporidium parvum*. Because UV disinfection is a physical process rather than a chemical process, different monitoring procedures are needed to determine the efficiency of the process. According to the LT2ESWTR, a UV facility must operate within the validated limits of the UV equipment to receive the required inactivation credits. If the reactor is operating outside of the validation limits for more than 5 percent of the water treated, it is considered to be off-specification.

Performance of UV systems—i.e., the delivered dose to the target organism—is affected by a water's chemical and physical characteristics, such as turbidity, transmittance, organic and inorganic constituents, and UV absorbance. Turbidity plays a major role in UV performance; both the number and nature of particles are important. Waters with a turbidity below 1 ntu are acceptable for UV treatment.

Natural organic matter, hardness, and other minerals can foul the lamps, causing a decrease in the critical dose. Dissolved inorganic constituents, such as iron, can precipitate on the lamps and decrease performance. Other organic and inorganic constituents may absorb the light at critical wavelengths, rendering the system ineffective at those wavelengths.

Low-pressure continuous wave mercury arc lamps, medium-pressure continuous wave mercury arc lamps, and pulsed blackbody ultraviolet radiation—an emerging technology—are three UV technologies used today to disinfect water and wastewater.

The low-pressure mercury arc lamps are efficient in generating UV light within the germicidal wavelength range. They generate UV light by transforming electrical energy into UV radiations. The low-pressure mercury arc lamp uses mercury vapor and argon gas to emit monochromatic radiation at 253.7 nm. About 35 to 40 percent of the input energy is converted to light, and approximately 85 percent of this light is at the wavelength of 253.7 nm.

Low-pressure mercury lamps are the source of UV energy in the majority of systems installed today. They last 8,000 to 10,000 hours before replacement and operate between 40°C (104°F) and 60°C (140°F). These lamps have been used to successfully disinfect secondary effluents. The UV radiation generated by low pressure is considered the safest disinfection alternative for wastewater treatment plants because no chemical agent is used. However, the industry and general public are moving away from mercury-based systems for health reasons. This is especially true for the drinking water industry.

Medium- to high-pressure mercury lamps generate higher UV intensities and offer a broader spectrum of output than the low-pressure units. They generate polychromatic ultraviolet radiation at wavelengths between 185 and 300 nm. Medium-pressure UV generates high UV intensity in discrete wavelengths. Medium-pressure lamps operate at temperatures between 500°C (932°F) and 800°C (1,472°F), generate medium-light intensity, and last between 3,000 and 5,000 hours.

Pulsed UV radiation uses a nonmercury flashlamp filled with an inert gas or a combination of inert gases. Electric current is discharged into the lamp in a series of pulses. The ultimate effect of the microsecond pulse is to drive the gas into a cold-plasma state with temperatures ranging from 10,000 kelvin (K) to 20,000 K. At these peak temperatures, a plasma radiates UV, visible, and infrared light at high peak powers and with extremely high numbers of photons (flux) per pulse—much more than conventional low- or medium-pressure mercury lamps. The wavelengths generated are in the interval of 185–400 nm. The mechanism of disinfection is not limited to absorbance of energy by the organism but also includes photo oxidation.

Some pulsed UV systems do not suffer from a decrease in performance caused by fouling, and one pulsed UV system manufacturer offers data that suggest that their system can function in waters with a very low transmittance.

Chemical Treatment

Although the primary use of chemical oxidants is for disinfection, these chemicals can serve other purposes during the disinfection process. In some cases, the choice of chemicals used in a treatment system is dictated by the ability of the chemicals to perform these secondary functions, which include the following:

- Control of biological growth in pipelines and basins
- Control of tastes and odors
- Removal of color
- Reduction of some organic compounds, particularly those that are precursors to the formation of DBPs
- Aid to flocculation
- Oxidation of iron and manganese so that they can subsequently be removed by precipitation

Chemicals used for treating potable water include the following:

- Bromine
- Iodine
- Ozone, alone or in combination with other chemicals
- Potassium permanganate
- Oxygen
- Chlorine dioxide
- Chlorine and chlorine compounds

The general effectiveness of commonly used oxidants in treating various water problems is summarized in Table 11-3. Bromine and iodine are not covered in this

Table 11-3 General effectiveness of water treatment oxidants

Purpose	Chlorine	Chloramines	Ozone	Chlorine Dioxide	Potassium Permanganate	Oxygen
Iron removal	E	N	E	E	E	E
Manganese removal*	S	N	E	E	E	N
Sulfide removal	E	N	S	S	S	E[†]
Taste-and-odor control	S	N	E	E	S[‡]	S[‡]
Color removal	E	N	E	E	S	N
Flocculation aid	E	N	E	U	S[**]	N
Trihalomethane formation potential control	N	N	E[††]	E	S	N
Synthetic organics removal	S[‡‡, ***]	N	S[††]	S[††]	S[††]	N
Biological growth control	E	S	N[†††]	E	S	N

Note: E = effective, S = somewhat effective, N = not effective, U = unknown.

*Above pH 7

[†]By stripping

[‡]Except earthy–musty odor-causing compounds

[**]May involve adsorption on manganese dioxide

[††]May increase problem at low doses

[‡‡]Depending on compound

[***]May form chlorinated by-products

[†††]Except with dual-stage ozonation

Source: *Water Quality and Treatment*. 4th ed. (1990).

table because they are rarely used for public water system treatment. Advantages and disadvantages of the principal water treatment oxidants are summarized in Table 11-4.

The concentration of chemical and the time needed to ensure disinfection are different for each chemical. A way to measure the effectiveness or degree of pathogenic inactivation of a disinfectant is the $C \times T$ value (see Chapter 3). The C is the disinfectant residual in mg/L. The T is the time in minutes that the chemical must be in contact with the water. The required $C \times T$ value to achieve disinfection is a function of the chemical used, the target pathogenic organism, and the water temperature.

Bromine Bromine is a dark reddish-brown liquid. It vaporizes at room temperature and has a penetrating, suffocating odor. The vapor is extremely irritating to the eyes, nose, and throat, and it is very corrosive to most metals. If splashed onto the skin, bromine causes painful burns that are slow to heal.

The residual formed when bromine is added to water is as effective a disinfectant as chlorine, but not as stable. Consequently, depending on the constituents in the water being treated, it may be necessary to add bromine at two or three times the concentration required for chlorine. Because of the higher cost of bromine and its handling hazards, liquid bromine is not used to disinfect public

Table 11-4 Advantages and disadvantages of water treatment oxidants

Oxidant	Advantages	Disadvantages
Chlorine	Strong oxidant Simple feeding Persistent residual Long history of use	Chlorinated by-products Taste-and-odor problems possible pH influences effectiveness
Chloramines	No trihalomethane (THM) formation Persistent residual Simple feeding Long history of use	Weak oxidant Some total organic halide formation pH influences effectiveness Taste, odor, and growth problems possible
Ozone	Strong oxidant Usually no THM or total organic halide formation No taste-or-odor problems Some by-products biodegradable Little pH effect Coagulant aid	Short half-life On-site generation required Energy intensive Some by-products biodegradable Complex generation and feeding Corrosive
Chlorine dioxide	Strong oxidant Relatively persistent residual No THM formation No pH effect	Total organic halide formation ClO_3^- and ClO_2^- by-products On-site generation required Hydrocarbon odors possible
Potassium permanganate	Easy to feed No THM formation	Moderately strong oxidant Pink water By-products unknown Causes precipitation
Oxygen	Simple feed No by-products Companion stripping Nontoxic	Weak oxidant Corrosion and scaling

water supplies. Bromine is sometimes used in a safer, but more costly, solid "stick form" (organobromine compound) to disinfect swimming pools.

Iodine   Iodine is a lustrous, blue-black solid that is about five times the density of water and has a peculiar chlorine-like odor. The solid can quickly change to a gas, releasing a characteristic violet vapor. Iodine has been used extensively for medicinal purposes.

Because of its possible adverse health effects, long-term consumption of iodine is not recommended. For this reason, it is not used as a disinfectant for water supplies serving permanent populations. However, it is occasionally used for water disinfection at campgrounds and other locations where use by most persons is limited to about two weeks. It can also be used for emergency disinfection of water and is available in small tablets for disinfecting small quantities of water. Crystalline iodine is available for use in saturator-type feeders.

Ozone   Ozone is a bluish, toxic gas with a pungent odor. It is a powerful oxidizing agent used in water treatment as a disinfectant. In air, it is considered a health hazard at low concentrations—the 8-hour Occupational Safety and Health Administration standard is 0.1 parts per million (ppm). It is formed photochemically in the atmosphere and is a constituent of smog.

Ozone (O_3) cannot be stored and is manufactured on-site by passing a high voltage through the air or oxygen between two electrodes. The electrical energy required to generate ozone is high, but its expense is sometimes offset by its effectiveness in controlling taste, odor, and color and in oxidizing organic substances.

Ozone has been used widely in Europe, and its use is gaining acceptance in the United States because of increasing concern and regulation of the by-products caused by disinfection with chlorine. Ozone offers other benefits and has been reported to improve coagulation, which lowers the cost of coagulant chemicals, reduces sludge disposal costs, and increases filter runs.

Ozone also produces by-products. Research is ongoing to determine the adverse health effects of those compounds. When bromides are present in a water, ozone treatment generates bromate, a potential carcinogen regulated by the Stage 1 Disinfectants/Disinfection By-Products Rule.

Ozone may convert large organic molecules into smaller, more biodegradable organic molecules, commonly referred to as *assimilable organic carbon* or *biodegradable dissolved organic carbon* (BDOC). BDOC serves as "food" for bacteria present in water or present in a biofilm attached to the pipes of a distribution system and can cause bacterial regrowth. To remove these organics, ozone treatment is often followed by granular activated carbon.

Potassium Permanganate   Potassium permanganate ($KMnO_4$) is an oxidant that was first used in 1910 for water treatment in London. However, widespread use of potassium permanganate did not occur until the 1960s, when its effectiveness for controlling tastes and odors had become recognized.

When added to water, permanganate turns the water purple until it finally dissipates after the completion of the oxidizing action. For this reason, it should be fed as early in the treatment process as possible to allow completion of the reaction before the water enters the distribution system. Concentrations as low as 0.05 ppm may still have some noticeable color.

Permanganate is frequently used as the initial chemical fed into surface water systems because it controls many taste- and odor-causing substances in the raw water. In particular, it will eliminate a number of taste-and-odor conditions that will not be controlled or may be accentuated by chlorine. It also works well in removing hydrogen sulfide, iron, and manganese. When permanganate alone is not completely successful in controlling tastes and odors, it may be used in combination with activated carbon.

Permanganate is also being used for trihalomethane (THM) control. The main cause of THMs is chlorination of precursors, primarily humic and fulvic acids, found in raw water. Feeding permanganate as the initial oxidant allows chlorine to be applied later in the treatment process, when the precursors have been reduced. THMs can usually be significantly reduced by this process.

Permanganate is also widely used by groundwater systems to oxidize iron and manganese (see Chapter 12). It has also been found effective for controlling zebra mussels and algae in reservoirs (see Chapter 6).

Although potassium permanganate is reported by many water systems to reduce coliforms, it is not registered with the US Environmental Protection Agency as a disinfectant. Some laboratory tests have shown its effectiveness against certain microorganisms, but its effectiveness against *Giardia lamblia* and viruses is still under study. Surface water systems electing to use permanganate as a disinfectant should contact their state drinking water agency for advice on the $C \times T$ (concentration multiplied by time) credit allowed under the SWTR.

Oxygen Oxygen is not effective in pathogen reduction, so it is not used for this purpose. It is frequently used to oxidize various contaminants for removal. The introduction of oxygen into water by aeration is covered in Chapter 17.

Chlorine Dioxide Chlorine dioxide (ClO_2) is a powerful oxidant that is normally prepared on-site. It is used by some water systems as an initial oxidant for water having high humic and fulvic substance levels, in order to reduce the formation of THMs. In some cases, it is used only when the THM precursor level in the raw water is high.

During the formation of chlorine dioxide, a small amount of chlorate and chlorite is formed. There is evidence that these substances can cause adverse health effects in some people. Water systems considering the use of chlorine dioxide should check with their state public water supply control agency for current requirements or restrictions on use.

Chlorine dioxide is capable of oxidizing iron and manganese, removing color, and lowering THM formation potential. It also oxidizes many organic and sulfurous compounds that cause taste-and-odor problems. Chlorine dioxide does add a specific taste to water that is objectionable to some people. The maximum residual that does not cause tastes or odors is about 0.4–0.5 mg/L as chlorine dioxide.

All chemicals used for disinfection must conform to standards set by the American Water Works Association and NSF International.

Chlorine and Chlorine Compounds

Chlorination, the addition of chlorine to water, is the most common form of disinfection currently practiced in the United States. When properly understood and correctly operated, the chlorination process is a safe, practical, and effective way to destroy disease-causing organisms.

Several secondary benefits are gained from using chlorine as the disinfectant for treated water, and chlorine may also be used as part of other treatment processes. Chlorine is useful for disinfecting storage tanks and pipelines; for oxidizing iron, manganese, and hydrogen sulfide; and for controlling tastes, odors, algae, and slime. These uses are discussed in greater detail in subsequent chapters.

Chlorine is available in gaseous, liquid, and solid forms. The chemicals and equipment used for chlorination depend primarily on the type of chlorine used.

Chlorine Chemicals

Hypochlorous acid (HOCl) and hypochlorite ion (OCl⁻) are the most effective residuals. They can be derived from the following three chemicals:

1. Chlorine, Cl_2
2. Calcium hypochlorite, $Ca(OCl)_2$
3. Sodium hypochlorite, NaOCl

A comparison of the chlorine content for these chemicals is given in Table 11-5.

Chemistry of Chlorination

To understand reactions of chlorine in natural water, consider the reaction of chlorine in distilled water. As shown in Figure 11-1, the amount of free chlorine residual is directly related to the amount (dose) of chlorine added. For example, if 2 mg/L of chlorine is added, 2 mg/L of free residual is produced. The reactions that occur are as follows:

$$Cl_2 + H_2O \longrightarrow HOCl + HCl \qquad (11\text{-}1)$$

| chlorine | water | hypochlorous acid | hydrochloric acid |

Table 11-5 Chlorine content of common disinfectants

Compound	Chlorine Percentage	Amount of Compound Needed to Yield 1 lb of Pure Cl
Chlorine gas or liquid (Cl_2)	100	1 lb (0.454 kg)
Sodium hypochlorite (NaOCl)*	15	0.8 gal (3 L)
	12.5	1.0 gal (3.8 L)
	5	2.4 gal (9.1 L)
	1	12.0 gal (45.4 L)
Calcium hypochlorite [$Ca(OCl)_2$]	65	1.54 lb (0.7 kg)

*Sodium hypochlorite is available in four standard concentrations of available chlorine. Ordinary household bleach contains 5% chlorine.

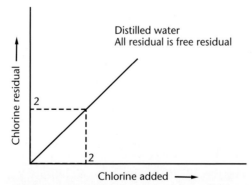

Figure 11-1 The reaction of chlorine in distilled water

The products are weak compounds that dissociate as follows:

$$HOCl \longrightarrow H^+ + OCl^-$$

hypochlorous   hydrogen   hypochlorite
acid   ion   ion

(11-2)

$$HCl \longrightarrow H^+ + Cl^-$$

hypochloric   hydrogen   chlorine
acid   ion   ion

(11-3)

Hypochlorous acid, one of two forms of free chlorine residual, is the most effective disinfectant available. When it dissociates, as in Equation 11-2, the hypochlorite ion (the second form of free chlorine residual) is formed. The hypochlorite ion is only 1 percent as effective as hypochlorous acid as a disinfectant. This is indicated in Table 11-6, which lists the estimated effectiveness of five types of residuals.

Natural water is not pure, and the reaction of chlorine with the impurities in the water interferes with the formation of a free chlorine residual. For example, if the water contains organic matter, nitrites, iron, manganese, and ammonia, the chlorine added will react as shown in Figure 11-2. Between points 1 and 2, added chlorine combines immediately with iron, manganese, and nitrites. These chemicals are reducing agents, and no residual can be formed until all reducing agents are completely destroyed by the chlorine.

Table 11-6 Estimated effectiveness of types of residual chlorine

Type	Chemical Abbreviation	Estimated Effectiveness Compared With HOCl
Hypochlorous acid	HOCl	1
Hypochlorite ion	OCl⁻	1/100
Trichloramine*	NCl_3	N/A†
Dichloramine	$NHCl_2$	1/80
Monochloramine	NH_2Cl	1/150

*Commonly called nitrogen trichloride

†No estimate; possibly more effective than dichloramine

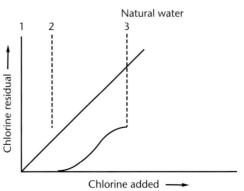

Figure 11-2 The reaction of chlorine with impurities in natural water

As more chlorine is added between points 2 and 3, the chlorine begins to react with ammonia and organic matter to form chloramines and chloroorganic compounds. These are called *combined chlorine residuals*. Because the chlorine is combined with other compounds, this residual is not as effective as a free chlorine residual.

Between points 2 and 3, the combined residual is primarily monochloramine—that is,

$$NH_3 \quad + \quad HOCl \quad \longrightarrow \quad NH_2Cl \quad + \quad H_2O$$

ammonia   hypochlorous   monochloramine   water   (11-4)
            acid

Adding more chlorine to the water actually decreases the residual (Figure 11-3). The decrease (shown from point 3 to point 4) results because the additional chlorine oxidizes some of the chloroorganic compounds and ammonia. The additional chlorine also changes some of the monochloramine to dichloramine and trichloramine.

$$NH_2Cl \quad + \quad HOCl \quad \longrightarrow \quad NHCl_2 \quad + \quad H_2O$$

monochloramine   hypochlorous   dichloramine   water   (11-5)
                 acid

$$NHCl_2 \quad + \quad HOCl \quad \longrightarrow \quad NHCl_3 \quad + \quad H_2O$$

dichloramine   hypochlorous   trichloramine   water   (11-6)
                 acid

As additional chlorine is added between points 3 and 4, the amount of chloramine reaches a minimum value. Beyond this minimum point, the addition of more chlorine produces free residual chlorine. The point at which this occurs (point 4 in Figure 11-4) is known as the *breakpoint*.

Past the breakpoint, an increase in the chlorine dose will usually produce a proportionate increase in the free chlorine residual; the free chlorine residual should be 85–90 percent of the total chlorine residual. The remaining percentage is combined residual consisting of dichloramines, trichloramines, and chloroorganic compounds. One group of the chloroorganic compounds—THMs—is discussed later in this chapter.

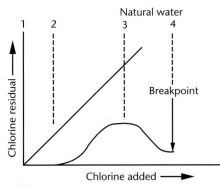

Figure 11-3 Decrease of chlorine residual

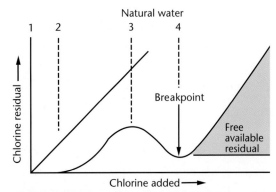

Figure 11-4 The chlorine breakpoint

Principle of Disinfection by Chlorination

The following five factors are important to the success of chlorination:

1. Concentration of chlorine
2. Contact time between the chlorine and water
3. Temperature of the water
4. pH of the water
5. Foreign substances in the water

Concentration and Contact Time The effectiveness of chlorination depends primarily on two factors, concentration C and contact time T. The destruction of organisms, often referred to as the *kill*, is directly related to these two factors as follows: kill is proportional to $C \times T$.

This means that if the chlorine concentration is decreased, then the contact time—the length of time the chlorine and the organisms are in physical contact—must be increased to ensure that the kill remains the same. Similarly, as the chlorine concentration increases, the contact time needed for a given kill decreases.

A combined chlorine residual, which is a weak disinfectant, requires a greater concentration, acting over a longer period of time, than is required for a free chlorine residual. Therefore, when the contact time between the point of chlorine application and the consumption of water by customers is short, only a free residual will provide effective disinfection.

It is important to know the contact time and type of residual chlorine available so that the proper concentration can be provided. Figure 11-5, which shows how many minutes are needed by different residual concentrations to achieve 99 percent destruction of *Escherichia coli* at 2–6°C (36–43°F), illustrates this point. In general, a minimum free chlorine residual of 0.2 mg/L should be maintained at the extremities of the distribution system.

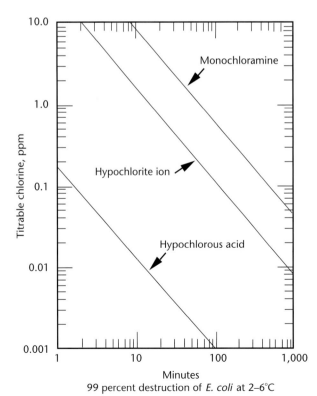

Figure 11-5 Efficiency of hypochlorous acid, hypochlorite ion, and monochloramine as disinfectants

Source: *Handbook of Chlorination and Alternative Disinfectants*. 4th ed. by Geo. Clifford White, copyright © 1998. Reprinted by permission of John Wiley & Sons, Inc.

Temperature The effectiveness of chlorination is also related to the temperature of the water. At lower temperatures, bacterial kill tends to be slower. However, chlorine is more stable in cold water, and the residual will remain for a longer period of time, compensating to some extent for the lower rate of disinfection. All factors considered, chlorination is more effective at higher water temperatures.

It is important for the operator to maintain a record of water temperatures. As temperatures change seasonally, the chlorine dosage will also need to be adjusted. The effectiveness of combined chlorine residuals is influenced more by low temperatures than that of free chlorine residuals.

pH The pH of the water affects the disinfecting action of chlorine because it determines the ratio of hypochlorous acid to hypochlorite ion. In other words, depending on the pH, either more hypochlorite ion or more hypochlorous acid could be present. As shown in Figure 11-6, the ratio of the ions will shift as the pH changes.

Hypochlorous acid dissociates poorly at low pH levels. The dominant residual is then hypochlorous acid. However, hypochlorous acid will dissociate almost completely at high pH levels, leaving hypochlorite ion as the dominant residual. Note in Figure 11-6 that temperature has very little effect on the dissociation at various pH levels.

Figure 11-7 summarizes the effects of pH on free and combined residuals. It is essential that the operator understand and use these relationships in order to obtain the most effective disinfectant. The pH of the water should be checked routinely. This is particularly important if the pH of the water is raised to control corrosion, because the chlorine dosage will have to be raised to maintain an effective level. Addition of chlorine gas lowers the pH of the water. The use of hypochlorites raises the pH slightly.

Interference Substances Chlorine acts as an effective disinfectant only if it comes in contact with the organisms to be killed. Turbidity, caused by tiny particles of dirt and other impurities suspended in the water, can prevent good contact and protect the pathogens. Therefore, for chlorination to be effective, turbidity must be reduced as much as possible through the use of coagulation, flocculation, and filtration.

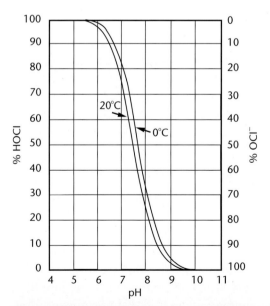

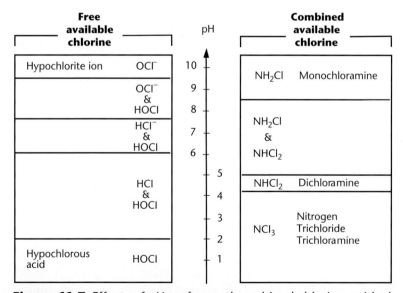

Figure 11-6 Distribution of hypochlorous acid (HOCl) and hypochlorite ion (OCl⁻) in water at indicated pH levels

Figure 11-7 Effects of pH on free and combined chlorine residual

As discussed earlier, chlorine reacts with other substances in water, such as organic matter and ammonia. Because these compounds result in the formation of the less-effective combined residuals, their concentrations are an important factor in determining chlorine dosages.

Superchlorination and Dechlorination

The process of superchlorination has typically been used in the treatment of poor-quality water, including water with high ammonia concentrations or severe taste-and-odor problems. In these cases, chlorine is added beyond the breakpoint, which oxidizes the ammonia nitrogen present.

The residual chlorine present at this point is usually higher than desired for the distribution systems, so the residual may have to be decreased before the water leaves the treatment plant. The chlorine residual can be reduced by dosing the water with a substance that reacts with the residual chlorine or accelerates its rate of decomposition. Compounds that can perform this function include thiosulfate, hydrogen peroxide, and ammonia. However, the chemicals most commonly used for plant-scale dechlorination are sodium bisulfite, sodium sulfite, and sulfur dioxide. Dechlorination can also be accomplished by passing the water through a bed of activated carbon.

Chloramination

Chloramines can be formed as a result of the reaction between applied chlorine and ammonia present in raw water. They can also be formed in the treatment process by the addition of ammonia to react with chlorine so that a combined chlorine residual will be formed. This practice has been used by many water systems for more than 70 years. In practice, the ammonia can be added before, at the same time as, or after the chlorine feed.

Chloramines have been used principally in systems requiring a reduction in tastes and odors, particularly where the raw water may contain phenol. Free chlorine normally reacts with phenol to form chlorophenol, which has a very disagreeable taste and odor. Many systems have also found that chloramines can be used to reduce the THM level in their water.

The primary disadvantage of chloramines is that they are a much weaker disinfectant than free chlorine, chlorine dioxide, or ozone. They are particularly weak for inactivating certain viruses. In most water systems that use chloramines as the principal disinfectant, the ammonia is added at a point downstream from the initial chlorine application so that microorganisms, including viruses, will be exposed to the free chlorine for a short period before chloramines are formed. To meet SWTR requirements, systems using chloramines must carry considerably higher residuals or provide a longer contact time than would be necessary if they were using free chlorine.

If a system changes from free chlorine to chloramines for disinfection, hospitals and kidney dialysis centers must be alerted. Cases of chloramine-induced hemolytic anemia in patients have been reported when their dialysis water was not appropriately treated.

Disinfectant Application Points

Disinfectants are commonly applied at two points: where the raw water enters a treatment plant and again after treatment has been completed. A growing number of treatment plants have also found it advantageous to add disinfectants at intermediate points in the treatment process.

Source Water Chlorination

As illustrated in Figure 11-8, most surface water systems apply chlorine (or alternative disinfectants) at two points. Source water chlorination (prechlorination) is performed for the following reasons:

- To begin the process of killing and/or inactivating pathogenic organisms
- To minimize operational problems and tastes and odors that could be caused by biological growths on filters, pipes, and basins
- To oxidize hydrogen sulfide, iron, and manganese that may be in the raw water
- To oxidize various organic substances in the raw water

Historically, the most common point for prechlorinating surface water has been the intake well or rapid-mix basin. Because the formation of THMs and other DBPs is a concern, many systems are moving the application point to later in the treatment process or feeding a different chemical oxidant as the water enters the treatment plant.

Postchlorination

Terminal disinfection (postchlorination) is the application of chlorine to treated water. This is necessary to meet federal and state requirements for maintaining a minimum chlorine residual in the water, both at the entry to the distribution system and at points throughout the distribution system. The presence of a residual indicates that a more than adequate amount of disinfectant has been added to complete the reaction. The residual is also considered to be a safeguard against contamination that could be introduced into the distribution system or customer plumbing systems.

Postchlorination is usually performed immediately before the clearwell or immediately before the sand filters. Although the clearwell is intended to provide some contact time with the chlorine to ensure adequate inactivation of pathogens, most clearwells do not have baffles, so there could be a short-circuiting of flow. To meet the $C \times T$ requirements of the SWTR, some systems may find it necessary to install baffles to ensure adequate contact time before the water enters the distribution system.

Systems having difficulty in maintaining the required chlorine residual in the distribution system may need to install booster chlorination facilities. A particularly good location for adding more chlorine is on the discharge from a storage reservoir.

Additional Application Points

In the process of balancing the multiple requirements of minimizing tastes and odors, reducing DBPs, and meeting the SWTR requirements, many systems have

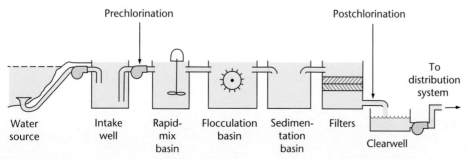

Figure 11-8 Common chlorination points in a conventional filtration plant

found it advantageous to use two or more types of disinfectants and to feed them at different points during the treatment process.

Figure 11-9 illustrates changes typically made to a surface water system to minimize DBPs; permanganate is applied at the intake, and the prechlorination point is moved to a later stage of the treatment process.

Figure 11-10 illustrates a system that has raw-water storage tanks. An initial disinfectant dose is added at the source, another application is added before treatment, and a third is applied as the water enters the distribution system. This situation is often ideal for meeting $C \times T$ requirements for poor-quality water, while still minimizing DBPs.

Groundwater Systems

Unless special treatment, such as iron removal or softening, is required, groundwater systems normally pump water directly from wells either to the distribution system or into a storage reservoir that pumps to the system. In either case, the chlorination point is usually located immediately past the wellhead.

Historically, most groundwater systems that required no special treatment did not chlorinate. In recent years, many states have enacted a requirement for all community public water supplies to chlorinate. The USEPA Ground Water Rule (Chapter 3) generally requires disinfection, although exemptions are granted under certain conditions.

Use of Multiple Disinfectants

There is a growing tendency for water systems to use multiple disinfectants. Many systems feed ozone, chlorine dioxide, or potassium permanganate as the initial oxidant and then apply chlorine later in the treatment process.

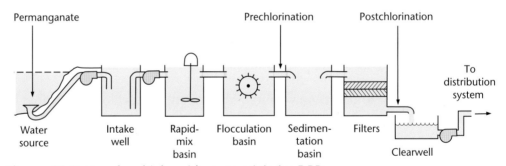

Figure 11-9 Use of multiple oxidants to minimize DBPs

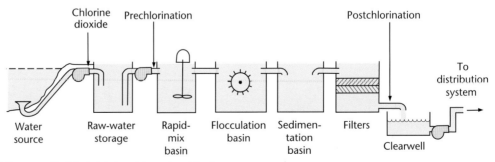

Figure 11-10 Initial oxidant feed before raw-water storage

Gas Chlorination Facilities

Chlorine gas, Cl_2, is about 2.5 times as dense as air. It has a pungent, noxious odor and a greenish-yellow color, although it is visible only at a very high concentration. The gas is very irritating to the eyes, nasal passages, and respiratory tract, and it can kill a person in a few breaths at concentrations as low as 0.1 percent (1,000 ppm) by volume. Its odor can be detected at concentrations above 0.3 ppm.

Chlorine liquid is created by compressing chlorine gas. The liquid, which is about 99.5 percent pure chlorine, is amber in color and about 1.5 times as dense as water. It can be purchased in cylinders, containers, tank trucks, and railroad cars (Figures 11-11 through 11-14).

Liquid chlorine changes easily to a gas at room temperatures and pressures. One volume of liquid chlorine will expand to about 460 volumes of gas. Dry chlorine gas will not corrode steel or other metals, but it is extremely corrosive to most metals in the presence of moisture.

Chlorine will not burn. But, like oxygen, *it will support combustion*; that is, it takes the place of oxygen in the burning of combustible materials. Chlorine is not explosive, but it will react violently with greases, turpentine, ammonia, hydrocarbons, metal filings, and other flammable materials. Chlorine will not conduct electricity, but the gas can be very corrosive to exposed electrical equipment. Because of the inherent hazards involved, chlorine requires special care in storage and handling.

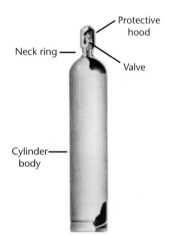

Figure 11-11 Chlorine cylinder

Courtesy of the Chlorine Institute.

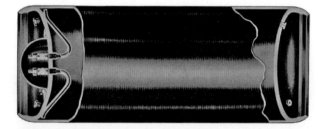

Figure 11-12 Chlorine ton container

Courtesy of the Chlorine Institute.

Figure 11-13 Chlorine ton container truck

Courtesy of PPG Industries, Inc.

Figure 11-14 Chlorine tank car

Courtesy of the Chlorine Institute.

Handling and Storing Chlorine Gas

Safe handling and storage of chlorine are vital to the operator and to the communities immediately surrounding a treatment plant. An error or accident in chlorine handling can cause serious injuries or even fatalities.

The containers commonly used to supply chlorine in smaller water treatment plants are 150-lb (68-kg) cylinders. Larger plants find it more economical to use ton containers. Some very large plants are equipped to draw chlorine directly from tank cars.

The decision of whether to use cylinders or ton containers should be based on cost and capacity. The cost per pound (kilogram) of chlorine in cylinders is usually substantially more than that of chlorine in ton containers. If a plant's needs for chlorine are lower than 50 lb/d (23 kg/d), cylinders should usually be selected. For systems that use large amounts, ton containers will probably be more economical.

Cylinders

Chlorine cylinders hold 150 lb (68 kg) of chlorine and have a total filled weight of 250–285 lb (110–130 kg). They are about 10.5 in. (270 mm) in diameter and 56 in. (1.42 m) high. As illustrated in Figure 11-11, each cylinder is equipped with a hood that protects the cylinder valve from damage during shipping and handling. The hood should be properly screwed in place whenever a cylinder is handled and should be removed only during use.

Cylinders are usually delivered by truck. Each cylinder should be unloaded to a dock at truck-bed height if possible. If a hydraulic tailgate is used, the cylinders should be secure to keep them from falling. Cylinders must never be dropped, including "empty" cylinders, which actually still contain some chlorine.

The easiest and safest way to move cylinders in the plant is with a hand truck. As shown in Figure 11-15, the hand truck should be equipped with a restraining chain that fastens snugly around the cylinder about two-thirds of the way up. Slings should never be used to lift cylinders, and a cylinder should never be lifted by the protective hood because the hood is not designed to support the weight of the cylinder. Cylinders should not be rolled to move them about a plant. Tipping the cylinders over and standing them up can lead to employee injury. In addition, the rolled cylinders might strike something that could break off the valve.

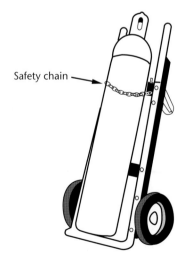

Safety chain

Figure 11-15 Hand truck for moving chlorine cylinders

Courtesy of the Chlorine Institute.

chlorine cylinder
A container that holds 150 lb (68 kg) of chlorine and has a total filled weight of 250–285 lb (110–130 kg).

Cylinders can be stored indoors or outdoors. If cylinders are stored indoors, the building should be fire resistant, have multiple exits with outward-opening doors, and be adequately ventilated. Outdoor storage areas must be fenced and protected from direct sunlight, and they should be protected from vehicles or falling objects that might strike the cylinders. If standing water accumulates in an outdoor storage area, the cylinders should be stored on elevated racks. Avoiding contact with water will help minimize cylinder corrosion.

Some operators find it convenient to hang "full" or "empty" identification tags on cylinders in storage, so that the status of the chlorine inventory can be quickly determined. Other plants maintain separate storage areas for full and empty cylinders, but all cylinders, full or empty, should receive the same high level of care. In addition, protective hoods should be placed on empty and full cylinders in storage. Even when a cylinder no longer has sufficient chlorine for plant use, a small amount of gas remains and could escape if the cylinder or valve were damaged. Both full and empty cylinders should always be stored upright and secured with a chain to prevent them from tipping over.

Ton Containers

The **ton container** is a reusable, welded tank that holds 2,000 lb (910 kg) of chlorine. Containers weigh about 3,700 lb (1,700 kg) when full and are generally 30 in. (0.76 m) in diameter and 80 in. (2.03 m) long. As shown in Figure 11-12, the ends are concave. The containers are crimped around the perimeter of the ends, forming good gripping edges for the hoists used to lift and move them. The ton container is designed to rest horizontally both in shipping and in use. It is equipped with two valves that provide the option of withdrawing either liquid or gaseous chlorine. The upper valve will draw gas, and the lower valve will draw liquid.

Handling the heavy containers is, by necessity, far more mechanized than handling cylinders. Containers are loaded or unloaded by a lifting beam in combination with a manual or motor-operated hoist mounted on a monorail that has a capacity of at least 2 tons (1,815 kg) (Figure 11-16). To prevent accidental rolling, containers are stored on trunnions, as illustrated in Figure 11-17. The trunnions

> **ton container**
> A reusable, welded tank that holds 2,000 lb (910 kg) of chlorine. Containers weigh about 3,700 lb (1,700 kg) when full and are generally 30 in. (0.76 m) in diameter and 80 in. (2.03 m) long.

Figure 11-16 Lifting beam with motorized hoist for ton containers

Figure 11-17 Ton containers stored on trunnions

allow the container to be rotated so that it can be positioned correctly for connection to the chlorine supply line.

Ton containers can be stored indoors or outdoors and require the same precautions as chlorine cylinders. The bowl-shaped hood that covers the two valve assemblies when the tank is delivered should be replaced each time the container is handled, as well as right after it has been emptied.

The chlorine storage area should provide space for a 30- to 60-day supply of chlorine. Some systems feed chlorine directly from this storage area. When ton containers are used, the chlorination feed equipment is usually housed in a separate room (Figure 11-18).

Feeding Chlorine Gas

Chlorine feeding begins where the cylinder or ton container connects to the manifold that leads to the chlorinator. The feed system ends at the point where the chlorine solution mixes into the water being disinfected. The system is composed of the following main components:

- Weighing scale
- Valves and piping
- Chlorinator
- Injector or diffuser

Weighing Scales

It is important that an accurate record be kept of the amount of chlorine used and the amount of chlorine remaining in a cylinder or container. A simple way to do this is to place the cylinders or containers on weigh scales. The scales can be calibrated to display either the amount used or the amount remaining. By recording weight readings at regular intervals, the operator can develop a record of chlorine-use rates. Figure 11-19 shows a common type of two-cylinder scale. Figure 11-20 shows a portable beam scale. Figure 11-21 shows a combination trunnion and scale for a ton container; this scale operates hydraulically and has a dial readout.

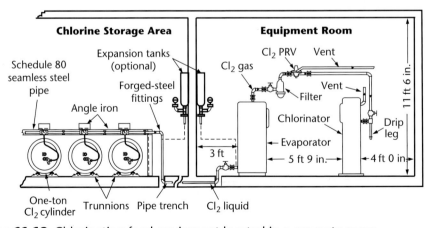

Figure 11-18 Chlorination feed equipment located in a separate room

Source: *Handbook of Chlorination and Alternative Disinfectants.* 4th ed. by Geo. Clifford White, copyright © 1998. Reprinted by permission of John Wiley & Sons, Inc.

Figure 11-19 Two-cylinder scale
Courtesy of US Filter/Wallace & Tiernan.

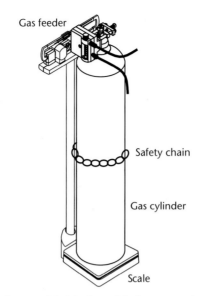

Figure 11-20 Portable beam scale
Courtesy of De Nora Water Technologies.

Figure 11-21 Combination trunnion and scale for a ton container
Courtesy of Force Flow.

Valves and Piping

Chlorine cylinders and ton containers are equipped with valves as shown in Figures 11-22 and 11-23. The valves must comply with standards set by the Chlorine Institute.

It is standard practice for an auxiliary tank valve to be connected directly to the cylinder or container valve, as illustrated in Figure 11-24. The connection is made with either a union-type or a yoke-type connector. The auxiliary valve can be used to close off all downstream piping, thus minimizing gas leakage during container changes. The auxiliary tank valve will also serve as an emergency

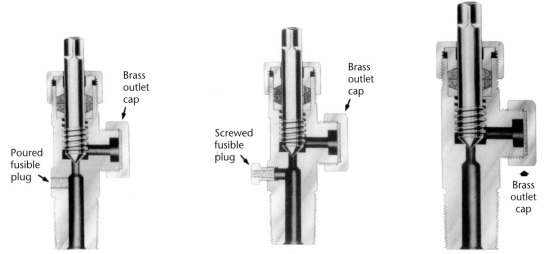

Figure 11-22 Standard cylinder valves: poured-type fusible plug (left) and screw-type fusible plug (right)

Courtesy of the Chlorine Institute.

Figure 11-23 Standard ton container valve

Courtesy of the Chlorine Institute.

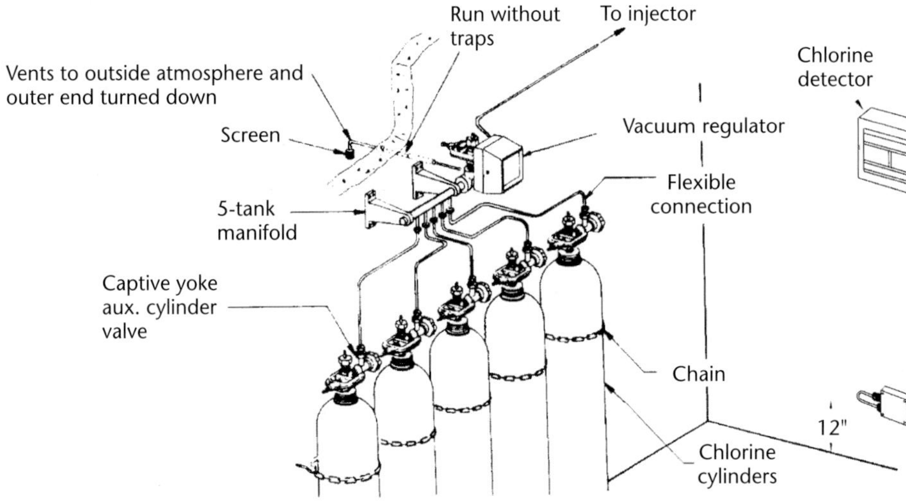

Figure 11-24 Auxiliary tank valve connected directly to container valve

Courtesy of US Filter/Wallace & Tiernan.

shutoff if the container valve fails. If a direct-mounted chlorinator is used, an auxiliary tank valve is not required (Figure 11-25).

The diagram in Figure 11-24 is of a typical valve assembly. The figure shows that the assembly is connected to the chlorine-supply piping by flexible tubing, which is usually 3/8-in. (10-mm) copper rated at 500 psig (3,500 kPa).

When more than one container is connected, a manifold must be used, as shown in Figure 11-24. The manifold channels the flow of chlorine from two or more containers into the chlorine-supply piping. The manifold and supply piping must meet the specifications of the Chlorine Institute. Manifolds may have from 2 to 10 connecting points. Each point is a union nut suitable for receiving flexible connections. Notice in Figure 11-24 that the header valve is connected at the manifold discharge end, providing another shutoff point. Additional valves are used along the chlorine supply line for shutoff and isolation in the event of a leak.

Figure 11-25 Direct-mounted chlorinator

Courtesy of De Nora Water Technologies.

Figure 11-26 Free-standing chlorinator cabinet

Courtesy of De Nora Water Technologies.

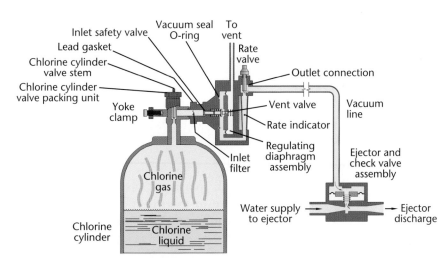

Figure 11-27 Schematic of direct-mounted gas chlorinator

Courtesy of De Nora Water Technologies.

Chlorinators

The **chlorinator** can be a simple direct-mounted unit on a cylinder or ton container, as shown in Figure 11-25. This type of chlorinator feeds chlorine gas directly to the water being treated. A free-standing cabinet-type chlorinator is illustrated in Figure 11-26. Cabinet-type chlorinators, which operate on the same principle as cylinder-mounted units, have a sturdier mounting and are capable of higher feed rates. Schematic diagrams of two typical chlorinators are shown in Figures 11-27 and 11-28

The purpose of the chlorinator is to meter chlorine gas safely and accurately from the cylinder or container and then accurately deliver the set dosage. To do this, a chlorinator is equipped with pressure and vacuum regulators that are actuated by diaphragms and orifices for reducing the gas pressure. The reduced pressure allows a uniform gas flow, accurately metered by the rotameter (feed rate indicator). In addition, a vacuum is maintained in the line to the injector for safety purposes. If a leak develops in the vacuum line, air will enter the atmospheric vent, causing the vacuum relief valve to close and stopping the flow of chlorine gas. To vary the chlorine dosage, the operator manually adjusts the setting of the rotameter.

chlorinator
Any device that is used to add chlorine to water.

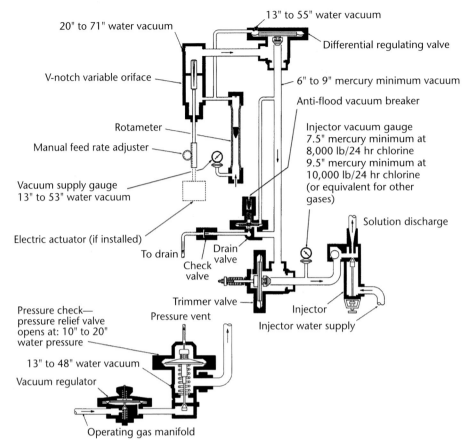

Figure 11-28 Schematic of cabinet-style chlorinator
Courtesy of US Filter/Wallace & Tiernan.

It is normally required that each treatment plant have at least one standby chlorinator ready for immediate use in the event that the primary chlorinator should fail. Automatic switchover equipment is also strongly recommended.

Injectors

An **injector** (or ejector) is located within or downstream of the chlorinator, as illustrated in Figure 11-27. It is a venturi device that pulls chlorine gas into a passing stream of dilution water, forming a strong solution of chlorine and water. The injector also creates the vacuum needed to operate the chlorinator. The highly corrosive chlorine solution (pH of about 2–4) is carried to the point of application in a corrosion-resistant pipeline. The type of pipe typically used is polyvinyl chloride (PVC), fiberglass, or steel pipe lined with PVC or rubber. A strainer should be installed on the water line upstream of the injector. This strainer prevents any grit, rust, or other material from entering and blocking the injector or causing wear of the injector throat.

Diffusers

A **diffuser** is one or more short lengths of pipe, usually perforated, that quickly and uniformly disperses the chlorine solution into the main flow of water. There are two types of diffusers: those used in pipelines and those used in open channels and tanks. A properly designed and operated diffuser is necessary for the complete mixing needed for effective disinfection.

injector

The portion of a chlorination system that feeds the chlorine solution into a pipe under pressure.

diffuser

A section of a perforated pipe or porous plates used to inject a gas, such as carbon dioxide or air, under pressure into water.

The diffuser used in pipelines less than 3 ft (0.9 m) in diameter is simply a pipe protruding into the center of the pipeline. Figure 11-29 shows a diffuser made from Schedule 80 PVC, and Figure 11-30 shows how the turbulence of the flowing water completely mixes the chlorine solution throughout the water. Complete mixing should occur downstream at a distance of 10 pipe diameters.

Figure 11-31 shows a perforated diffuser for use in larger pipelines. A similar design is used to introduce chlorine solution into a tank or open channel, as shown in Figure 11-32. (During normal operations, the diffuser would be completely submerged, but in the figure, the water level has been dropped, for illustrative purposes only, to show the chlorine solution passing out of each perforation.)

Gas Chlorination Auxiliary Equipment

A variety of auxiliary equipment is used for chlorination. The following discussion describes the functions of the more commonly used items.

Booster Pumps

A booster pump (Figure 11-33) is usually needed to provide the water pressure necessary to make the injector operate properly. The booster pump is usually a low-head, high-capacity centrifugal type. It must be sized to overcome the pressure in the line that carries the main flow of water being treated, and it must be rugged enough to withstand continuous use.

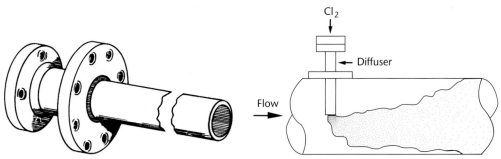

Figure 11-29 Diffuser made from Schedule 80 PVC

Figure 11-30 Chlorine solution mixing in a large-diameter pipeline

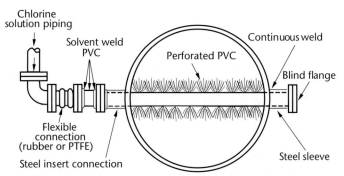

Figure 11-31 Perforated diffuser for pipelines larger than 3 ft (0.9 m) in diameter

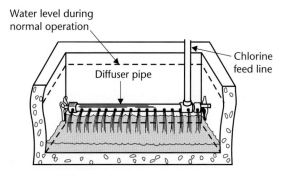

Figure 11-32 Open-channel diffuser

Source: *Handbook of Chlorination and Alternative Disinfectants.* 4th ed. by Geo. Clifford White, copyright © 1998. Reprinted by permission of John Wiley & Sons, Inc.

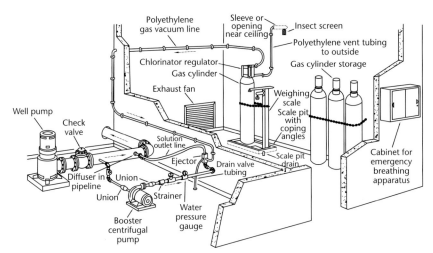

Figure 11-33 Typical chlorinator deep-well installation showing booster pump
Courtesy of De Nora Water Technologies.

Automatic Controls

If a chlorination system is to be manually operated, adjustments must be made each time the flow rate or the chlorine demand changes. For constant or near-constant flow rate situations, a manual system is suitable.

However, when flow rate or chlorine demand is continually changing, the operator is required to change the rotameter settings frequently. In these situations, automatic controls are valuable. Although many automatic control arrangements are possible, there are two common types: flow proportional control and residual flow control.

Flow Proportional Control   If chlorine demand rarely changes and it is necessary to compensate only for changes in the pumping rate, flow proportional control works well. It will automatically increase or decrease the chlorine feed rate as the water flow rate increases or decreases. The required equipment includes a flowmeter for the treated water, a transmitter to sense the flow rate and send a signal to the chlorinator, and a receiver at the chlorinator. The receiver responds to the transmitted signal by opening or closing the chlorine flow rate valve.

Residual Flow Control   If the chlorine demand of the water changes periodically, it is necessary to make corresponding changes in the rate of feed to provide adequate disinfection. Residual flow control, also called *compound loop control*, automatically maintains a constant chlorine residual, regardless of chlorine demand or flow rate changes. The system uses an automatic chlorine residual analyzer (Figure 11-34) in addition to the signal from a meter measuring the flow

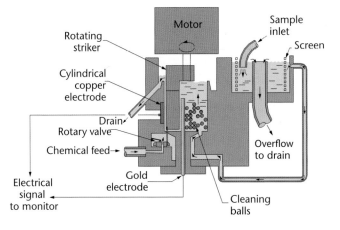

Figure 11-34 Automatic chlorine residual analyzer
Courtesy of De Nora Water Technologies.

rate. The analyzer uses an electrode to determine the chlorine residual in the treated water. Signals from the residual analyzer and flow element are sent to a receiver in the chlorinator, where they are combined to adjust the chlorine feed rate to maintain a constant residual in the treated water.

Evaporators

A **chlorine evaporator** is a heating device used to convert liquid chlorine to chlorine gas. Ton containers are equipped with valves that will draw either liquid or gas. At 70°F (21°C), the maximum gas withdrawal rate from a ton container is 400 lb/d (180 kg/d). If higher withdrawal is required, the liquid feed connection is used and connected to an evaporator. The evaporator accelerates the evaporation of liquid chlorine to gas, so that withdrawal rates up to 9,600 lb/d (4,400 kg/d) can be obtained.

An evaporator (Figure 11-35) is a water bath heated by electric immersion heaters to a temperature of 170–180°F (77–82°C). The pipes carrying the liquid chlorine pass through the water bath, and liquid chlorine is converted to gas by the heat.

Automatic Switchover Systems

For many small water systems, it is either impossible or uneconomical to have an operator available to monitor operation of the chlorination system at all times. An automatic switchover system provides switchover to a new chlorine supply when the online supply runs out. The switchover is either pressure or vacuum activated. The vacuum type of installation is shown in Figure 11-36. The automatic changeover mechanism has two inlets and one outlet. As the online supply is exhausted, the vacuum increases, causing the changeover mechanism to close on the exhausted supply and open the new chlorine supply. The unit can also send a signal to notify operating personnel that the one tank is empty and should be replaced. Figure 11-37 shows a

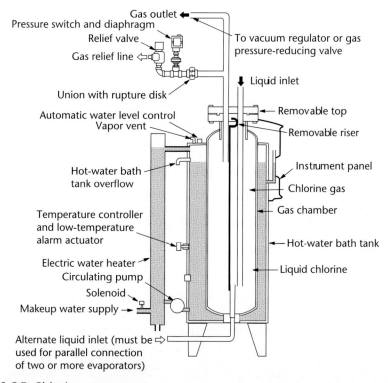

Figure 11-35 Chlorine evaporator

Courtesy of US Filter/Wallace & Tiernan.

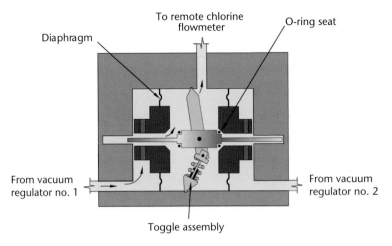

Figure 11-36 Automatic switchover unit

Courtesy of De Nora Water Technologies.

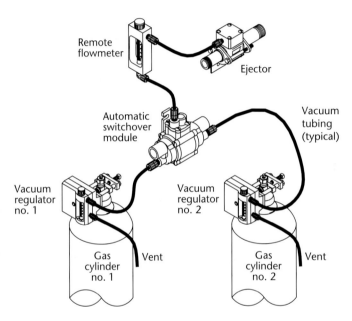

Figure 11-37 Typical installation of switchover system

Courtesy of De Nora Water Technologies.

typical installation. This system is ideal for remote locations to ensure uninterrupted chlorine feeding.

Chlorine Alarms

Chlorinators are often equipped with a vacuum switch that triggers an alarm when it senses an abnormally low or high vacuum. A low-vacuum condition can mean an injector failure, vacuum line break, or booster pump failure. A high-vacuum condition can be caused by a plugged chlorine supply line or by empty chlorine tanks.

Safety Equipment

Safety in and around the gas chlorination process is important to prevent serious accidents and equipment damage. Certain items of equipment, such as the following, are essential for the safe operation of a chlorination facility:

- Chlorine detectors
- Self-contained breathing apparatus
- Emergency repair kits

Hypochlorination Facilities

Hypochlorination is a chlorination method increasingly used by water treatment plants because of its relative safety (as compared to gaseous chlorine) and its ease of use. Sodium hypochlorite is fed as a liquid, and many operators prefer to feed liquids rather than gases.

Hypochlorite Compounds

The two most commonly used compounds are calcium hypochlorite and sodium hypochlorite. Table 11-7 lists the properties of both compounds.

Calcium Hypochlorite

Calcium hypochlorite, $Ca(OCl)_2$, is a dry, white or yellow-white, granular material. It is also available in compressed tablets. It normally contains 65 percent available chlorine by weight. This means that when 1 lb (0.5 kg) of the powder is added to water, only 0.65 lb (0.3 kg) of pure chlorine is being added. Conversely, if 1 lb (0.5 kg) of chlorine is added, 1.5 lb (0.7 kg) of calcium hypochlorite must be added (Table 11-5).

Calcium hypochlorite requires special storage to avoid contact with organic material. Its reaction with any organic substances can generate enough heat and oxygen to start and support a fire. When calcium hypochlorite is mixed with water, heat is given off. To provide adequate dissipation of the heat, the dry chemical should be added to the water; the water should *not* be added to the chemical.

Calcium hypochlorite is used mostly for disinfection of new and repaired water mains, water storage tanks, and small water volumes, such as swimming pools.

Sodium Hypochlorite

Sodium hypochlorite, $NaOCl$, is a clear, light-yellow liquid commonly used for bleach. Ordinary household bleach contains 5 to 6 percent available chlorine. Industrial bleaches are stronger, containing from 9 to 15 percent.

The sodium hypochlorite solution is alkaline, with a pH of 9 to 11, depending on the available chlorine content. For common strengths, Table 11-5 shows the amount of solution needed to supply 1 lb (0.5 kg) of pure chlorine. Large systems can purchase the liquid chemical in carboys, drums, and railroad tank cars. Very small water systems often purchase it in 1-gal (3.8-L) plastic jugs.

There is no fire hazard in storing sodium hypochlorite, but the chemical is quite corrosive and should be kept away from equipment susceptible to corrosion damage. At its maximum strength of 12 to 15 percent, sodium hypochlorite solution can lose 2 to 4 percent of its available chlorine content per month at room temperature. It is therefore recommended that it not be stored for more than 15–25 days. Instability of the chemical increases with increasing temperature, solution strength, and exposure to sunlight. Sodium hypochlorite solutions of 6 percent are more stable. Water plant design specifications usually call for the

Table 11-7 Properties of hypochlorites

Property	Sodium Hypochlorite	Calcium Hypochlorite
Symbol	NaOCl	Ca(OCl)$_2$
Form	Liquid	Dry granules, powder, or tablets
Strength	Up to 15% available chlorine	65–70% available chlorine, depending on form

hypochlorination
Chlorination using solutions of calcium hypochlorite or sodium hypochlorite.

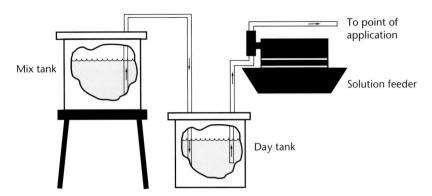

Figure 11-38 Mix tank and day tank

dilution of the 12 percent stock chemical to 6 percent, unless special storage facilities are built that keep out sunlight and heat.

Common Equipment

Disinfecting facilities using calcium hypochlorite should be equipped with a cool, dry storage area to stockpile the compound in the shipping containers. A variable-speed chemical feed pump (hypochlorinator), such as a diaphragm pump, is all that is required for feeding the chemical to the water. A mix tank and a day tank (Figure 11-38) are also required. After calcium hypochlorite is mixed with water, impurities and undissolved chemicals settle to the bottom of the mix tank. The clear solution is then transferred to the day tank for feeding. This prevents any of the solids from reaching and plugging the hypochlorinator or rupturing the diaphragm.

Because sodium hypochlorite is a liquid, it is simpler to use than calcium hypochlorite. It is fed neat (as the 12 percent stock chemical) or at the 6 percent strength, usually with peristaltic pump equipment that uses a quality-grade tubing. Redundant pumps are needed and operators must get used to changing the tubing on a frequent basis to prevent failure.

Off-gassing is a major issue with the equipment used for storing and feeding sodium hypochlorites. Equipment failure and damage are common occurrences when hypochlorite feed systems are poorly designed or poorly maintained.

 WATCH THE VIDEO
Water Disinfection (www.awwa.org/wsovideoclips)

Study Questions

1. The two most important factors impacting the effectiveness of chlorination are
   a. the pH of the water and the content of foreign substances in the water.
   b. the concentration of chlorine and the content of foreign substances in the water.
   c. the concentration of chlorine and the contact time.
   d. the pH and the temperature of the water.

2. Of the organisms that cause the following illnesses, which is the hardest to kill?

   a. Cholera

   b. Typhoid

   c. *Cryptosporidiosis*

   d. Infectious hepatitis

3. At which range of temperatures will fusible plugs on chlorine cylinders melt?

   a. 147–152°F (64–67°C)

   b. 155–159°F (68–71°C)

   c. 157–162°F (69–72°C)

   d. 167–171°F (75–77°C)

4. When a chlorine cylinder or container is changed, a new gasket should be used

   a. every time.

   b. after 2 uses.

   c. after 3 uses.

   d. after 4 or 5 uses.

5. A(n) _____ is one or more short lengths of pipe, usually perforated, that quickly and uniformly disperses the chlorine solution into the main flow of water.

   a. cylinder

   b. injector

   c. chlorinator

   d. diffuser

6. What is the term for the treatment process used to destroy or inactivate disease-causing (pathogenic) organisms, such as viruses, bacteria, fungi, or protozoa?

7. What element is a dark reddish-brown liquid that vaporizes at room temperature and has a penetrating, suffocating odor?

8. In the chlorination process, what term refers to the point beyond which the addition of more chlorine produces free residual chlorine.

9. Which condition, caused by tiny particles of dirt and other impurities suspended in the water, can prevent good contact and protect pathogens during the disinfection process?

Iron and manganese are often present in groundwaters and surface waters. Iron is more prevalent in groundwaters. When manganese is found in groundwaters, it is usually accompanied by iron.

Iron and manganese found in groundwaters originate when rock strata rich in iron and manganese are exposed to acidic water devoid of oxygen from anaerobic activity. In groundwaters, iron may also be present as soluble ferrous bicarbonate in alkaline wells or as soluble ferrous sulfate in acid mine drainage waters, or in waters high in sulfur. Iron is present as suspended insoluble ferric hydroxide in groundwater exposed to air and as a product of pipe corrosion.

At times iron and manganese in the oxidized form are present in surface waters, usually as organic complexes.

Excessive Iron and Manganese

Excessive iron and manganese in drinking water can result in aesthetic and operational problems, potentially causing customers to seek out alternate supplies of drinking water that may not be safe.

Aesthetic Problems

Iron and manganese in the concentrations that occur naturally in groundwater and surface water have no known adverse health effects. However, the aesthetic problems they can cause may be quite serious from a consumer's standpoint. Iron and manganese in raw water are generally in the soluble, reduced, divalent state. The water is clear, and the substances are not noticeable aside from the taste and odor effect that they may cause at high concentrations. When they are oxidized, iron and manganese change and discolor the water from turbid yellow to black, depending on their concentration and the presence or absence of other contaminants.

When a groundwater system pumps water directly from wells to the distribution system and uses no disinfection or other treatment, dissolved iron in the water usually first becomes oxidized when it is exposed to the oxygen in air. After a customer fills a glass, bathtub, or washing machine with water, the iron gradually oxidizes and changes color. This property results not only in water that is unpalatable for consumption, but also in stained porcelain fixtures and discolored laundry (Figure 12-1).

The reaction between the high levels of iron and the tannic acid in tea and coffee can also cause customer complaints. In some cases, the beverage will darken so that it looks like ink.

iron

An abundant element found naturally in the earth. As a result, dissolved iron is found in most water supplies. When the concentration of iron exceeds 0.3 mg/L, it causes red stains on plumbing fixtures and other items in contact with the water. Dissolved iron can also be present in water as a result of corrosion of cast-iron or steel pipes. This is usually the cause of red-water problems.

manganese

An abundant element found naturally in the earth. Dissolved manganese is found in many water supplies. At concentrations above 0.05 mg/L, it causes black stains on plumbing fixtures, laundry, and other items in contact with the water.

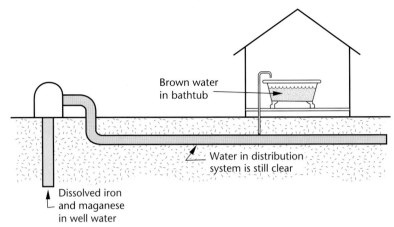

Figure 12-1 Iron and manganese oxidized after being exposed to air in a customer's plumbing fixtures

The presence of iron or manganese in the distribution system often provides a food source for bacterial growth. The bacterial slimes contribute to aesthetically objectionable tastes and odors. The presence of manganese is a problem because it creates brown spots on laundry. It is also a major problem for industries that incorporate water into their product because it will react with other chemicals to form undesirable tastes, odors, or colors. Manganese also tends to accumulate, corrode, and clog industrial fixtures. The maximum desirable level of manganese is 0.05 mg/L, and the point at which it creates an undesirable taste is about 5 mg/L.

Operational Problems

The presence of iron in a water distribution system may also be caused by corrosion of metal pipes in the system. In this case, the problem must be corrected by corrosion control, as discussed in Chapter 15.

If a disinfectant is added to the water, or if iron and manganese are fully or partially oxidized by any means before entering the distribution system (Figure 12-2), the oxidized iron and manganese will precipitate in the distribution system. The following problems may occur:

- Much of the precipitate could settle out in the mains. The worst problems will usually be in dead-end mains, where velocity is the lowest. If the iron and manganese problem in the system is not very serious, sometimes only the customers on dead ends will continually have a problem with rusty water.
- Sudden demands for extra water, such as the opening of a fire hydrant, may disrupt the normal flow in the system. The sediment that has accumulated on the bottom of mains will then be put back into suspension. Parts of the system, or even the whole system, will then have rusty water for a few hours or even a day or two. Customers will register complaints during and after the event—particularly those who were doing laundry at the time.

The presence of iron and manganese in the distribution system, in either the dissolved or oxidized state, can also provide a food source for bacterial growth in the system. The bacterial slimes that form can have the following detrimental effects:

- Reduction in pipeline flow capacity
- Clogging of meters and valves
- Further discoloration of the water as a result of the bacterial growth
- Increased chlorine demand

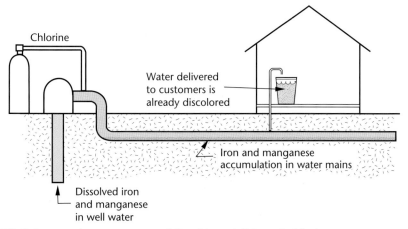

Figure 12-2 Iron and manganese oxidized by addition of chlorine

Control Processes

Iron and manganese are controlled or removed from water using sequestration for control and precipitation for removal. Precipitation is discussed first.

Precipitation

In the precipitation process, the soluble forms of iron and manganese are oxidized to insoluble ferric and manganic compounds, similar to the mechanism that rusts iron. Oxidized iron and manganese precipitate as ferric oxide or oxyhydroxides and manganese hydroxide. Following oxidation, the precipitates are removed from the water by a combination of settling and filtration, direct filtration, or membrane filtration.

Both iron and manganese are effectively removed by lime softening, but costs associated with chemical usage and sludge disposal usually make the process too costly to use unless water softening is also desired. This process is discussed in detail in Chapter 16.

Oxidation

In the precipitation of iron and manganese from water, the first step is oxidation to the insoluble state. The Stage 1 Disinfectants/Disinfection By-products (D/DBP) Rule limits trihalomethanes and haloacetic acids. Iron and manganese treatment strategies must be evaluated in light of this rule.

Air is often used to oxidize iron. If manganese is present, chlorine, either as sodium or calcium hypochlorite, ozone, chlorine dioxide, or potassium permanganate is required.

Unless there is past experience with a specific water supply, each oxidant must be evaluated using bench-scale jar testing to select the best process conditions.

The pH of the water must be adjusted to an optimum value, determined not only by the solubility of the precipitate but also by its charge. It may be necessary to determine the zeta potential in selecting the optimum pH adjustment. For example, lime is usually more effective than caustic soda at the same pH, and this may very well be attributed to the charge on the particles and charge neutralization.

The optimum pH value will establish detention time—that is, the time required for oxidation to occur at a given concentration (percentage of stoichiometric). A number of relationships involving the concentrations of iron or manganese and the pH, temperature, and oxidant used affect the detention time.

In cases where only iron is present at low concentration, the reaction is almost instantaneous. In other cases, particularly where manganese is present, detention times up to an hour may be required for complete oxidation. If the reaction has not been completed when the water is filtered, the soluble forms will pass through the filter and will later precipitate in the distribution system.

Once the iron has been oxidized and precipitated, the volume of sludge produced must be examined to determine whether the treated water can then be clarified by direct filtration or will require treatment through a sedimentation tank prior to filtration. In general, where the iron is less than 5 mg/L, the oxidized water can be fed directly to a filter. The filter used is either a mixed-media filter provided with air scour devices so that the bed can be kept clean, a pleated membrane filter, or a hollow-fiber membrane operated in a dead-end mode.

Very effective oxidation of iron and manganese can be achieved by using ozone. However, ozone alone is rarely used for this purpose because of the high cost of equipment, operation, and maintenance. Ozone can also be used to control trace organics, if this happens to be a problem in the water. Another factor that must be considered is that excessive amounts of ozone can oxidize manganese to permanganate, which will cause pink water.

Chlorine dioxide is a powerful oxidant, second only to ozone in biocidal efficacy, but without ozone's high costs. Chlorine dioxide does not generate ozonation by-products or biodegradable organic by-products, such as aldehydes and carboxylic acids. A by-product of concern in using chlorine dioxide as an oxidant is the formation of chlorite, a reduction by-product regulated under the Stage 1 D/DBP Rule at 1.0 mg/L maximum contaminant level. Chlorine dioxide instantaneously reacts with soluble iron and manganese to form insoluble precipitates easily removed by filtration.

Potassium permanganate is very effective in oxidizing both iron and manganese, and the reaction is rapid. Another benefit of using permanganate is that it reacts with hydrogen sulfide, cyanides, phenols, and other taste-and-odor compounds if present. Again, no trihalomethanes are known to be formed. Care, however, must be taken not to overfeed permanganate, as purple water will be discharged to the distribution system.

Removal

After the precipitates of iron and manganese are formed by the oxidation process, they are removed by filtration.

Granular Media Filters   Granular media filters are generally used for removing iron and manganese precipitates. If the solids concentration is relatively low (under approximately 5 mg/L), then the water can usually be processed directly by filtration, without sedimentation (Figure 12-3). If the solids concentration is higher, the water must be clarified using a sedimentation step to remove as much precipitate as possible before the water is filtered. Lime is often added to provide alkalinity and facilitate iron precipitation. If the loading is not properly reduced through sedimentation, then filter backwashing will be excessive.

Manganese Greensand Filters   Manganese greensand filters use a special type of medium that removes iron and manganese by a combination of both adsorption and oxidation. In the process, permanganate is added ahead of the greensand filter to allow the grains of the medium to become coated with oxidation products. The oxidized greensand then adsorbs the dissolved iron and manganese from the water, after which the substances are oxidized with permanganate and removed by the filtering action of the filter bed. A potassium permanganate backwash is used to regenerate the bed, or permanganate is fed continuously in a small dose.

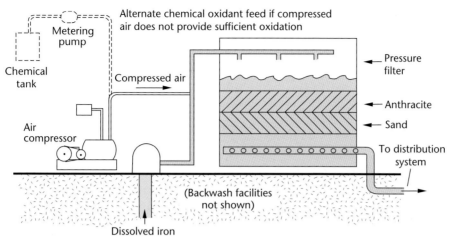

Figure 12-3 Low concentration of iron oxidized with compressed air or oxidant chemical and removed with a pressure filter

Greensand grains are somewhat smaller than silica sand, so the head loss can quickly become excessive under a heavy loading. The length of filter runs can be increased by adding a layer of anthracite above the greensand.

When the lowest concentrations of iron and manganese are required, and when footprint and chemical disposal issues are critical, membrane filtration should be considered. Membrane systems are able to reduce pumping costs by operating without breaking head; that is, the water is pumped directly from the well to the membrane and subsequently to the distribution system without the need to collect filtered water in a clearwell or other storage vessel.

Pleated Membrane Microfiltration An emerging microfiltration technology offers the economy of pleated media filtration with the removal performance of fine membranes. Although the patented pleated filter configuration was specifically designed for iron removal from groundwater, this technology is currently in operation in France, processing 40 million gallons per day (mgd; 150 ML/d) of river water as pretreatment to final-stage nanofilters.

The membrane module, known as Septra XS, is a high-area, coreless, single, open-ended, pleated cartridge with an outside-to-inside flow pattern. The membrane traps within the filter matrix all debris and particles 0.1 micron and larger. The filter system is operated in the dead-end mode at high pressure, which allows treatment without breaking head. Every 2 to 4 hours, air is injected at the feed inlet, mixing with the water in the filter to remove any iron or particulate particles trapped in the filter matrix. This infrequent cleaning maintains a stable flux while keeping recovery at or above 99 percent.

Recovery is the ratio of the volume of product water, or filtrate produced, to the volume of raw water treated. Process recovery is a function of the filtrate flow rate, length of the filtration cycle, and volume of water used in a backwash. At 99 percent recovery, less than 1 percent of feedwater must be handled as waste. The high flow capacity and high-pressure properties of the filter allow the unit to operate without excessive head loss.

Membrane Filtration Hollow-fiber microfiltration and ultrafiltration membrane technology are effective in iron and manganese removal.

Microfiltration systems use uniquely designed filtration modules with a hollow-fiber membrane made of materials such as polyvinylidene fluoride (PVDF).

After suitable oxidation with aeration, chlorine, potassium, permanganate, ozone, or chlorine dioxide, microfiltration systems with pore sizes about 0.1 micron remove turbidity, iron, and manganese from groundwaters.

In the case of PVDF hollow fibers, no requirement exists to remove the oxidant prior to contact with the membrane. The microfiltration systems are highly permeable, resulting in high water production rates with a very small footprint and minimal operator attention.

Ultrafiltration has been showcased together with ozone for iron and manganese removal. Typically cross-flow energy costs make this technology operationally impractical.

In theory, nanofiltration and reverse osmosis remove iron and manganese in a reduced state without oxidation. These technologies are operationally impractical because of membrane fouling concerns, and capital and operating costs.

Sequestration

In the sequestration process, polyphosphates or sodium silicates are added before the water is exposed to air or disinfectants. The total phosphates applied should not exceed the amount specified by the chemical supplier. If effective, sequestration tends to keep iron and manganese soluble in the finished water. Because it does not *remove* the iron and manganese, bacterial slimes may still form in the distribution system as a result of bacterial growth. In addition, a chlorine residual of at least 0.2 mg/L should be maintained in the system at all times.

Sequestration is effective only for groundwater with a relatively low level of dissolved iron and manganese and no dissolved oxygen. It is not usually recommended if the concentration of iron, manganese, or a combination of the two exceeds 1.0 mg/L.

Study Questions

1. Virgin greensand can be regenerated by soaking the filter bed for several hours in a solution of chlorine containing
   a. 50 mg/L Cl_2.
   b. 75 mg/L Cl_2.
   c. 100 mg/L Cl_2.
   d. 200 mg/L Cl_2.

2. Which process works best for sequestering manganese?
   a. Sodium silicate alone
   b. Sodium silicate and chlorine
   c. Polyphosphates alone
   d. Polyphosphates and chlorine

3. When should polyphosphates used for sequestration of iron and manganese from a well be injected into the process?
   a. Right after disinfection
   b. Immediately after aeration to remove unwanted gases
   c. Right after clarification
   d. Right after the water leaves the well

4. Which oxidant should be fed as early as possible in the treatment process to allow for complete reaction before it enters the distribution system?
   a. Ozone
   b. Chlorine dioxide
   c. Chloramines
   d. Potassium permanganate

5. Which adverse effects does the secondary contaminant manganese have?
   a. Unappealing to drink, undesirable taste, and possible indication of corrosion
   b. Discolored laundry and changed taste of water, coffee, tea, and other beverages
   c. Undesirable metallic taste and possible indication of corrosion
   d. Added total dissolved solids and scale, indication of sewage contamination and tastes

6. When they are oxidized, iron and manganese change and discolor water from_____, depending on their concentration and the presence or absence of other contaminants.
   a. turbid yellow to black
   b. clear to yellow
   c. clear to white
   d. dark yellow to white

7. The presence of iron or manganese in the distribution system often
   a. reduces the need for chlorine.
   b. provides a food source for bacterial growth.
   c. rids the system of bacteria.
   d. improves taste-and-odor problems.

8. What type of filter uses a special type of medium that removes iron and manganese by a combination of both adsorption and oxidation?

9. Process recovery is a function of the filtrate flow rate, length of the filtration cycle, and what other factor?

10. What is sequestration?

Chapter 13

Fluoridation

Fluoride is an ion from the element fluorine. It is a constituent of the earth's crust and consequently is found naturally, to some degree, in all drinking water sources. A small amount of fluoride in the diet is essential for proper tooth and bone formation.

Fluoride may be found in drinking water as a natural contaminant or as an additive intended to provide public health protection from dental caries. **Fluoridation** is the deliberate adjustment of the fluoride concentration in a public water supply. Some public water supplies contain naturally occurring fluoride. Many bottled water products contain fluoride ranging from levels barely detectable to levels higher than 1.3 mg/L. The benefits of fluoride in reducing tooth decay were discovered through comparisons of the teeth of children from areas that have different concentrations of natural fluoride in their drinking water. Fluoridation is a safe, effective, and economical process endorsed by the American Dental Association, the American Water Works Association, and public health groups worldwide.

The Centers for Disease Control and Prevention keeps statistics on the number of people in the United States who receive drinking water with added fluoride. An update in 2006 showed that out of the approximately 266,000,000 people served by community water systems in this country; slightly more than 184,000,000 (about 69 percent) received fluoridated drinking water.

Process Description

Reasons for Fluoridation

At optimal levels, fluoride can greatly reduce the incidence of tooth decay among children. The amount of fluoride consumed with drinking water is generally based on the total amount of water consumed each day. Water consumption usually depends on the temperature in a region; people in warm climates tend to drink more water than people in cold climates. Consequently, the optimal fluoride concentration in drinking water varies across the country and is set in relation to the average air temperature. The fluoride levels shown in Table 13-1 are for annual averages of maximum daily air temperatures, which must be determined for a 5-year period. Each state health department uses this information to establish optimal fluoride levels for the state.

To achieve the maximum benefits of fluoridation, the optimal fluoride concentration in the water supply must be continuously maintained. A drop of only 0.3 mg/L below optimal can reduce fluoride's benefits by as much as two-thirds.

fluoride
An ion from the element fluorine. It is a constituent of the earth's crust and consequently is found naturally, to some degree, in all drinking water sources. A small amount of fluoride in the diet is essential for proper tooth and bone formation.

fluoridation
The water treatment process in which a chemical is added to the water to increase the concentration of fluoride ions to an optimal level. The purpose of fluoridation is to reduce the incidence of dental cavities in children.

Table 13-1 Optimal fluoride concentrations

Annual Average of Maximum Daily Air Temperature,*		Recommended Control Limits of Fluoride Concentration, mg/L		
°F	°C	Lower	Optimal	Upper
53.7 and below	12.0 and below	0.9	1.2	1.7
53.8–58.3	12.1–14.6	0.8	1.1	1.5
58.4–63.8	14.7–17.6	0.8	1.0	1.3
63.9–70.6	17.7–21.4	0.7	0.9	1.2
70.7–79.2	21.5–26.2	0.7	0.8	1.0
79.3–90.5	26.3–32.5	0.6	0.7	0.8

*Based on temperature data for a minimum of 5 years.

However, concentrations above 1.5 mg/L over the optimal level do not significantly reduce tooth decay any further and can cause mottling of the teeth.

Effects of Excessive Fluoride in Water

Surface water normally contains only trace amounts of fluoride; groundwater often contains fluoride near the optimal level. Some wells have fluoride levels up to four or five times the optimal level. When children are exposed to excessive levels of fluoride, a condition known as fluorosis occurs. In its mildest form, fluorosis appears as very slight, opaque, whitish areas (called mottling) on the tooth surface. More severe fluorosis causes teeth to darken, turning from shades of gray to black. When the fluoride concentration is over 4 mg/L, teeth are likely to be pitted; they then become more susceptible to cavities and wear. Studies have shown that fluorosis starts to occur when children younger than 8 years old regularly drink water containing twice the optimal fluoride level for 3 months or longer.

When a water source contains fluoride concentrations slightly higher than optimal, the water utility may be required to provide periodic public notification to warn customers that fluorosis may occur in their children's teeth. If levels exceed the maximum contaminant level, the utility must stop supplying the water to the public. Details of regulations concerning excessive fluoride are provided in Chapter 14.

Fluoridation Facilities

The facilities used for fluoridation are similar to those used for feeding other water treatment chemicals. The type of equipment depends primarily on how much water is to be treated and the type of chemical being used.

Fluoride Chemicals

The following three chemical compounds are used for fluoridation:

1. Sodium fluoride
2. Fluorosilicic acid
3. Sodium fluorosilicate

The characteristics of these compounds are summarized in Table 13-2. Only chemicals meeting applicable standards should be used for addition to potable water.

fluorosis
Staining or pitting of the teeth due to excessive amounts of fluoride in the water.

Table 13-2 Characteristics of fluoride compounds

Item	Sodium Fluoride, NaF	Sodium Fluorosilicate, Na$_2$SiF$_6$	Fluorosilicic Acid, H$_2$SiF$_6$
Form	Powder or crystal	Powder or very fine crystal	Liquid
Molecular weight	42.00	118.1	144.08
Commercial purity, %	97–98	98–99	20–30
Fluoride ion, % (100% pure material)	45.25	60.7	79.2
Pounds required per mil gal for 1.0 ppm F at indicated purity	18.8, 98%	14.0, 98.5%	35.2, 30%
pH of saturated solution	7.0	3.5–4.0	1.2 (1% solution)
Sodium ion contributed at 1.0 ppm F, ppm	1.17	0.40	0.00
F ion storage space, ft^3/100 lb	22–34	23–30	54–73
Solubility at 77°F, g/100 mL water	4.0	0.762	Infinite
Weight, lb/ft^3	65–90	85–95	10.5 lb/gal, 30%
Shipping containers	100-lb bags, 125- to 400-lb fiber drums, bulk	100-lb bags, 125- to 400-lb fiber drums, bulk	13-gal carboys, 55-gal drums, bulk

Because of the relatively small quantities of chemicals required to maintain the optimal dosage, chemical costs for fluoridation are very small in relation to the overall operation cost of a water system.

Sodium Fluoride

The first compound used in practicing controlled fluoridation was sodium fluoride (NaF), which is still widely used today. It is a white, odorless material that comes as free-flowing crystals or in a coarse crystalline form.

The solubility of sodium fluoride is an almost constant 4 g NaF/100 mL water within the common range of water temperatures of 32–77°F (0–25°C). It is available in 100-lb (45-kg) multiply paper bags, in drums that hold up to 400 lb (180 kg), and in bulk.

Additional information can be found in AWWA B701, Standard for Sodium Fluoride.

Fluorosilicic Acid

Fluorosilicic acid (H$_2$SiF$_6$), otherwise known as hydrofluorosilicic acid, is a clear, colorless to straw-yellow-colored, fuming, and very corrosive liquid. It has a pungent odor, can cause skin irritation, and will even etch glass.

All commercial solutions of fluorosilicic acid have a low pH, ranging from 1.0 to 1.5. In highly alkaline waters, the addition of the acid usually will not appreciably affect the pH of the treated water. However, in low-alkaline (poorly buffered) waters, the addition of fluorosilicic acid can reduce the pH, so its use is not recommended without a study of the possible side effects.

Fluorosilicic acid is available in 13-gal (50-L) or 55-gal (210-L) drums for small users, and in tank cars or trucks for large users. Because it contains a high proportion of water (about 70 percent), fluorosilicic acid is costly to ship

sodium fluoride
A dry chemical used in the fluoridation of drinking water. It is commonly used in saturators.

fluorosilicic acid
A strongly acidic liquid used to fluoridate drinking water.

compared to the dry chemicals. However, the greater ease of feeding a liquid that is already prepared more than offsets this disadvantage for many users.

If the acid must be diluted, care should be taken to avoid dilutions between the ranges of 10 to 1 and 20 to 1 (parts water to parts acid). Within these ranges, an insoluble silica precipitate often forms, which can clog feeders, orifices, and other equipment.

Additional information can be found in AWWA B703, Standard for Fluorosilicic Acid.

Sodium Fluorosilicate

The most inexpensive chemical available for fluoridation is **sodium fluorosilicate** (Na_2SiF_6), formerly known as sodium silicofluoride. It is a white or yellowish-white, slightly hygroscopic, crystalline powder with limited solubility in water. Although odorless, it has an acidic taste.

Unlike sodium fluoride, its solubility decreases as water temperature decreases. At 60–70°F (16–21°C), it takes 60 gal (230 L) of water to dissolve 1 lb (0.45 kg) of sodium fluorosilicate. The pH of the saturated solution is quite low, between 3.0 and 4.0, but this is not a problem because the solution is diluted once it is added to drinking water. Sodium fluorosilicate is available in the same size containers as sodium fluoride.

Additional information can be found in AWWA B702, Standard for Sodium Fluorosilicate.

Chemical Feeders

Fluoride is fed into the water system by either a dry feed system or a solution feed system. Either system will feed a specific quantity of chemical into the water at a preset rate. Table 13-3 lists the required equipment and other characteristics for several methods of feeding fluoride.

Dry Feeders

A dry feeder meters a dry powder or crystalline chemical at a given rate. It is typically used to add fluoride to systems that produce 1 mgd (3.8 ML/d) or more. The two basic types are volumetric and gravimetric dry feeders.

Volumetric feeders (Figures 13-1 and 13-2) are simple to operate and less expensive to purchase and maintain than gravimetric feeders. However, they are usually less accurate. The feed mechanism delivers the same volume of dry chemical to the dissolving tank for each complete revolution of the screw or roll. Varying the speed of rotation varies the feed rate.

Gravimetric dry feeders can deliver large quantities and are extremely accurate, but they are relatively expensive. They can readily be adapted to automatic control and recording. The belt-type feeder (Figure 13-3) delivers a certain weight of material for each revolution of the conveyor belt. The feed rate is adjusted by varying the speed of the belt. The loss-of-weight–type feeder (Figure 13-4) matches the weight lost by the feed hopper to the preset weight of the required dosage. Because gravimetric feeders control the weight of material, not the volume, variations in density have no effect on feed rate. This accounts for the extreme accuracy of this type of feeder.

The steady stream of dry material discharged from a dry feeder falls into a solution chamber or tank, where it is dissolved into water. The tank is usually equipped with a mixer to ensure that the chemical is thoroughly dissolved. The resulting fluoride solution either flows by gravity into the clearwell or is pumped

sodium fluorosilicate

A dry chemical used in the fluoridation of drinking water. It is derived from fluorosilicic acid.

Table 13-3 Fluoridation checklist

Operating Parameters	Sodium Fluoride, Manual Solution Preparation	Sodium Fluoride, Automatic Solution Preparation	Fluorosilicic Acid, Diluted	Fluorosilicic Acid, 23–30%	Sodium Fluorosilicate Dry Feed	Sodium Fluoride, Dry Feed
Water flow rate	Less than 500 gpm (2,000 L/m)	Less than 2,000 gpm (7,500 L/m)	Less than 500 gpm (2,000 L/m)	More than 500 gpm (2,000 L/m)	More than 100 gpm (400 L/m)	More than 2 mgd (8 ML/d)
Population served by system or each well of multiple-well system	Less than 5,000	Less than 10,000	Less than 10,000	More than 10,000	More than 10,000	More than 50,000
Equipment required	Solution feeder, mixing tank, scales, mixer	Solution feeder, saturator, water meter	Solution feeder, scales, measuring container, mixing tank, mixer	Solution feeder, day tank, scales, transfer pump	Volumetric dry feeder, scales, hopper, dissolving chamber	Gravimetric dry feeder, hopper, dissolving chamber
Feed accuracy	Depends on solution preparation and feeder	Depends on feeder	Depends on solution preparation and feeder	Depends on feeder	Usually within 3%	Usually within 1%
Chemical specifications and availability	Crystalline NaF, dust-free, in bags or drums; generally available	Downflow: coarse crystalline NaF in bags or drums, may be scarce. Upflow: fine crystalline NaF, generally available	Low-silica or fortified acid in drums or carboys; generally available	Bulk acid in tank cars or trucks; available on contract	Powder in bags, drums, or bulk; generally available	
Handling requirements	Weighing, mixing, measuring	Dumping whole bags only	Pouring or siphoning, measuring, mixing, weighing	All handling by pump	Bag loaders or bulk-handling equipment required	
Feeding point	Injection into filter effluent line or main	Injection into filter effluent line or main	Injection into filter effluent line or main	Injection into filter effluent line or main	Gravity feed from dissolving chamber into open flume or clearwell, pressure feed into filter effluent line or main	
Other requirements	Solution water may require softening	Solution water may require softening	Dilution water may require softening	Acid-proof storage tank, piping, etc.	Dry storage area, dust collectors, dissolving-chamber mixers, hopper agitators, eductors, etc.	
Hazards	Dust, spillage, solution preparation error	Dust, spillage	Corrosion, fumes, spillage, solution preparation error	Corrosion, fumes, leakage	Dust, spillage, arching, and flooding in feeder and hopper	

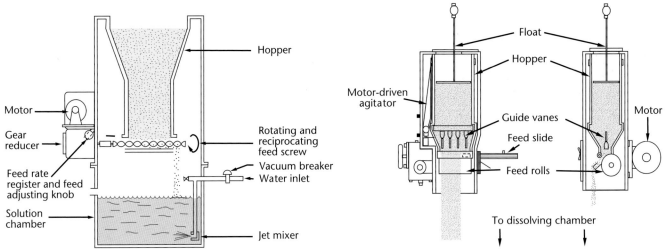

Figure 13-1 Screw-type volumetric dry feeder

Figure 13-2 Roll-type volumetric dry feeder

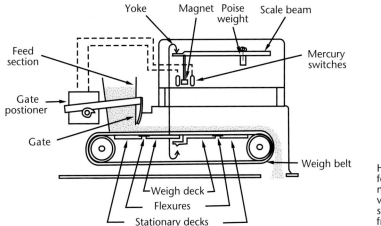

Figure 13-3 Belt-type gravimetric dry feeder

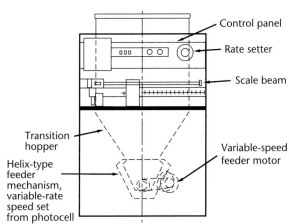

Figure 13-4 Loss-of-weight–type gravimetric dry feeder

into a pressure pipeline. Either of the dry chemicals can be used in a dry feeder, but sodium fluorosilicate is most often used for dry chemical feed because it is less expensive.

Solution Feeders

Solution feeders are often the most economical way for water systems to fluoridate water (Table 13-3). The feeders are small pumps that feed a sodium fluoride or fluorosilicic acid solution from a tank or saturator into the water system at a preset rate.

Diaphragm pumps and piston pumps are normally used for fluoride feed because they are accurate and can operate against a pressure if the chemical is being fed into a pipeline.

Diaphragm pumps are the same as those used for hypochlorination systems. They consist of a flexible pumping diaphragm made of rubber, plastic, or thin metal, which is actuated by a reciprocating shaft driven by a cam. To vary the feed rate, either the cam speed or the pump shaft stroke is adjusted. The pumps can usually be electronically controlled based on flow rate.

Piston pumps are similar, but instead have a rigid piston that moves back and forth within a cylinder that serves as the metering chamber. By varying the stroke length, the pump can vary the feed rate. Some piston pumps are capable of delivering chemicals at very low rates and against high pressure.

Manual Solution Feed

The manual solution feed method, as shown in Figure 13-5, is sometimes used by small systems feeding sodium fluoride. The chemical is added to the mixing tank for dissolving. Then the concentrated solution is transferred to the day tank and fed by a metering pump. The day tank is placed on a platform scale, which allows one to determine how much solution is fed. The major disadvantage of this system is that the sodium fluoride must be manually weighed and added to the mixing tank

Saturators

A saturator retains the simplicity of the manual feed system but eliminates the disadvantage of constant chemical handling. The principle behind the saturator is that a saturated solution of 40 g/L sodium fluoride will result if water at normal temperatures is allowed to trickle through a bed of sodium fluoride crystals. In other words, no matter how much chemical is in the saturator tank, the fluoride solution will stabilize at 4 percent. This solution of known concentration can then be pumped to the water supply at a controlled rate by a metering pump. A saturator is ideal for small systems because of its low initial cost, low maintenance requirements, and ease of operation.

There are two types of saturators. Upflow saturators (Figure 13-6A) have water introduced at the bottom of a 50-gal (190-L) polyethylene tank beneath crystals of sodium fluoride. The water moves slowly upward, forming the saturated solution.

Downflow saturators (Figure 13-6B) are constructed so that the sodium fluoride crystals rest on a bed of sand and gravel, which in turn rests on a collection system, such as a perforated pipe manifold. Water enters the top of the tank and moves slowly through the chemical layer; it is a saturated solution by the time it reaches the collection manifold. The layer of sodium fluoride crystals should be maintained at least 6 in. (150 mm) thick.

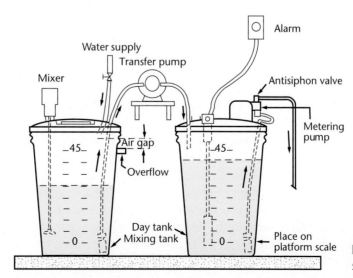

Figure 13-5 Manual solution feed installation

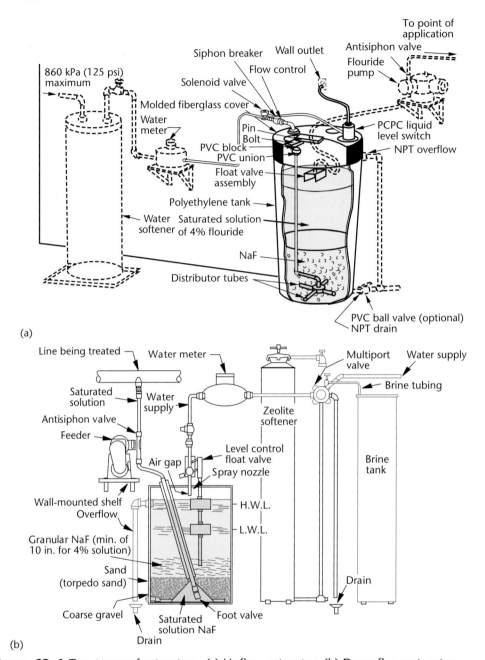

Figure 13-6 Two types of saturators. (a) Upflow saturator. (b) Downflow saturator.

Acid Feed Systems

An acid feed system is generally the simplest installation. Fluorosilicic acid can be fed directly from the shipping container into the water supply, as shown in Figure 13-7. The shipping container rests on a scale, which allows one to determine the amount of acid used. However, for water systems treating less than 500 gpm (32 L/sec), it is usually impractical to feed the acid directly from the container because the metering pump cannot be set at a low enough rate to provide a constant feed. In those cases, the dilution system shown in Figure 13-8 can be used. The acid is then diluted to one-half strength or some other proportion, so the metering pump can be operated at a moderate rate.

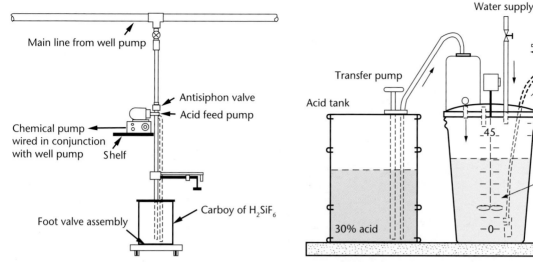

Figure 13-7 Acid feed installation

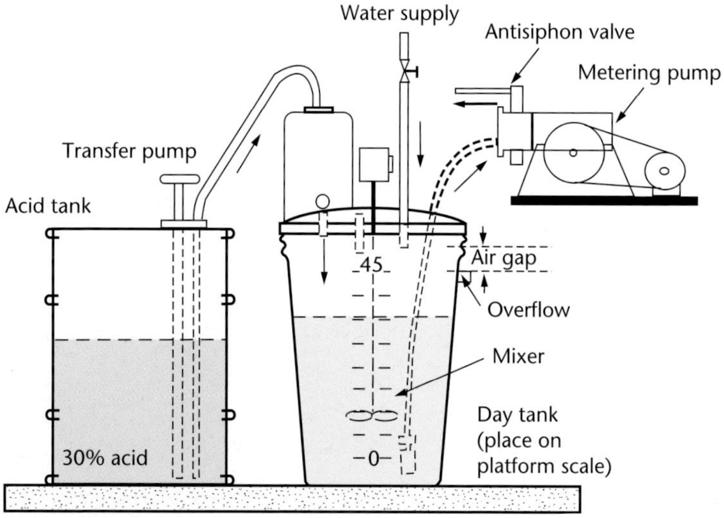

Figure 13-8 Diluted-acid feed system

Larger water systems purchase fluorosilicic acid in tank truck loads and store it in large tanks. In this case, the acid is normally pumped periodically from storage to a day tank on a scale, so that the amount used can be monitored. From there it is metered to the water supply.

Auxiliary Equipment

The following are descriptions of the more common types of auxiliary equipment used with the feed systems described in this chapter.

Scales

Scales are needed for determining the quantity of solution being fed and the quantity of dry fluoride compound or acid delivered by the feeders. They are necessary in all systems except those using saturators. The most common type is the platform scale, on which a solution tank, a carboy of acid, or an entire volumetric dry feeder is placed.

The scale must have sufficient capacity to weigh a full tank and give measurements to the nearest pound (half kilogram) or better. An example of a platform scale installation is shown in Figure 13-9.

Softeners

When sodium fluoride solutions are used with hard water, insoluble compounds of calcium and magnesium fluoride can form. These compounds can clog the feeder, the feeder suction line, the gravel bed in a downflow saturator, and other equipment.

For this reason, water being fed a sodium fluoride solution should be softened if the hardness exceeds 75 mg/L as calcium carbonate. Only the water used in preparing the solution (the makeup water) need be softened. Because this amount of water is quite small, a household-type ion exchange water softener is usually adequate. It can be installed directly in the pipeline used for solution makeup (Figure 13-6A).

Figure 13-9 Platform scale installation

Dissolving Tanks

The dry chemical discharged from a feeder must be continuously dissolved in a chamber located beneath the feeder. This chamber, referred to as the *solution pot*, *dissolving tank*, *solution tank*, or *dissolving chamber*, may be a part of the feeder or may be a separate unit. The chemical can be pumped to the water system only when it is completely dissolved. Slurry feed cannot be used because the buildup of undissolved chemical can cause inaccurate feed rates and clogging and deposits in the tanks or water system.

Mixers

Whenever solutions are prepared, it is important that the solution be thoroughly mixed. A fractional horsepower mixer with a stainless-steel shaft and propeller is satisfactory for preparing sodium fluoride solution. All immersed parts of a mixer used for fluorosilicic acid must be plastic coated or made of a corrosion-resistant alloy.

A jet mixer, like the one illustrated in Figure 13-1, is sometimes used for dissolving sodium fluorosilicate, but a mechanical mixer is usually preferred. Because of sodium fluorosilicate's low solubility, particularly in cold water, and the limited detention time in the dissolving tank, violent agitation is usually necessary to prevent discharge of a slurry. Mechanical mixers should never be used in conjunction with saturators.

Water Meters

The solution makeup water for a saturator must be metered for the fluoride feed rates to be determined accurately (Figure 13-6). Because the flow is very small, the smallest available meter is usually sufficient.

Flowmeters

Measuring the total flow through a treatment plant serves two important functions for effective fluoridation. First, the meter indicates the flow rates at which the feeder must be set to provide the correct concentration. Second, it can be designed to provide a signal that will allow automatic adjustment (known as *pacing*) of the feed rates so that those rates will be proportional to flow.

Day Storage Tanks

A day storage tank is a plastic tank that holds enough fluoride solution for one day, or in the case of a large plant, enough for one shift. A tank is essential for large systems that feed acid from bulk storage. Acid is siphoned or pumped into the small tank located on a platform scale, and from there it is metered to the system. As shown in Figures 13-5 and 13-8, day tanks are also used with manual solution and diluted-acid feed systems.

Hoppers

Most dry feeders come equipped with a small hopper. In large installations, an additional or extension hopper is provided over the main hopper to provide more storage capacity. As shown in Figure 13-10 this extension hopper is located one floor over the feeder. The chemicals are then stored on the upper floor and can be conveniently loaded into the hopper.

In small plants, the hopper should be large enough to hold slightly more than one bag or drum of chemical. A hopper that holds less than one bag will cause additional dust and spillage when partially filled bags are handled. Hoppers for large plants are designed to hold several bags at one time. An electric vibrator should be installed on the hopper to keep the chemicals flowing and to prevent "bridging."

Bag Loaders

A bag loader is usually necessary when the hopper of a dry feeder is directly above the feeder and the operator must lift the bag of chemical a considerable height to fill the hopper. A bag loader is a hopper extension large enough to hold a single bag of chemical (Figure 13-11). The front of the loader is hinged to swing

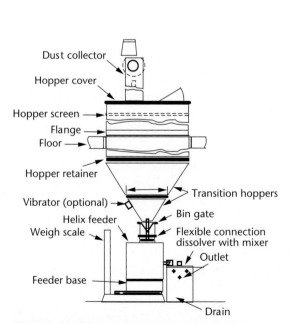

Figure 13-10 Dry feed hoppers and dust collectors

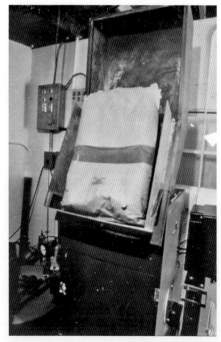

Figure 13-11 Bag loader

down to a more accessible height. The operator fastens the bag by running an attached rod through the bottom of the bag. The bag is then opened, and the loader is swung back into position. Although this device minimizes dust, the operator should still wear a dust mask during the operation.

Dust Collectors and Wet Scrubbers

The handling of powdered dry chemicals always generates dust. When small quantities of fluoride are being handled, ordinary care will minimize dust, and good housekeeping plus an exhaust fan will keep the storage and loading areas relatively dust-free. However, when larger quantities are handled, dust prevention and collection facilities should be provided.

A dust canopy, completely enclosing the hopper-filling area and equipped with an exhaust fan, will prevent dust from spreading throughout the loading area. Dust filters are incorporated into the exhaust system to prevent dust from escaping into the air outside the plant. The hoppers on some large feeders have dust collectors and exhaust fans incorporated into the hopper unit.

Wet scrubbers can also be used to remove dust from exhausted air. The air flows through a chamber in which there is a continuous water spray. The air is thus "scrubbed" clean, and the dust particles are carried down the drain with the wastewater.

Weight Recorders

If a platform scale is used to weigh the dry chemicals or solutions, a recorder can be attached to keep a record of the weight of chemical fed. Many volumetric dry feeders have recorders available as an accessory along with the scale.

Alarms

Alarms can be included with either solution or dry feed systems to alert the operator of problems, such as a low level in the solution day tank or a low dry-chemical level in the feeder hopper. The alarms are triggered by level switches, flow switches, or pressure switches.

Vacuum Breakers

A cross-connection is possible whenever there is a water connection to a chemical solution. That is, under certain conditions, concentrated chemicals could flow back into the potable water system. Particularly vulnerable locations are the supply line to a dissolving tank or the discharge of a solution feeder.

The simplest way to prevent backflow is to provide an air gap in the water fill connection. An air gap is a vertical separation between the water line and the tank or device receiving the water (Figures 13-5 and 13-8).

When pressure must be maintained in the system, a vacuum breaker (or antisiphon device) must be used. This is a valve that is kept closed by water pressure. However, if the water pressure fails, the valve opens to the atmosphere so that the chemical will not be siphoned into the water system. The vacuum breaker should be installed as close to the chemical feeder as possible. In some states, mechanical vacuum breakers are not permitted and air gaps must be used.

Study Questions

1. Teeth are likely to become pitted when the fluoride concentration in drinking water goes above which amount?
   a. 3 mg/L
   b. 4 mg/L
   c. 5 mg/L
   d. 6 mg/L

2. Sodium fluoride
   a. was once called silly acid.
   b. is a straw yellow color.
   c. has a solution pH of about 1.0 pH units.
   d. is odorless.

3. How often should the fluoride concentration of treated water be measured?
   a. Every 8 hours
   b. Every 12 hours
   c. Every day
   d. Continuously

4. Which is the commercial purity of fluorosilicic acid?
   a. 20–30%
   b. 20–40%
   c. 30–40%
   d. 35–48%

5. Which type of fluoride chemical should be used in downflow saturators?
   a. Tablets of sodium fluorosilicate
   b. Granular sodium silicofluoride
   c. Crystalline sodium fluoride
   d. Powdered sodium fluoride

6. A small amount of fluoride in the diet is essential for
   a. proper tooth and bone formation.
   b. healthy skin.
   c. sharp vision.
   d. a healthy heart.

7. Fluoride is fed into the water system by either a solution feed system or a(n)
   a. acid feed system.
   b. dry feed system.
   c. manual feed system.
   d. continuous feed system.

8. A small amount of fluoride in the diet serves what essential anatomical function?

9. What is the most inexpensive chemical available for fluoridation?

10. Compared to gravimetric feeders, what are two advantages of volumetric feeders?

Chapter 14
Water Quality Testing

Water Quality Monitoring

All public water systems monitor water quality to some extent. Small systems with consistently good-quality water from deep wells may need to provide only occasional monitoring. Because surface water is more prone to variations in water quality, systems using surface-water sources are required to monitor their water on a more frequent or continuous basis than systems using groundwater.

Water quality is monitored to meet federal, state, and local requirements and for process control. The contaminants that are monitored under US Environmental Protection Agency (USEPA) requirements are extensive, and public water systems must monitor water quality to ensure proper and economic treatment as well as to comply with regulations.

Sampling

Importance of Sampling

Sampling is a vital part of monitoring the quality of water in a water treatment process, distribution system, and supply source. As such, water plant operators take samples every day. Water in the plant and the distribution system is sampled frequently for two reasons: to ensure the water is safe for human consumption through compliance testing and to measure the efficiency of the treatment process.

Errors can occur easily when recording water quality information. Every precaution must be taken to ensure that the sample collected is as representative as is feasible of the water source or process being examined. Water treatment decisions based on incorrect data may be made if sampling is not correctly performed. Representative analytical results depend on the water treatment plant operator ensuring that

- the sample is representative of the water source under consideration,
- the proper sampling techniques are used,
- the samples are protected and preserved until they are analyzed, and
- the proper sample containers are used.

Types of Samples

Improper sampling is a common cause of error in water quality analysis. Because the results of an analysis can show only what is actually in the sample, the sample must have the same content as the water from which it was taken. Water laboratory analysts refer to this as a **representative sample**, and it is achieved through the use of grab samples, composite sample, or continuous sampling.

representative sample

A sample containing all the constituents that are in the water from which it was taken.

283

Grab Samples   A grab sample is a single-volume sample collected at one time from one place. An operator taking a 100-mL sample from a distribution system for bacteriological analysis is taking a grab sample. Similarly, an operator taking a few milliliters of settled water for turbidity analysis is taking a grab sample. As such, these samples represent the quality of water in those locations only at the time that the sample was obtained.

A grab sample may be preferred over a composite sample when

- the water to be sampled does not flow on a continuous basis,
- the water's characteristics are relatively constant, or
- the water is to be analyzed for water quality indicators that may change with time, such as dissolved gases, coliform bacteria, residual chlorine, disinfection by-products, temperature, volatile organics, certain radiological parameters, and pH.

A grab sample might not give an accurate representation of the quality (over time) of a flowing river that is subject to intermittent pollution from upstream wastewater plants or chance rainfall events.

Figures 14-1 and 14-2 illustrate this point. Figure 14-1 shows the changes in surface water dissolved oxygen (DO) over a 24-hour period. A grab sample represents the DO level only at the time the sample was taken. DO can change rapidly—for example, because of the growth of algae or plants in the water (diurnal effect). Online process instruments are good examples of instruments that perform grab sample analyses; they analyze a continuous string of grab samples and produce a series of individual analyses that, when plotted, illustrate trends such as those in the figures.

Figure 14-2 shows that levels of total dissolved solids (TDS) in the same water change very little. A grab sample can be representative of the water quality in a stable supply such as a deep well for perhaps a month. TDS levels are a function of the minerals dissolved from rocks and soil as the water passes over or through them and may change only in relation to seasonal runoff patterns. The TDS in groundwater (e.g., wells) may also change if certain water-bearing zones in the well become plugged, changing the dilution or zones from which the water is being drawn.

grab sample
A single water sample collected at one time from a single point.

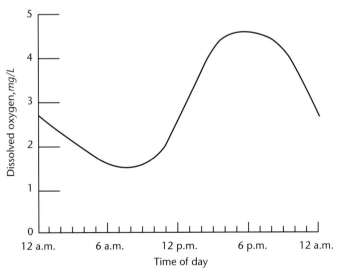

Figure 14-1 Example of hourly changes in dissolved oxygen for a surface water source

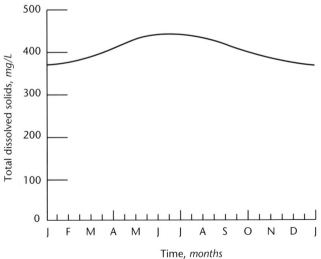

Figure 14-2 Example of monthly changes in total dissolved solids for the surface water source shown in Figure 14-1

Composite Samples   In many processes, water quality changes with time. A continuous sampler–analyzer provides the most accurate results in these cases. Often the operator is the sampler–analyzer, and continuous analysis could prove costly. A Except for tests that cannot wait because of rapid physical, chemical, or biological changes of the sample (such as tests for DO, pH, and temperature), a fair compromise may be reached by taking samples throughout the day at hourly or 2-hour intervals. Each sample should be refrigerated immediately after collection. At the end of 24 hours, each sample is vigorously mixed and a portion of each sample is then withdrawn and mixed with the other samples. The size of the portion is in direct proportion to the flow when the sample was collected (aliquot) and the total size of sample needed for testing. For example, if hourly samples are collected when the flow is 1.2 mgd, use a 12-mL portion of the sample, and when the flow is 1.5 mgd, use a 15-mL portion of the sample. The resulting mixture of portions of samples is a **composite sample**.

An example of a time-composite sample is 100-mL samples of backwash water taken at 1-minute intervals for the length of the wash and mixed together to measure total solids. When the samples are taken, they can either be set aside or combined as they are collected. In both cases, they should be stored at a temperature of less than 40°F (4°C) but above freezing until they are analyzed.

Flow-proportional composite samples consist of different volumes of sample taken from the same location at different times; the volume collected each time is dependent on the flow rate of the water at the sample location. When composite samples of raw water in a water treatment plant are needed and the raw water flow rate varies over the day, a proportional composite sample is sometimes taken because it more accurately represents the water quality over time.

Composite samples allow the laboratory analyst to determine the average concentration of a constituent over time, without having to perform the analysis every time a sample is taken. Automatic samplers can be used to take samples at night, which enables the chemist who comes to work in the morning to perform the analysis.

There are drawbacks to composite samples. The high and low points, or ranges, of a contaminant cannot be known because they are averaged. Also, some constituents, such as pH, dissolved gases, chlorine residual, and temperature, begin to change immediately after the sample is taken and therefore should not be composited. Bacteriological samples, such as those taken for coliform analysis, must always be taken as grab samples because the number of bacteria in the samples begins to change immediately after sampling. *In no instance should a composite sample be collected for bacteriological examination.*

Continuous Sampling   This type of sampling is used in online or process control sampling devices/instruments. Some of the new regulations call for this type of sampling for the larger systems for chlorine residual under the new Ground Water Rule (GWR) and for surface water filtration or groundwater under the direct influence of surface water (GWUDI) filtration systems. Continuous sampling is used in certain circumstances to monitor distribution systems for chlorine levels and for other parameters associated with security monitoring. It is also used by larger systems on the incoming surface water for turbidity, pH, and streaming current measurements for treatment control. As technology becomes more sophisticated and affordable, this type of monitoring will become more prevalent in the industry. Some systems use this technology to monitor levels of nitrate and other specific ions during the treatment process and fluoride levels of water leaving the treatment facility. Examples of the online instruments are shown in Figures 14-3 and 14-4.

composite sample
A series of individual or grab samples taken at different times from the same sampling point and mixed together.

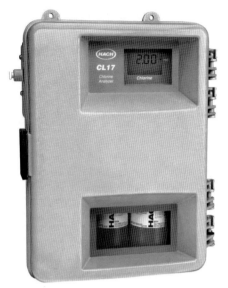

Figure 14-3 Online chlorine residual analyzer
Courtesy of HACH Inc.

Figure 14-4 Online particle counter
Courtesy of HACH Inc.

Sampling Point Selection

Careful selection of representative sample points is an important step in developing a sampling procedure that will accurately reflect water quality. The criteria used to select a sample point depend on the type of water sampled and the purpose of the testing. Check with primacy regulations as to *compliance samples* versus *process samples*. Any sample taken from a *compliance sample tap* may have to be reported as a *performance sample* even if it is just being collected for process control. Samples are generally collected from three broad types of areas:

- Raw-water supply
- Treatment plant
- Distribution system

These first two areas are discussed below.

Raw-Water Sample Points The choice of collection points for raw-water samples depends on the type of system being sampled. There are at least three general types of systems:

- Raw-water transmission lines
- Groundwater (wells)
- Rivers, reservoirs, and lakes

Raw-water transmission lines and groundwater sources are sampled directly from the transmission line or well-discharge pipe. After a sampling point has been selected (prior to any chemical addition or treatment), the pipeline is equipped with a small sample valve or tap, often called a *sample cock* (Figure 14-5). The valve must be fully opened before sampling to flush out any standing water and accumulated sediment. The flow may then be adjusted to achieve the optimal flow for the type of sample being collected. For example, a slow, steady stream to prevent aeration is best for analysis of volatile organics or DO.

Most of the physical factors known to promote mixing in surface waters are absent or are much less effective in groundwater systems. Wells usually draw

Figure 14-5 Sample cock attached to pipeline for sampling

water from a considerable thickness of saturated rock and often from several different strata. These water components are mixed by the turbulent flow of water in the well before they reach the surface and become available for sampling. Most techniques for well sampling and exploration are usable only in unfinished or nonoperating wells. Usually the only means of sampling the water tapped by a well is to collect a pumped sample. The operator is cautioned to remember that well pumps and casings can contribute to sample contamination. If a pump has not run for an extended period of time prior to sampling, the water collected may not be representative of the normal water quality. Good records of static and pumping levels of the wells should be kept to determine if the well is performing as designed and when the sample should be drawn to be representative of the water in the well column.

Rivers To adequately determine the composition of a flowing stream, each sample (or set of samples taken at the same time) must be representative of the entire flow at the sampling point at that instant. The sampling process must be repeated at a frequency sufficient to show changes of water quality that may occur over time in the water passing the sampling point.

On small- or medium-sized streams, it is usually possible to find a sampling point at which the composition of the water is presumably uniform at all depths and across the stream. Obtaining representative samples in these streams is relatively simple. For larger streams, more than one sample may be required. A portable conductivity meter is very useful in selecting good sample sites.

Reservoirs and Lakes Water stored in reservoirs and lakes is usually poorly mixed. Thermal stratification and associated depth changes in water composition (such as DO) are among the most frequently observed effects. Single samples can therefore be assumed to represent only the spot of water from which the sample came. Therefore, several samples must be collected at different depths and from different areas of the impoundment to accurately sample reservoirs and lakes. See Figures 14-6 and 14-7.

Treatment Plant Sample Points Treatment plants are sampled to evaluate the treatment efficiency of unit processes or to evaluate operational changes. Selection of in-plant sample points is an important step in developing an overall process control program for a water treatment plant. Samples from the points selected can be tested to determine the efficiency of the various treatment processes. The test results will also help to indicate operational changes that will improve contaminant removal efficiencies or reduce operating costs.

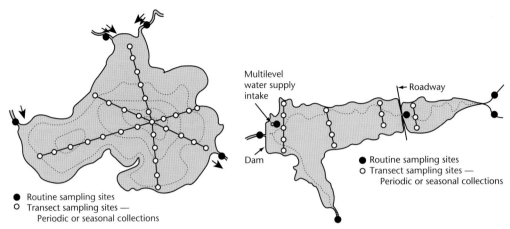

Figure 14-6 Routine and transect sample points in a natural lake

Source: Mackenthun and Ingram. 1967.

Figure 14-7 Routine and transect sample points in a reservoir

Source: Mackenthun and Ingram. 1967.

Collection of representative samples in the water treatment plant is similar to sample collection in a stream or river. The operator must ensure that the water sampled is representative of the water passing that sample point. In many water plants, money has been spent to purchase sample pumps and piping only to find that the sample from that point is not representative of the passing water. A sample tap in a stagnant area of a reservoir or on the floor of a process basin serves little purpose in helping the plant operator with control of water quality. The operator is urged to ensure that each and every sample point is located to provide useful and representative data. If the sampling point is improperly located, the operator should make arrangements to move the piping to a better location. Multiple sample locations for the same analysis point may be needed if changes in plant conditions, such as flow, affect the quality of the sample. For example, if using a streaming current detector or other instruments such as an oxidation–reduction meter, flow can change mixing times and affect the validity of the value read on the instrument.

Treatment plants vary widely in the kinds of treatment processes used and the configurations of the processes. In general, in-plant sample points are established at every place where, because of a treatment method or group of methods, a measurable change is expected in the treated-water quality. Simply put, if you are adding something to the process, either chemically or mechanically, you should have some way of determining the effect. Other in-plant sampling sites may have to be selected and installed for changes in testing needed by changes in governmental laws and regulations. Figure 14-8 identifies 10 suggested locations where process control samples are routinely collected in a plant employing several different treatment processes. These locations are described as follows:

- Between sample points 1 and 2, test results should show a reduction in algae and the associated tastes and odors (the result of chemical pretreatment), a reduction in sediment load (the result of presedimentation), and a reduction in debris (the result of screening).
- Between points 2 and 3, aeration should cause oxidation of iron and manganese and a significant reduction in undesirable dissolved gases while increasing the oxygen content.

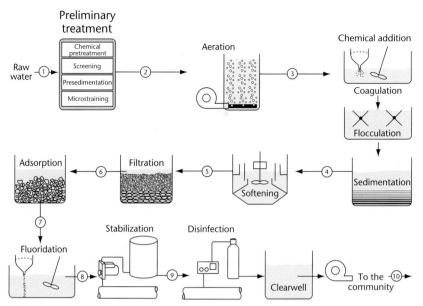

Figure 14-8 Suggested in-plant sample points (indicated by numbered circles)

- Between points 3 and 4, the combined effects of coagulation, flocculation, and sedimentation should cause a reduction in turbidity and color.
- Water quality changes between sample points 4 and 5 will allow the operator to monitor the effectiveness of the softening process.
- Sample points 5 and 6 allow monitoring of the efficiency of filtration in removing turbidity and previously oxidized iron and manganese as well as the reduction in pathogenic organisms.
- Sampling at points 6 and 7 will indicate the efficiency of the adsorption process in removing organic chemicals.
- Point 8 is used for the measurement of fluoride concentration to ensure that water entering the distribution system contains the proper level.
- Sampling at point 9 will provide a final check on pH and alkalinity for corrosion control.
- Point 10 is used for monitoring chlorine residual, turbidity, and the presence of coliform bacteria in the finished water.

In the selection of in-plant sample collection points and times, certain precautions should be kept in mind. Sampling immediately after chemical addition or at points immediately downstream from chemical additions should be avoided because proper mixing and reaction may not have had time to take place. Sampling of combined filter effluent turbidity should take place before post-treatment chemicals are added to avoid measuring added turbidity, such as from lime or phosphates. Operators should always take samples from the main stream of flow, avoiding areas of standing water, algae mats, and floating or settled debris.

Finished-water sample points are normally established downstream of the final treatment process at or just before the point where the water enters the distribution system, such as the point of discharge from the clearwell. For example, turbidity samples required by the National Primary Drinking Water Regulations (NPDWRs) must be collected before the water enters the distribution system while avoiding an area where added chemicals (e.g., lime or corrosion inhibitors) may affect the results.

Collection of Samples

The steps described in the following sections are general sample collection procedures that should be followed regardless of the constituent tested. Special collection procedures required for certain tests are described later in this chapter.

Note that the volume of sample will vary according to the testing procedures used and often is set by regulations. For example, coliform compliance sampling requires a 100-mL grab sample. The laboratory analyst will provide instructions for sample volume.

Only containers designed for water sampling and provided by the laboratory should be used. Mason jars and other recycled containers cannot be trusted to function properly no matter how well they are cleaned, and they are generally not accepted by a laboratory for water analysis. Some laboratories reuse sample containers by washing them under carefully controlled conditions and sterilizing them prior to reuse. In other cases, it has been found more economical to dispose of used bottles and provide only new ones for collection.

When a container with a screw-on lid is used, the lid should be removed and held threads-down while the sample is collected in the container. The lid can easily be contaminated if the inside is touched or if it is set facedown or placed in a pocket. A contaminated lid can contaminate the sample, which will necessitate resampling, costing a great deal of time and expense unnecessarily.

Raw-Water Sample Collection

If no raw-water sample tap is available and the sample must be taken from an open body of water, the following procedures should be used.

On a well supply, if no raw-water sample tap is available, the well should be put to waste with any treatment shut off, the samples collected, the treatment restarted, and the well placed back in service. A clean, wide-mouth sampling bottle should be used for raw-water sampling. The bottle should not be rinsed; this is especially important if the bottle has been pretreated or contains a preservative. The open bottle should be held near its base and plunged neck downward below the surface of the water. The bottle should then be turned until the neck points slightly upward for sampling, with the mouth directed toward any current present. Care must be taken to avoid floating debris and sediment. In a water body with no current, the bottle can be scooped forward to fill the bottle. Once the bottle has been filled, it is retrieved, capped, and labeled.

If the sampler is wading, the sample bottle should be submerged upstream from that person. If a boat is being used for stream sampling, the sample should be taken on the upstream side.

When samples are being taken from a large boat or a bridge, the sample bottle should be placed in a weighted frame that holds the container securely. The opened bottle and holder are then slowly lowered toward the water with a rope or with the handle that comes with certain devices available through water supply equipment catalogs, DO sampling cans, "swing samplers" on poles, long-handled dippers, or weighted bailers. When the bottle or sample device approaches the surface, the unit is dropped quickly into the water. Slack should not be allowed in the rope because the bottle could hit bottom and break, or it could pick up mud and silt. After the bottle is filled, it is pulled in, capped, and labeled. There are also specialized sampling devices to be used as required for specific samples. For example, for DO, the device with the sample bottles is lowered into the water and then the stopper is remotely removed, the sample container is filled, and the stopper is replaced before the unit is removed from the water. This type of device can also be used when sampling at a certain depth to ensure the water is from the zone desired.

Treatment Plant Sample Collection

The procedure used to collect samples from an open tank or basin or in an open channel of moving water is essentially the same as for raw-water sampling. Treatment plants should be equipped with sample taps. These faucets provide a continuous flow of water from various locations in the treatment plant, including raw-water sources. In some plants, these taps do not run continuously because of operational constraints, so the operator may have to turn the taps on and run the water for a specific amount of time to obtain a representative sample. To collect a sample, the operator or laboratory technician draws the required volume from the sample tap. Figure 14-9 shows a typical bank of sample faucets in a laboratory.

Monitoring for Chemical Contaminants

Drinking water may contain contaminants considered a threat to the public. The contaminants of concern may occur naturally in the water, be human-made, or be formed during the water treatment process. The chemicals are broken into four general classes for regulation:

1. Inorganic chemicals
2. Synthetic organic chemicals
3. Volatile organic chemicals
4. Radionuclides (covered in Chapter 1)

The need to establish regulations for new chemical contaminants has presented USEPA with the problem of creating, adapting, proving, and promulgating analytical techniques. The method must be for a specific chemical and not for a "contaminant" defined by a physical description such as a boiling fraction. An example of this distinction can be found in kerosene, which is a member of the petroleum distillates; these chemicals boil at between 150°C and

Figure 14-9 Sample faucets in a laboratory

275°C (300–530°F), which results in a mixture of organic chains of 6 to 16 carbon atoms in each compound. Before a requirement to monitor for a contaminant can be imposed, the testing methods must be developed to ensure that an adequate number of laboratories will be available to perform the tests and that they will get consistent, reliable results. Many of the chemicals now being added to the list of regulated contaminants must be analyzed at the parts-per-billion level or in even smaller concentrations.

Faucets selected should be on the lines connected directly to the main. Only cold-water faucets should be used for sample collection. A sampling faucet must not be located too close to a sink bottom. Contaminated water or soil may be present on the exteriors of such faucets, and it is difficult to place a collection bottle beneath them without touching the neck's interior against the faucet's outside surface. In most instances, samples should not be taken from the following types of faucets (Figure 14-10):

- Leaking faucets, which allow water to flow out around the stem of the valve and down the outside of the faucet
- Faucets with threads
- Faucets connected to home water-treatment units, including water softeners and hot-water tanks
- Faucets that swivel, because the swivel joint may act as a siphon and introduce contamination
- Faucets with single-lever handles that do not guarantee that only the cold-water sample is being selected

 WATCH THE VIDEO
Water Sampling (www.awwa.org/wsovideoclips)

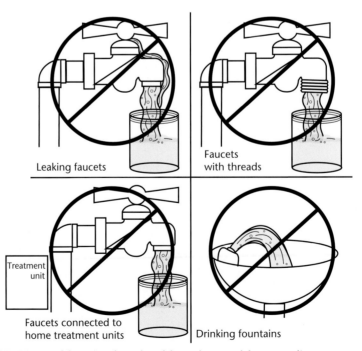

Figure 14-10 Types of faucets that should not be used for sampling

Quality Assurance and Quality Control

Standard Methods for the Examination of Water and Wastewater defines **quality assurance (QA)** as "a definitive plan for laboratory operation that specifies the measures used to produce data of known precision and bias." It defines **quality control (QC)** as a "set of measures within a sample analysis methodology to assure that the process is in control."

A QA program of a laboratory consists of a QA manual, written procedures, work instructions, and records. For example, an organizational chart that lists the training, capabilities, and responsibilities of each lab analyst would be part of a QA program. Quality control is also part of the overall QA program. Note that the processes discussed so far in this chapter relate directly to QA. Choosing the proper location and method of gathering a sample, for example, is the result of applying the laboratory's predefined practices.

In a QC program, each analyst demonstrates his or her capability to obtain acceptable results for an analysis. This is demonstrated by analyzing a set of "blind" standards. Analysts are given samples that contain a specific amount of a chemical. The analyst runs the samples, and the results are reported to an agency that knows the correct levels of chemicals in the samples. The agency then rates the laboratory and the analyst on their performance. This type of testing is commonly called a *performance evaluation* or PE. PEs are typically run twice a year and determine if a laboratory is "certified" to run the analysis.

Another type of continuous laboratory evaluation is performed through the use of "known" standards. Known standards are samples that contain a predetermined amount of a chemical. These standards along with each set of samples are run by an analyst. This allows an analyst to determine how well a particular set of analyses has been performed in each analytical trial. Power fluctuations or other daily hazards may affect laboratory equipment, and the evaluation of known samples will let an analyst determine if a particular run is satisfactory. Sometimes these known samples are referred to as *standards*. For example, known turbidity standards are run before each set of filter turbidity grab samples is run, thus allowing an operator to determine if the instrument is properly measuring turbidity.

A final set of samples is also used to determine data quality. These samples are referred to as *spiked samples*, *laboratory control samples*, or *laboratory fortified matrix (LFM) samples*. Spiked samples are made in the laboratory by adding a known quantity of the chemical being measured to the collected samples. The analyst splits one sample into two aliquots and then adds a precise amount of the chemical being analyzed to one of the aliquots. The two aliquots are run and the results compared. The sample to which the chemical was spiked should have a level of chemical equal to the known addition plus the results of the unaltered sample. This type of sample is important because it allows the analyst to determine if some other chemistry in the sample is interfering with how the instrument measures the contaminant. Regulations and reference to *Standard Methods for the Examination of Water and Wastewater* determine the frequency of this type of QA sampling. Different analyses require different numbers of QA samples; this will affect the number of samples an operator may be required to take for any given parameter.

Another way to evaluate laboratory performance is by reviewing historical analytical performance. In differentiating quality *assurance* and quality *control*, this historical review is generally considered the latter, quality *control*. The results of known samples and spiked samples are graphed and reviewed for trends

quality assurance (QA)

A plan for laboratory operation that specifies the measures used to produce data of known precision and bias.

quality control (QC)

A laboratory program of continually checking techniques and calibrating instruments to ensure consistency in analytical results.

over time. This is important because the efficiency of analytical equipment can decrease over time, or an analyst can improve his or her performance with experience. For example, a decrease in the amount of a known sample result over time can indicate that a probe or detector needs to be replaced.

The importance of laboratory QA/QC to overall plant operations cannot be overstressed. It is critical that test results be reliable because they are a measure of how a plant is performing and a measure of the safety of the water the plant is producing. Performance must be measured accurately, and the accuracy of analysis depends on sample quality and analytical quality. All laboratories should strictly adhere to the laboratory practices described in this section and be willing to produce QA/QC information as requested.

Laboratory Certification

Each of the approximately 155,000 public water systems affected by the Safe Drinking Water Act (SDWA) must routinely monitor water quality to determine if the water is adequately protected from regulated microbiological, chemical, and radiological contaminants. It is imperative that the analyses for all of this monitoring be performed by standard methods approved for compliance testing so that the results are comparable for all systems. Consequently, states are required by federal regulations to consider analytical results from water systems only if samples have been analyzed by a certified laboratory. Some exceptions are measurements for turbidity, chlorine residual, temperature, and pH, which may be performed by a person acceptable to the state using approved equipment and methods.

Federal regulations require each state with primary enforcement responsibility to have available laboratory facilities that have been certified by USEPA, with capacities sufficient to process samples for water systems throughout the state. Certified laboratories fall into the following general classes:

- State-operated laboratories
- Water-system laboratories
- Commercial laboratories

In most states, the necessary capacity is provided by a combination of all three types of laboratories. Some laboratories may be certified to perform only one type of analysis; for instance, some laboratories are set up to handle only microbiological analyses. Analyses requiring expensive equipment and highly trained technicians, such as for organic chemical and radiological monitoring, are also generally handled by specialized laboratories.

Consistency among laboratories in analytical results is overseen by USEPA and by state primacy programs for each of the types of analyses for which the laboratories are certified. Periodically, an independent vendor contracted by USEPA provides to each laboratory carefully prepared proficiency testing samples containing a known concentration of a contaminant. The values of the samples are unknown to the laboratory, and its staff must be able to determine the contaminant concentration within an appropriate tolerance to maintain the laboratory's certification. The results determined by the laboratory are submitted to the agency having primacy for laboratory certification for the particular state.

Historically, most states have operated their own laboratories to process water system samples. But the number of samples has increased severalfold in recent years, so it is difficult for the states to continue providing laboratory service with state funding only. Some states have instituted charges to water systems to help fund the laboratory services. Other states process only a certain number of samples from any one water system, and if more are required, commercial laboratories must be used.

Record Keeping and Sample Labeling

Records should be kept for every sample that is collected. A sample identification label or tag should be filled out at the time of collection. Each label or tag should include at least the following information:

- Water utility name
- Water system's public water system identification number
- Date on which the sample was collected
- Time when the sample was collected
- Location where sample was collected
- Type of sample—grab or composite
- Tests to be run
- Name of person sampling
- Preservatives used
- Bottle number

The samples provided to laboratories should always be clearly labeled. The information on the label should also be entered on a record-keeping form that is maintained as a permanent part of the water system's records and placed on the chain-of-custody forms submitted to the laboratory. Each laboratory may have its own forms that request the required information for compliance with regulations.

Sample Preservation, Storage, and Transportation

Samples cannot always be tested immediately after they are taken. Ensuring that the level of the constituent remains unchanged until testing is performed requires careful attention to techniques of sample preservation, storage, and transportation. It is also extremely important that records be kept of the chain of custody of samples collected for SDWA compliance.

Preservation and Storage

After a sample has been collected, its quality may change because of chemical and/or biological activity in the water. Some characteristics (alkalinity, pH, dissolved gases, disinfectant residuals, temperature, and odor) can change quickly and quite significantly, and so samples to be analyzed for these parameters should not be stored under any conditions. The tests for disinfectant residuals, pH, and temperature must be completed in the field at the time of collection. Other parameters, such as pesticides and radium, change more slowly and much less noticeably, and these samples can usually be stored for considerable lengths of time if necessary.

Regulated parameters have specific directions for sampling, preservation, and storage before testing. These requirements are listed in the regulatory agency compliance regulations. Some agencies have adopted the USEPA requirements, and some have separate, additional requirements. Many, including USEPA, have referred to *Standard Methods for the Examination of Water and Wastewater*. Consult the regulatory agency for requirements in the utility's location.

Sample-Preservation Techniques   To extend the storage time of samples requiring chemical analysis, sample-preservation techniques have been developed that slow the chemical or biological activity in the sample. Sample preservation usually involves one or both of the following steps:

- *Refrigeration:* For some samples, storage time can be prolonged by keeping samples refrigerated until the analysis is performed. In some cases, it is recommended that samples be transported or shipped to the laboratory in a portable cooler containing an ice pack.
- *Use of preservatives:* Agents used to preserve samples include chemical preservatives, quenching agents, and pH-adjustment chemicals.

These techniques can facilitate sample preservation and/or storage, thereby extending the shelf life of the sample and allowing more time for analysis, as might be needed when transporting a sample to the laboratory. They also allow the analyst to collect all the necessary samples and then perform a single analysis, greatly reducing errors that may otherwise occur during calibration. Further, these techniques are useful because it is more efficient and less costly to perform one calibration for multiple samples than it is to calibrate for each individual sample.

Often the laboratory provides bottles for specific analyses with the preservative already added. It is particularly important not to allow these containers to overflow as they are filled; if overflow occurs, some of the preservative will be lost. These containers must also be kept out of the reach of children, because the preservative material could be harmful to a child who opens a container. If preservatives are to be added by the sampler, specific instructions on the procedures should be obtained from the laboratory that will perform the analyses.

Storage Containers   Glass and carbonate plastic sample containers are most often used in water utilities, but glass is avoided where there is a greater chance of breakage, such as in shipping. Also, glass is not used when sampling for fluoride because fluoride will adhere to the glass and not provide accurate results. Plastic can also be problematic because certain organic chemicals can permeate the plastic, and therefore the organic chemicals will not be detected in the subsequent analysis. Some types of plastics may actually release organic chemicals into the sample, thereby invalidating the results.

Samples for total trihalomethane and haloacetic acid analyses are taken in glass vials, usually colored brown to filter out sunlight, and shipped in coolers.

Time of Sampling   Most laboratories do not maintain a full staff on weekends, so they generally request that samples with short holding times, such as bacteriological samples, be collected and shipped early in the week. If a sample arrives on a weekend and cannot be processed, the delay will probably exceed the required holding time and the sample will be rejected. However, most laboratories accept emergency samples on weekends.

Samples that must be submitted within a specified compliance period should generally be collected and sent to the laboratory early in the compliance period. Some of the problems that can require resampling are described in the following list:

- The sample is frozen or broken during shipment.
- The sample is lost or delayed in shipment and arrives at the laboratory after the specified holding time has elapsed.
- The laboratory makes an error in processing the sample.
- The laboratory analysis is inconsistent or shows an increase in the MCL, and another sample to confirm the results is required.

- The sample was not properly preserved or was too warm, or no preservative was present.
- The sample container used was not the proper container for the required sample, size, volume, or material.

Sampling early in the compliance period ensures that time is available for one or more resamplings, if necessary, before the end of the period. If resampling has not been completed before the end of a compliance period, a water system is usually deemed out of compliance and will be instructed by the state to provide public notification.

Transportation

If samples arrive at a laboratory past the specified holding time following collection, the laboratory must reject the samples. New sample bottles must then be shipped to the water system, and another set of samples will have to be collected and shipped back.

The mail is usually the best and easiest method of shipment, except for microbiological or certain radiological samples that require delivery within about a 24-hour period. If regular mail service fails to deliver samples reliably within the required time period, overnight shipping services or package delivery services may be tried. In some cases, changing to a laboratory at a different location may improve delivery time. Some water system operators who are located near a laboratory have found it best just to drive the samples directly to the laboratory or arrange with the laboratory for pickup of the samples as part of the analysis price. Depending on distance and availability of personnel, a bonded courier service may be used.

If samples are shipped, it is important to make sure the bottle caps are tight to prevent leakage. Systems that have had bottle caps loosen during shipment have found that wrapping the lids with electrical or packing tape is an easy method of further securing them. Samples must be packed in a sturdy container with enough cushioning material to prevent breakage. The box should be marked to indicate which end is up, that the contents are fragile, that they must not be allowed to freeze, and that priority should be given to the shipment.

Chain of Custody

As more and more parameters are added to the list of regulated and unregulated contaminants, and with the MCLs and MCLGs in the micrograms per liter range, the practice of good QA/QC procedures becomes very important. One essential part of QA/QC is maintaining a written record of the sample's history of SDWA compliance, from the time of collection to the time of analysis and subsequent disposal. This record, called the **chain of custody**, is important if the analyses are ever challenged and need to be defended.

Maintaining an accurate chain of custody is more complicated when samples are stored or transported. The delay in analyzing these samples and the additional processing steps to which they are exposed introduce more opportunities for errors to occur. As such, their results will be met with greater scrutiny. Chain-of-custody requirements vary by state, so water system operators should be sure that the requirements for their state are being met.

chain of custody
A written record of the sample's history of SDWA compliance, from the time of collection to the time of analysis and subsequent disposal.

Field Log Sheet   One method of establishing the chain-of-custody record is to use a daily field log sheet, which should contain the following information:

- Date the samples were collected
- Name of the sampler

- List of all the samples collected by the sampler on this date
- List of all the sample locations for this date
- Time of day each sample was collected
- Comments concerning any unusual situations
- Signature of the individual receiving the samples from the sampler
- Date and time the samples were received by the laboratory
- Location or identification of the laboratory

This log sheet states that the samples were in the custody of the sampler until they were turned over to the shipper. The laboratory record then follows the history of the sample to disposal.

Sampler's Liability If the results of an analysis of a specific sample are ever questioned, the sampler will be asked to verify that the sample was in his or her custody until it was turned over or sent to the laboratory. The sampler will be asked to verify that the sample was collected, stored, and transported using proper procedures and that no other person could have in any way altered the concentrations of any contaminant(s) present.

Sampler's Responsibility The sampler has the basic responsibility to ensure that the sample is properly collected, labeled, stored, and transported to the laboratory. The sample collector must be able to testify that the sample was under his or her custody at all times. The sample collector is also responsible for knowing and performing the proper sampling routine for each type of analysis required, including preservation.

Common Water Utility Tests

Having discussed the general procedures for gathering and ensuring the validity of water samples, we will now consider some of the more common parameters that water plant operators frequently measure, including their significance. Where applicable, cross-references to other chapters are given.

Alkalinity

The buffering capacity of the water is measured by its alkalinity. This test can determine the concentration of carbonate (CO_3^{-2}), bicarbonate (HCO_3^-), and hydroxide (OH^-) alkalinity. These measurements are useful to determine the corrosive nature of the water in combination with other factors and to optimize the lime–soda ash softening process.

The test involves careful titration of a measured quantity of water with a standard 0.02 N sulfuric acid solution to pH end points of 8.3 and 4.5 (these are indicated by color change indicators or by using a pH meter). The carbonate, bicarbonate, and hydroxide alkalinity levels are then calculated from the results.

Carbon Dioxide

Water that contains high concentrations of free carbon dioxide (CO_2) can cause the consumption of lime when using this method of softening. Also, carbon dioxide is a factor affecting corrosion.

The test usually used is to titrate a measured water sample with a standard solution of sodium hydroxide. The end point is signified by a change in color for phenolphthalein or a pH of 8.3.

Chlorine (Free or Total)

For water plants that use chlorine for disinfection or oxidation, this is one of the most important tests performed by operators. After any addition of chlorine, a measurement should be taken routinely. This test will verify the correct dosage and reveal changes that may affect plant performance and the safety of the water supply. Many plants use both free and total (or combined) forms of chlorine in their processes.

The test most often used is the N,N diethyl p-phenylenediamine sulfate (DPD) color test. The DPD (either for free or total chlorine testing) is added to a water sample, and the intensity of the color indicates the amount of chlorine present in the sample. Most plants use a digital read-out colorimeter to give an accurate re-sult. Some color comparison portable test devices are used as well; however, they are not always accurate. Another test method is amperometric titration. This test is usually performed in the laboratory. A special meter is used to determine the end points when titrating a measured sample with a standard phenylarsine oxide (PAO) solution. This method is very accurate and is capable of determining many chlorine species that may be present. There are several other chlorine residual test methods that can be considered (see *Standard Methods for the Examination of Water and Wastewater*).

Both the DPD color test and amperometric titration are used in online instru-ments for continuous chlorine monitoring. As with any instrument, these devices must be calibrated and checked frequently to ensure accuracy.

Chlorine demand can be determined using the residual test method. This mea-surement can be used to predict residual chlorine over a specified time. Jar testing apparatus may be used for this test. A sample is taken and the chlorine residual is measured immediately. After a specified time, the residual is measured again and the difference is the demand. Care is needed to duplicate the conditions (light, temperature, holding time) that are of interest.

Chlorine Dioxide

See Chapter 11 for a discussion of chlorine dioxide disinfection, generation, and operation. Also, Chapters 12 and 17 include information regarding ion exchange for iron and manganese removal and greensand filter operation. Chlorine dioxide residual is limited to 0.8 mg/L (USEPA maximum residual disinfectant level), and a by-product, chlorite, is also regulated with an MCL of 1.0 mg/L.

The test methods for chlorine dioxide are similar to those for chlorine. There are DPD and amperometric test methods, but some of the test conditions have been modified to yield chlorine dioxide–specific results. Also, there is an ion chro-matography method that requires trained technicians in a certified laboratory.

Coliform

Coliforms (see Chapter 1) are a group of bacteria that produces gas bubbles in lactose or lauryl tryptose broth at 35.5°C (96°F) within 24 to 48 hours. They are considered indicator organisms, meaning that their presence may indicate the presence of other more harmful bacteria and organisms. Because total coli-forms are easier to analyze in the average water utility laboratory than the actual disease-causing microorganisms, total coliform testing is used in place of more tedious, more expensive testing for these other organisms.

Most laboratories use one of two methods to test for coliforms. One method is the membrane filter technique, in which water samples are passed through a 0.45-µm filter. The filter paper is fine enough to trap bacterial particles as the water passes through. The filter paper is then placed onto a growth medium (such as M-endo) and incubated. Any bacterial colonies that are present will grow in size, will be visible to the naked eye, and can be counted after a period of time (usually 24 hours).

Another method is the MMO-MUG (minimal medium) technique. This method allows for inoculation of water sample bottles with powder. The substance in the bottle will feed any total coliform that may be present and produce a color change during incubation.

Samples for coliform testing are always collected in sterile bottles and in quantities sufficient for testing (Figure 14-11). Most bacteriological samples require a minimum of 100 mL (approximately 4 oz) for analysis. Samples should be analyzed the same day as they are collected but can be refrigerated for 8 hours prior to analysis. Coliform samples are taken in the plant at various stages to test for process efficiency; they are also taken in the distribution system for regulatory compliance. The number of samples that must be taken in the distribution system is a function of the population served. Many water treatment plants also take coliform samples of the raw or source water.

Conductivity

This test (more correctly named *specific conductance*) measures the ability of water to conduct electricity. This is an indirect measure of the ions or minerals in the water. It is sometimes used to estimate the TDS content due to its ease of measurement and the availability of inexpensive mobile field instruments.

A conductivity meter is connected to an electrode, and this is immersed in a water sample. An instrument setting to match the sample temperature is often used to adjust for extremes. The conductivity reading is in microsiemens per centimeter (µs/cm).

Cryptosporidium

Cryptosporidium is a parasite regulated under the Long-Term 2 Enhanced Surface Water Treatment Rule (LT2ESWTR). It is a regulated pathogen, and its measurement is necessary to ensure adequate treatment depending on the occurrence in the untreated water supply.

Figure 14-11 Autoclave used for sterilization. Bacteriological equipment must be sterilized in steam under pressure.

Source: Conneaut, Ohio, Water Department.

The method involves filtration, specialized separation, and identification methods. This test can be performed only by laboratories approved for this method. Plant operations personnel will use the test results to determine compliance with the LT2ESWTR.

Disinfectant By-products (DBPs)

Several organic compounds are created when chlorine is used in water treatment. Two groups of these by-products are regulated: trihalomethanes and haloacetic acids. Compounds in both groups have been classified as probable carcinogens.

The test methods for both groups involve procedures that must be performed by trained analysts in approved laboratories. Compliance testing is, therefore, not usually performed by plant operating personnel. Online instruments are available for continuous monitoring, but the instruments should be checked periodically by the same approved laboratory procedures. Operator-performed screening tests can be used to indicate levels for plant monitoring, but these methods are not approved for compliance testing.

Dissolved Oxygen

The amount of **dissolved oxygen** (DO) in the source water may be an indicator of the condition of the lake or reservoir being used. Lack of oxygen may be a predictor of water quality problems due to anoxic conditions. The DO concentration in the treated water may be a factor contributing to the rate of corrosion.

The DO test involves the use of a dedicated meter and specific sensor probe. Also, there are color methods where the intensity of the color from the addition of the indicator is a measure of the concentration present in the water.

Fluoride

Fluoride reduces tooth decay. Fluoride may be naturally occurring or added during water treatment as directed by local health authorities. The optimum amount of fluoride needed to provide health benefits depends on several factors. The MCL for fluoride in drinking water is 4.0 mg/L.

There are both instrumental and colorimetric tests for fluoride in water. Operations personnel usually use the color methods. The color indicator is added to the water, and the color intensity measures the amount of flouride present.

Giardia lamblia

Giardia lamblia is a parasite found in untreated water supplies, and it is pathogenic. It is regulated by a treatment technique in which disinfectant concentration and contact time are prescribed to ensure adequate inactivation. Separate requirements are specified for chlorine, chloramine, ozone, and ultraviolet radiation.

The method involves filtration, specialized separation, and identification methods. This test can be performed only by laboratories approved for this method. Plant operations personnel will use the test results to determine compliance with the Surface Water Treatment Rule.

Hardness

Hardness is attributed primarily to the amount of calcium and magnesium in the water. Softening treatment plants must carefully monitor hardness as a process control. Most other water systems regularly monitor for this parameter as a basic measure of water quality.

There are several methods for hardness testing. Although hardness can be determined by separately analyzing the calcium and magnesium levels, most water

dissolved oxygen (DO)
The oxygen dissolved in water, wastewater, or other liquid, usually expressed in milligrams per liter, parts per million, or percent of saturation.

systems use a color titration method for total hardness results. A measured sample is titrated with a standard solution (EDTA) to a color change end point.

Inorganics (Heavy Metals)

Some metals are toxic in high amounts (such as cadmium or chromium), and others are not (such as iron or manganese). There are MCL regulations for many heavy metals and secondary limits for those that can cause aesthetic concerns. Most regulated metals are included in the primary drinking water regulations, and some, such as lead and copper, have special rules.

The test methods for metals are tremendously varied. Instrumental and color methods predominate. Only approved methods can be used for compliance testing. Operations personnel may elect to use unapproved screening methods for process monitoring. The more precise methods require trained analysts and must be performed by approved laboratories.

Iron and Manganese

These metals are often grouped together because they are similar in their role in water quality and often occur together. Both cause staining of fixtures and are not generally toxic at normally encountered concentrations. Treatment processes have been developed to remove one or both of these substances. Secondary standards (nonenforceable) are established for both.

There are several test methods for both of these metals. Many treatment plants use a color method for process control. These methods are typical where an indicator is used, and the intensity of the color is measured to determine the amount present.

Lead and Copper

These metals are grouped together because of the USEPA regulatory rule requirements. Both substances are toxic at elevated levels; thus, they are regulated. Generally, these contaminants are somewhat unique in that they are not often found in source water but are the result of dissolution from piping components (see the Lead and Copper Rule description in Chapter 3). Therefore, testing is performed primarily in the distribution system rather than the treatment plant.

The test methods vary from instrumental laboratory procedures to simple field-test color methods. The laboratory methods require trained analysts and are not usually conducted by operations personnel. Screening tests using colorimetric methods are often employed by plant operators for process control.

Microbiological Organisms

Many microbiological organisms are found in untreated water. Bacteria, viruses, protozoan, algae, and plankton are examples of the multitude of possibilities. Some of these are pathogenic; others can produce toxic substances. The array of consequences is very broad. Some are regulated in drinking water. The coliform group of bacteria is used to indicate the possibility of contamination. Another useful bacteria indicator is the heterotrophic plate count. This is a general bacteria population measurement that may indicate the presence of other pathogens.

Test methods are as varied as the organisms. Many involve growing colonies on selective nutrients and counting the number from a measured sample. Other samples may be examined by microscope and the organisms identified by experts. Some chemical by-products are analyzed by instrumental methods capable of detecting minute amounts. Generally, trained analysts must perform most of these procedures. The exceptions are the coliform tests that have been developed using color changes to both detect and enumerate these bacteria.

Nitrate, Nitrite, and Ammonia

These three inorganic nitrogen compounds are often encountered in water supplies. Contamination from agricultural activities is often the source in surface water, but another significant source is wastewater discharges. Nitrate and nitrite are regulated contaminants with enforceable MCLs. Ammonia is not regulated in drinking water but is a compound that may encourage the growth of nitrifying bacteria. Ammonia is often associated with the chloramination process.

Several test methods are available for these substances. Operational control testing is usually conducted using colorimetric methods. Special precautions are needed when testing for free ammonia in the presence of chloramines in order to ensure accurate results.

Orthophosphate and Polyphosphate

Phosphate can be naturally occurring in surface water, where it may be the result of urban runoff or waste discharges. Orthophosphate and polyphosphate are often used as corrosion inhibitors in water supplies. These substances are not considered toxic, but the amount is carefully monitored to ensure optimum effectiveness.

There are instrumental methods for phosphate that require approved laboratories and trained analysts. Most operational control testing uses colorimetric tests. Selecting the correct test may require knowledge of the type of phosphate used for corrosion control.

pH

This is one of the most common tests performed in water treatment and drinking water monitoring. The pH value (Chapters 1 and 15) is an indicator of the acidity or alkalinity of the water. There is not an MCL for pH in drinking water. However, there is a secondary standard range of 6.5–8.5.

pH testing uses a scale from 0 to 14, with the midpoint of 7 being neutral (i.e., the acidity and alkalinity are balanced). Below 7, the acidity of the water predominates; above 7, the alkalinity of the water predominates. With each unit increase or decrease, the concentration or intensity changes 10-fold.

For example, for the pH to change from 5 to 6, the acidity must decrease by a factor of 10. The pH of water is significant because it affects the efficiency of chlorination, coagulation, softening, and corrosion control. Also, pH testing can provide early warning of unit process failure. For example, the addition of alum to the rapid-mix stage should produce a predictable drop in pH. If it does not, a malfunction of coagulant feed could be indicated.

Samples for pH should be collected in glass or plastic containers and analyzed as quickly as possible. Samples should not be agitated because dissolved carbon dioxide could be liberated, which will change the pH.

A pH meter is used for the test in combination with a suitable probe. The meter must be periodically calibrated using a known standard. The pH value for a water sample may change while standing due to a change in temperature or exposure to air. Therefore, measurements are usually taken immediately upon sampling.

Radiologic Substances

Contamination from radiological substances is more common in groundwater than surface water. Several of these substances have MCL regulations. There are numerous possible radioactive isotopes that may be encountered; therefore, screening water supplies for general radioactivity (gross alpha and gross beta activity) may be prudent before employing specific substance testing.

Testing for radioactive substances often requires specialized equipment and procedures. Approved laboratories are required for compliance testing, and analysts with specific training are needed. Test results for radioactivity are sometimes expressed as pCi/L (picoCuries/L), but, depending on the substance, µg/L or mrem/yr may be used.

Solids—Settleable, Dissolved, Suspended

The solids contained in a water supply are all of the substances that are not H_2O. These can be inorganic, organic, volatile, nonvolatile, suspended, settleable, or dissolved. There are not MCLs for solids content, but there is a secondary standard for TDS levels of 500 mg/L.

The test method involves taking a measured sample and heating it to remove the water and then weighing the remaining residue (solids). The temperature used for heating can define the volatility of the residue. Also, filtration before heating can be used to give a dissolved result. TDS is the most used solids measurement in drinking water. TDS is a gross measure of the inorganic content of the water (because organic substances usually are a minor part of the total).

Synthetic Organic Chemicals

This is a large group of organic compounds that is regulated and has MCL standards. Many of these compounds are pesticides and herbicides that for the most part are not currently manufactured in the United States. Most of these compounds are probable carcinogens and, therefore, have MCLG limits of 0. These must be tested according to the requirements of the Primary Drinking Water Regulations.

The test methods for this group of compounds involve complex chemistry instrumental procedures. Only approved laboratories with trained analysts can perform these tests. A few of these substances have intricate rapid test methods that are not approved for regulatory compliance. These methods may be suitable for screening surveys or other occurrence evaluations.

Taste and Odor

Consumers often react to taste and odor as their only way to evaluate the quality of the drinking water. A disagreeable response may result in a poor perception, so it is imperative that the water utility seek to provide water that is pleasing to its customers. There is no regulatory MCL for taste or odor, but there is a secondary standard MCL for threshold odor number (TON) of 3.

There are several tests for taste and odor. One is the flavor profile analysis (FPA). This test involves a trained panel to routinely evaluate the water. Several utilities use this method with good results. However, most utilities find this method to be labor intensive and instead use the older TON method. This method enlists a panel to smell water samples of various dilutions. The consensus of the dilution where an odor was detected is the TON for the sample. Although this test can be a bit subjective, it can also be useful to detect odor problems and to assess the effectiveness of treatment.

Temperature

This is probably the test most frequently performed on drinking water. There is no MCL for temperature. Differences in temperature can indicate probable water quality problems. Also, water supply changes are often linked to temperature.

A thermometer is used and the water must be tested at the sample location. The result is usually expressed in °C because this scale is used for many other test procedures.

Total Organic Carbon

This parameter is a nonspecific measure of the organic content of the water. There is no MCL for total organic carbon (TOC), but the Disinfectants and Disinfection By-products Rule (DBPR) uses TOC measurements to determine if precursor removal is needed to comply with the rule. Enhanced coagulation or other means may be required to reduce the TOC.

The test uses a TOC instrument either in the laboratory or online. Calibration is required by analyzing known standards and adjusting the instrument to provide an accurate result. Specific training is necessary to calibrate and use the instrument to provide the best results.

Volatile Organic Chemicals

Several volatile organic chemicals are regulated and have MCLs. Although these compounds are volatile, it is possible that water under pressure may contain these substances, and when the pressure is released, the compounds could be inhaled.

Test methods for this class of compounds involve careful sample collection (zero headspace). The samples are purged with an inert gas, and the vapor is analyzed by gas chromatograph (instrument). This test must be performed in an approved laboratory by trained analysts. Operational personnel may assess the results and compare them to regulatory standards.

Study Questions

1. Under no circumstances should a composite sample be collected for which type of analysis?
   a. Bacteriological
   b. Total dissolved solids
   c. Alkalinity
   d. Turbidity

2. The number of monthly distribution system chlorine residual samples required is
   a. based on water withdrawal permit limit.
   b. based on system size.
   c. based on population.
   d. different for each state.

3. Which of the following are the ideal indicator for pathogens?
   a. Salmonella species
   b. Coliform group bacteria
   c. Gram-negative cocci
   d. Gram-negative coccobacilli

4. A _____ is a single-volume sample collected at one time from one place.
   a. composite sample
   b. continuous sample
   c. random sample
   d. grab sample

5. Consistency among laboratories in analytical results is overseen by _____ and by state primacy programs for each of the types of analyses for which the laboratories are certified.
   a. OSHA
   b. AWWA
   c. USEPA
   d. NIOSH

6. If samples arrive at a laboratory past the specified holding time following collection, the laboratory
   a. must reject the samples.
   b. can proceed with the samples only if the chain of custody is intact.
   c. must reconstitute the samples.
   d. must visually inspect the samples to determine their viability.

7. How frequently do water plant operators take samples?

8. What are three broadly classified areas from which samples are generally collected?

Chapter 15
Corrosion Control

Many water systems must apply special chemical treatment because their source water either causes damaging **corrosion** or deposits scale (a process known as **scaling**) on pipelines and plumbing fixtures. The treatment process for controlling these problems is known as **stabilization**. Many more systems must provide corrosion control treatment under new federal and state regulations enacted to protect the public from the health dangers of lead and copper, and other trace metals in drinking water.

Water system operators are cautioned that complicated interactions often occur in the control of water corrosion and scaling. A seemingly simple change to improve one characteristic may have an adverse effect on some other water characteristic or treatment process. This chapter offers an overview of the need for corrosion and scaling control and their related processes. However, because of all the complex variables involved, it is not intended to be a guide for the best treatment method for any particular system. It is best to get professional guidance and state approval before beginning any new stabilization treatment.

Purposes of Corrosion and Scaling Control

Corrosion and scaling are controlled for the following reasons:

- Protect public health
- Improve water quality
- Extend the life of plumbing equipment
- Meet federal and state regulations

Protecting Public Health

Corrosive water can leach toxic metals from distribution and household plumbing systems. Lead and copper are the metals most likely to be a problem because they are commonly used in plumbing systems.

In addition, corrosion of cast-iron mains can cause the formation of iron deposits, called **tubercles**, in the mains. These deposits can protect bacteria and other microorganisms from chlorine, allowing them to grow and thrive. Changes in water velocity or pressure can then cause the microorganisms to be released, creating a potential for disease outbreaks. Some bacteria shielded by the tubercles can also accelerate the corrosion process.

corrosion

The gradual deterioration or destruction of a substance or material by chemical action. The action proceeds inward from the surface.

scaling

Metal deposits left in pipelines and plumbing fixtures.

stabilization

The water treatment process intended to reduce the corrosive or scale-forming tendencies of water.

tubercle

A knob of rust formed on the interior of cast-iron pipes as a result of corrosion.

Table 15-1 Estimated effect of scale on boiler fuel consumption

| Scale Thickness, | | Fuel Consumption, |
in.	mm	% increase
1/50	0.5	7
1/16	1.6	18
1/18	3.2	39

Improving Water Quality

Corrosive water attacking metal pipes can cause taste, odor, and color problems in a water system. Red-water problems occur when iron is dissolved from cast-iron mains by corrosive water. The iron will stain a customer's plumbing fixtures and laundry and make the water's appearance unappealing for drinking and bathing. The dissolved iron also acts as a food source for a group of microorganisms called *iron bacteria*, which can cause serious taste-and-odor problems. Corrosion of copper pipes can cause a metallic taste, as well as blue-green stains on plumbing fixtures and laundry.

Extending the Life of Plumbing Equipment

Unstable water can also result in significant costs to water systems and customers. Aggressive water can significantly reduce the life of valves, unprotected metal, and asbestos–cement (A–C) pipe. It can also shorten the service life and performance of plumbing fixtures and hot water heaters.

Buildup of corrosion products (a process known as *tuberculation*) or uncontrolled scale deposits can seriously reduce pipeline capacity and increase resistance to flow. This impaired flow in turn reduces distribution system efficiency and increases pumping costs. If scale deposits or tuberculation go unchecked, pipes can become completely plugged, requiring expensive repair or replacement. Scaling can also increase the cost of operation of hot water heaters by increasing their fuel consumption, as shown in Table 15-1.

Meeting Federal and State Regulations

As detailed in Chapter 3, the Lead and Copper Rule enacted by the US Environmental Protection Agency (USEPA) in 1991 requires water systems to check if their water is corrosive enough to cause lead and copper corrosion products to appear in customers' water at levels exceeding the new action level. If the level is exceeded, the system is required to take action to reduce the corrosivity of the water.

Water System Corrosion

red water

Rust-colored water resulting from the formation of ferric hydroxide from iron naturally dissolved in the water or from the action of iron bacteria.

Corrosion can be broadly defined as the wearing away or deterioration of a material because of chemical reactions with its environment. The most familiar example is the formation of rust (oxidized iron) when an iron or steel surface is exposed to moisture. Corrosion is usually distinguished from erosion, which is the wearing away of material caused by physical causes, such as abrasion. Water that promotes corrosion is known as *corrosive* or *aggressive* water.

In water treatment operations, corrosion can occur to some extent with almost any metal that is exposed to water. Whether corrosion of a material will be extensive enough to cause problems depends on several related factors, such as the type of material involved, the chemical and biological characteristics of the water, and the electrical characteristics of the material and its environment.

The relationships among these factors, as well as the process of corrosion itself, are quite complex. As a result, it is difficult to make general statements about what combinations of water and equipment will or will not have corrosion problems. The discussions in this chapter cover only basic principles; the operator faced with persistent corrosion in a given installation may require the assistance of corrosion-control specialists.

Chemistry of Corrosion

The chemical reactions that occur in the corrosion of metals are similar to those that occur in an automobile battery. In fact, corrosion generates an electrical current that flows through the metal being corroded. The chemical and electrical reactions that occur during **concentration cell corrosion** of iron pipes are illustrated in Figure 15-1.

As shown in Figure 15-1A, minor impurities and variations (present in all metal pipes) have caused one spot on the pipe to act as an electrical anode in relation to another spot that is acting as an electrical cathode. At the anode, atoms of iron (Fe^{+2}) are breaking away from the pipe and going into solution in the water. As each atom breaks away, it ionizes by losing two electrons, which travel through the pipe to the cathode.

In Figure 15-1B, it is shown that chemical reactions within the water balance the electrical and chemical reactions at the anode and cathode. Many of the water molecules (H_2O) have dissociated into H^+ ions and OH^- radicals. This is a normal condition, even with totally pure water. The Fe^{+2} released at the anode combines

> **concentration cell corrosion**
>
> A form of localized corrosion that can form deep pits and tubercles.

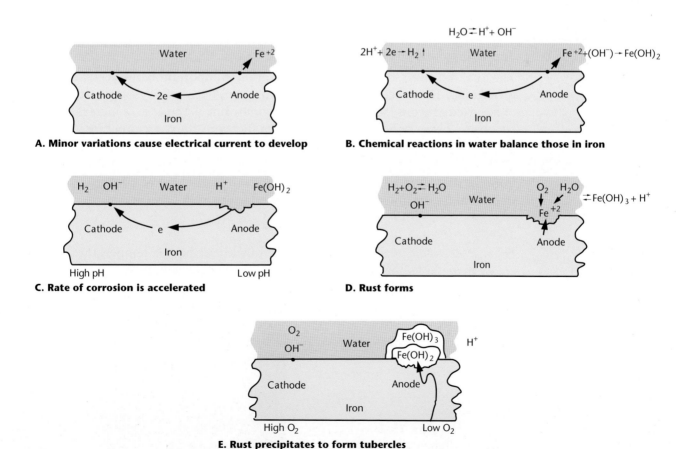

A. Minor variations cause electrical current to develop

B. Chemical reactions in water balance those in iron

C. Rate of corrosion is accelerated

D. Rust forms

E. Rust precipitates to form tubercles

Figure 15-1 Chemical and electrical reactions that occur during corrosion of iron pipe

with two OH⁻ radicals from dissociated water molecules to form $Fe(OH)_2$, ferrous hydroxide. Similarly, two H^+ ions from the dissociation of the water molecules near the cathode pick up the two electrons originally lost by the iron atom then bond together as H_2, hydrogen gas.

The formation of $Fe(OH)_2$ leaves an excess of H^+ near the anode, and the formation of the H_2 leaves an excess of OH^- near the cathode. This change in the normal distribution of H^+ and OH^- accelerates the rate of corrosion and causes increased pitting in the anode area (the concentration cell), as shown in Figure 15-1C.

If the water contains dissolved oxygen (O_2)—most surface water does—then $Fe(OH)_3$, ferric hydroxide, will form (Figure 15-1D). Ferric hydroxide is common iron rust. The rust precipitates, forming tubercles (Figure 15-1E). The existence of tubercles further concentrates the corrosion, increasing both pitting at the anode and growth of the tubercle. Tubercles can grow into large nodules (Figure 15-2), significantly reducing the carrying capacity of a pipe. During rapid pressure or velocity changes, some of the $Fe(OH)_3$ can be carried away, causing "red water."

Factors Affecting Corrosion

The rate of corrosion depends on many site-specific conditions, such as the characteristics of the water and pipe material. Therefore, there are no established guidelines that determine the rate at which a pipe will be corroded.

Chemical reactions play a critical role in determining the rate of corrosion at both the cathode and the anode. Any factor that influences these reactions will also influence the corrosion rate.

Dissolved Oxygen

The concentration of dissolved oxygen (DO) in water is a key part of the corrosion process. As the concentration of DO increases, the corrosion rate will also increase.

Total Dissolved Solids

The total dissolved solids (TDS) concentration is important because electrical flow is necessary for the corrosion of metal to occur. Pure water is a poor conductor of electricity because it contains very few ions. But as the TDS is increased, water becomes a better conductor, which in turn increases the corrosion rate.

Alkalinity and pH

Both the alkalinity and the pH of the water affect the rate of chemical reactions. In general, as pH and alkalinity increase, the corrosion rate decreases.

Temperature

Because chemical reactions occur more quickly at higher temperatures, an increase in water temperature usually increases the corrosion rate.

Figure 15-2
Tuberculated pipe
Courtesy of Girard Industries.

Flow Velocity

The velocity of water flowing past a piece of metal can also affect the corrosion rate, depending on the nature of the water. If the water is corrosive, higher flow velocities cause turbulent conditions that bring DO to the corroding surface more rapidly, which increases the corrosion rate. However, if chemicals are being added to stabilize the water, the higher velocities will decrease the corrosion rate, allowing the chemicals (such as calcium carbonate) to deposit on the pipe walls more quickly.

Type of Metal

Metals that easily give up electrons will corrode easily. Table 15-2 lists metals commonly used in water systems, with those at the top being most likely to corrode. This listing is called the *galvanic series of metals*. Where dissimilar metals are electrically connected and immersed in a common flow of water, the metal highest in the galvanic series will immediately become the anode, the other metal will become the cathode, and corrosion will occur. This process is termed **galvanic corrosion** (as opposed to concentration cell corrosion).

The rate of galvanic corrosion will depend largely on how widely separated the metals are in the galvanic series. Widely separated metals will exhibit extremely rapid corrosion of the anode metal (the highest in the series), and the cathode metal will be protected from corrosion. A common example of galvanic corrosion occurs when a brass corporation cock is tapped into a cast-iron main and attached to a copper service line. The copper will be protected at the expense of the brass and cast iron.

Electrical Current

If electrical current is passed through any corrodible metal, corrosion will be accelerated. The two causes of electrical current in water mains are improperly grounded household electrical systems and electric railway systems.

Table 15-2 Galvanic series for metals used in water systems

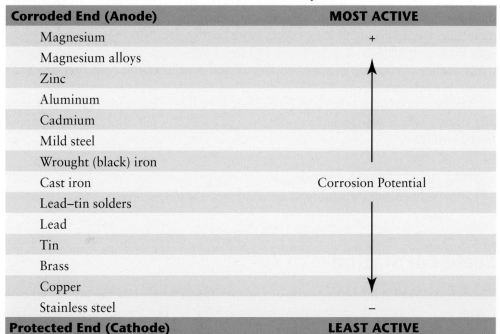

Corroded End (Anode)	MOST ACTIVE
Magnesium	+
Magnesium alloys	
Zinc	
Aluminum	
Cadmium	
Mild steel	
Wrought (black) iron	
Cast iron	Corrosion Potential
Lead–tin solders	
Lead	
Tin	
Brass	
Copper	
Stainless steel	–
Protected End (Cathode)	**LEAST ACTIVE**

galvanic corrosion
A form of localized corrosion caused by the connection of dissimilar metals in an electrolyte, such as water.

Bacteria

Certain types of bacteria can accelerate the corrosion process because they produce carbon dioxide (CO_2) and hydrogen sulfide (H_2S) during their life cycles, which can increase the corrosion rate. These bacteria can also produce slime, which will entrap precipitating iron compounds and increase red-water problems and the amount of tuberculation.

Two groups of bacteria cause the most problems. Iron bacteria, such as *Gallionella* and *Crenothrix*, can form considerable amounts of slime on pipe walls, particularly if the water contains enough dissolved iron to allow them to survive. The iron present in the water can be naturally occurring in the source water or can be caused by corrosion of the pipe material. Beneath this slime layer, CO_2 production by the bacteria can significantly lower the pH, which will speed up the corrosion rate.

The periodic sloughing of these slime accumulations can cause other major problems, such as tastes and odors. The slimes can also prevent the effective deposition of a protective calcium carbonate ($CaCO_3$) layer by enmeshing it within the slime layer. As this layer sloughs away, it carries away the $CaCO_3$ and leaves the pipe surface bare.

Sulfate-reducing bacteria, such as *Desulfovibrio desulfuricans*, can accelerate corrosion when sulfate (SO_4^{2-}) is present in the water. They reduce the SO_4^{2-} under anaerobic conditions, which occur under the slime layer where oxygen is depleted by other bacteria. The products formed are iron sulfide (Fe_2S_2) and hydrogen sulfide (H_2S), which causes obnoxious odors and black-colored water. The CO_2 formed can also lower the pH of the water.

All of these factors interact with each other and with metal pipes, tanks, and various equipment in water plants, the distribution system, and the customer's plumbing. As the factors change, the corrosion rate will also change. The only factors over which the operator has significant control are pH, alkalinity, and the bacteriological content of the water. The techniques used to control these parameters are discussed later in this chapter.

Types of Corrosion

Corrosion in water systems can be divided into two broad classes: localized and uniform. Localized corrosion, the most common type in water systems, attacks metal surfaces unevenly. It is usually a more serious problem than uniform corrosion because it leads to a more rapid failure of the metal. Two types of corrosion that produce pitting are galvanic corrosion and concentration cell corrosion (discussed previously).

Uniform corrosion takes place at an equal rate over the entire surface. It usually occurs where waters having very low pH and low alkalinity act on unprotected surfaces.

WATCH THE VIDEO
External Corrosion (www.awwa.org/wsovideoclips)

Scale Formation

The formation of mild scale on the interior of pipes can protect the pipe from corrosion by separating the corrodible pipe material from the water. However, uncontrolled scale deposits can significantly reduce the carrying capacity of a distribution system. Figure 15-3 shows a pipe that is almost completely blocked by scale.

Figure 15-3
Scaling of pipe
Courtesy of Johnson Controls.

Chemistry of Scale Formation

Scale is formed when the divalent metallic cations associated with hardness, primarily magnesium and calcium, combine with other minerals dissolved in the water and precipitate to coat pipe walls. (See Chapter 16 for further discussion of hardness.) The most common form of scale is calcium carbonate ($CaCO_3$). Other scale-forming compounds include magnesium carbonate ($MgCO_3$), calcium sulfate ($CaSO_4$), and magnesium chloride ($MgCl_2$).

Factors Affecting Scale Formation

Water can hold only so much of any given chemical in solution. If more is added, it will precipitate instead of dissolve. The point at which no more of the chemical can be dissolved is called the **saturation point**. The saturation point varies with other characteristics of the water, including pH, temperature, and TDS.

The saturation point of calcium carbonate ($CaCO_3$) depends primarily on the pH of the water. For example, if water with a certain temperature and TDS concentration can maintain 500 mg/L of $CaCO_3$ in solution at pH 7, then the same water will hold only 14 mg/L of $CaCO_3$ in solution if the pH is raised to 9.4.

Temperature also affects the saturation point, although not as dramatically as pH. The solubility of $CaCO_3$ in water decreases as temperature increases. The most common example is when the higher temperature in hot water heaters and boilers causes scale to precipitate out of the water and build up on pipe and tank walls. Because the presence of other minerals in the water affects the solubility of $CaCO_3$, the TDS concentration must be known in order to determine the $CaCO_3$ saturation point. As the TDS concentration increases, the solubility of $CaCO_3$ increases.

Corrosion and Scaling Control Methods

The following are the basic methods used for stabilizing water to protect against the problems of corrosion or scaling:

- Adjustment of pH and alkalinity
- Formation of a calcium carbonate coating
- Use of corrosion inhibitors and sequestering agents

The selection of which method or methods are finally used on any water system depends on both the chemical characteristics of the raw water and the effects of other treatment processes being used.

The type of source water, the number of sources, and the hydraulics and flow patterns of the system can also have a bearing on the choice of corrosion-control

saturation point
The point at which a solution can no longer dissolve any more of a particular chemical. Precipitation of the chemical will occur beyond this point.

measures that should be taken. Systems that have multiple sources with different chemistry may have particularly complex problems. The pH of the water is sometimes critical in the use of chemical corrosion-control measures; some measures work properly only within a narrow pH range. The principal treatment techniques for corrosion and scaling control are summarized in Table 15-3.

Table 15-3 Summary of treatment techniques for controlling corrosion and scaling

Treatment	Application	Effectiveness	Comments or Problems
To Prevent Corrosion			
Lime alone or lime with sodium carbonate or sodium bicarbonate	Increase pH Increase hardness Increase alkalinity	Most effective in water with low pH and hardness Excellent protection for copper, lead, and asbestos–cement pipe in stabilized waters Good protection for galvanized and steel pipe	May be best overall treatment approach Oversaturation may cause calcium deposits
Sodium hydroxide	Increase pH	Most effective in waters with sufficient hardness and alkalinity to stabilize water May provide adequate protection against lead corrosion in low-alkalinity, soft waters	Should not be used to stabilize waters without the presence of adequate alkalinity and hardness May cause tuberculation in iron pipes at pH 7.5–9.0
Sodium hydroxide and sodium carbonate or sodium bicarbonate	Increase pH Adjust alkalinity	Most effective in water with low pH and sufficient hardness Excellent protection for lead corrosion in soft waters at pH 8.3	Combination of high alkalinity and hardness with low pH is more effective than combination of high pH with low hardness and alkalinity
Inhibition with phosphates (primarily sodium zinc phosphate and zinc orthophosphate)	Form a protective film on pipe surfaces	Effective at pH levels above 7.0 Good protection for asbestos–cement pipe Addition of lime may increase effectiveness of treatment for copper, steel, lead, and asbestos	May cause leaching of lead in stagnant waters May encourage the growth of algae and microorganisms May cause red water if extensive tuberculation is present May not be effective at low pH levels
Inhibition with silicates	Form a protective film on pipe surfaces	Most effective in waters having low hardness and pH below 8.4 Good protection for copper, galvanized, and steel pipe	May increase the potential of pitting in copper and steel pipes May not be compatible with some industrial processes
To Prevent Scale Formation			
Carbon dioxide or sulfuric acid	Decrease pH Decrease alkalinity	Effective with high-pH, high-alkalinity water such as lime-softened water	Overfeeding can cause low pH and corrosion
Sequestering with phosphates (primarily sodium hexametaphosphate and tetrasodium polyphosphate)	Sequester scale-forming ions	Effective in controlling scale formation from lime-softened waters and iron in the source water	Can loosen existing deposits and cause red-water complaints Compounds lose sequestering ability in hot water heaters, causing precipitation of calcium carbonate or iron

Adjustment of pH and Alkalinity

In general, soft waters that have a pH of less than 7 and that are slightly buffered will be corrosive to lead and copper. Water that has too much alkalinity can also be quite corrosive. Water that is nominally corrosive naturally can also have the corrosivity increased by the addition of other water treatment chemicals. For instance, gaseous chlorine will reduce pH levels.

Usually, a moderate increase in pH and alkalinity levels can reduce corrosion, and a decrease can prevent scale formation. The formation of a protective film on the interior of lead and copper pipes is also usually aided by increasing pH.

Lime is normally used to increase both pH and alkalinity because it is less expensive than other chemicals having the same effect. Soda ash (sodium carbonate) can be added along with the lime to further increase the alkalinity. Sodium bicarbonate is sometimes used instead of sodium carbonate because it will also increase alkalinity without as much of an increase in pH. The increased alkalinity buffers the water against pH changes in the distribution system. This has proven particularly effective in controlling corrosion of lead and copper service pipes. Instead of lime, caustic soda with soda ash or sodium bicarbonate can be used to increase pH and alkalinity.

Lime-softened water can cause severe scale problems if it is not stabilized (see Chapter 16). Stabilization after softening is accomplished by the addition of carbon dioxide (a process called *recarbonation*) or sulfuric acid. Both chemicals lower the pH so that calcium carbonate will not precipitate in the distribution system.

Formation of a Calcium Carbonate Coating

Because corrosion attacks the surface of a pipe, a protective coating on the pipe surface can inhibit corrosion. A coating of cement, plastic, or asphaltic material is commonly applied to the interior of pipes and tanks and on metal equipment to protect them from corrosion. Although these coatings form an effective barrier against corrosion, very aggressive water can sometimes attack the coatings. In addition, if there are any breaks in the coating, corrosion will be particularly severe at these points.

As a result, many systems apply an additional protective coating by controlling the chemistry of the water. A common protective-coating technique is to adjust the pH of the water to a level just above the saturation point of calcium carbonate. When this level is maintained, calcium carbonate will precipitate and form a protective layer on the pipe walls. This process must be closely controlled. A pH that is too low may result in corrosion, and a pH that is too high may result in excessive precipitation, which will cause a clogging of service pipes and a restriction of flow in the distribution system. Lime, soda ash, sodium bicarbonate, or sodium hydroxide can be used to raise the pH level. Lime is often used because it also adds needed calcium (hardness) and alkalinity.

Use of Corrosion Inhibitors and Sequestering Agents

Some waters do not contain enough calcium or alkalinity to make the formation of calcium carbonate coatings economical. Water obtained primarily from snowmelt is an example, having alkalinity and calcium concentrations as low as 2 mg/L as calcium carbonate. In this event, other chemical compounds can be used to form protective coatings.

The most common compounds are polyphosphates and silicates. The chemical reactions by which these compounds combine with corrosion products to form a protective layer are not completely understood; however, the chemicals have proven successful in many water systems.

Some polyphosphates can also be used as sequestering agents to prevent scale formation. These compounds sequester, or chemically tie up, the scale-forming ions of calcium and magnesium so that they cannot react to form scale. Because these compounds remain in solution, they are eventually ingested by consumers. Therefore, any sequestering agent selected must be suitable for use in drinking water.

Polyphosphates also sequester iron, whether it is dissolved in water from the source or from corrosion of the system. This prevents the precipitation of the iron compounds, so red water will not result. However, this effect does not prevent corrosion; it merely prevents the corrosion by-products from being noticed.

Study Questions

1. The treatment process that controls corrosion or scaling is known as
   a. chemical control.
   b. stabilization.
   c. passivation.
   d. corrosion kinetics.

2. Which of the following is the principal scale-forming substance in water?
   a. Zinc orthophosphate
   b. Sodium carbonate
   c. Calcium
   d. Calcium carbonate

3. The buildup of corrosion products is a process known as
   a. deposition.
   b. electrochemical deposition.
   c. physiochemical deposition.
   d. tuberculation.

4. Iron deposits caused by the corrosion of cast-iron mains are called
   a. rust specks.
   b. floc.
   c. tubercles.
   d. scale.

5. Which of the following is *not* a reason that corrosion and scaling are controlled?
   a. To improve water quality
   b. To reduce the need for quality sampling
   c. To meet federal and state regulations
   d. To protect public health

6. _____ can be broadly defined as the wearing away or deterioration of a material because of chemical reactions with its environment.
   a. Corrosion
   b. Rust
   c. Oxidization
   d. Scaling

7. What are the basic methods for controlling corrosion or scaling?

8. What are the primary reasons to control corrosion and scaling?

9. Certain types of bacteria can accelerate the corrosion process because they produce carbon dioxide and what other product?

10. In general, soft waters that have a pH of less than 7 and that are slightly buffered will have what effect on lead and copper?

Chapter 16
Lime Softening Basics

Natural water contains dissolved impurities, some of which impart a quality known as **hardness**. Technically, hardness is any material that forms a precipitate with the sodium salt of fatty acids (i.e., soap). Consumers frequently complain about problems attributed to hard water, such as the formation of scale in cooking utensils and hot water heaters, and an increased consumption of soap.

The first section of this chapter discusses the occurrence, chemistry, and effects of hard water. The remainder of the chapter describes the **softening** processes that remove the hardness-causing minerals.

The precipitation process most frequently used is known as *cold process lime–soda softening* or the **lime–soda ash process**. Because of the special facilities required and the complexity of the process, it is applicable only to medium- or large-sized water systems where all treatment can be accomplished at a central location. This process provides softened water at the lowest cost. Lime softening is used for treatment of either groundwater or surface water sources.

The other commonly used method of softening is ion exchange, as detailed in Chapter 17. This process has the advantages of a lower initial cost and ease of use by small systems or by larger systems at multiple locations. The principal disadvantage is that operating costs are higher. Ion exchange is used for direct treatment of groundwater, provided turbidity and iron levels are not excessive. For treatment of surface water, the process is preceded by conventional treatment.

Softening can also be accomplished using nanofiltration membrane technology, electrodialysis, distillation, and freezing. Of these, membrane methods (as described in Chapter 17) have gained the widest use. Nanofiltration membrane softening is currently used to soften brackish water.

Effects of Hard and Soft Water

Occurrence of Hard Water

Hard water is caused by the presence of multivalent cations, such as calcium and magnesium, in combination with anions, such as bicarbonate, carbonate, sulfate, nitrate, or chloride. The principal cations that cause water hardness are calcium and magnesium. Strontium, aluminum, barium, iron, manganese, and zinc can also cause hardness in water, but they are not usually present in large enough concentrations to contribute significantly to the total hardness.

As shown in Figure 16-1, water hardness varies in different geographic areas of the contiguous 48 states. This is caused by different geologic formations

---

hardness

A characteristic of water, caused primarily by the salts of calcium and magnesium. Hardness causes deposition of scale in boilers, damage in some industrial processes, and sometimes objectionable taste.

softening

The water treatment process that removes calcium and magnesium, the hardness-causing constituents in water.

lime–soda ash process

A precipitation process used to remove hardness from water.

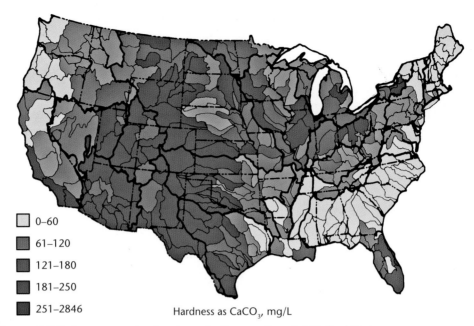

0–60
61–120
121–180
181–250
251–2846

Hardness as CaCO₃, mg/L

Figure 16-1 Average water hardness in the continental United States

and is also a function of the contact time between water and these formations. Calcium is dissolved as water passes over and through limestone deposits. Magnesium is dissolved as water passes over and through dolomite and other magnesium-bearing minerals. Because groundwater is in contact with these formations for a longer time than surface water, groundwater is normally harder than surface water, although this too depends on the geologic formation in which it is stored.

Expressing Hardness Concentration

Water hardness is most often expressed as a concentration of calcium carbonate ($CaCO_3$), in terms of milligrams per liter as $CaCO_3$. The degree of hardness that consumers consider objectionable varies, depending on other qualities of the water and the hardness concentration to which they have become accustomed. Table 16-1 shows two different classifications of the relative hardness of water.

Types of Hardness

Hardness is generally categorized as temporary (carbonate) or permanent (noncarbonate). Total hardness is the sum of calcium, magnesium, and all multivalent cations.

The calcium–magnesium distinction is based on the minerals involved. Hardness caused by calcium is called *calcium hardness*, regardless of the anions associated with it, which include calcium sulfate ($CaSO_4$), calcium chloride ($CaCl_2$), and others. Likewise, hardness caused by magnesium is called *magnesium hardness*. Calcium and magnesium are normally the only significant minerals that cause hardness. Iron, aluminum, and manganese cause hardness but are usually only present in low concentrations. It is generally assumed that

total hardness = calcium hardness + magnesium hardness

The carbonate–noncarbonate distinction, however, is based on hardness from either the bicarbonate salts of calcium or the normal salts of calcium and

Table 16-1 Comparative classifications of water for softness and hardness

Classification	mg/L as CaCO$_3$*	mg/L as CaCO$_3$†
Soft	0–75	0–60
Moderate	75–150	61–120
Hard	150–300	121–180
Very hard	Over 300	Over 180

*Per Sawyer (1960).
†Per Briggs and Ficke (1977).
Adapted from Sawyer 1960 and Briggs and Ficke 1977.

magnesium involved in causing water hardness. Carbonate hardness is caused primarily by the bicarbonate salts of calcium and magnesium, which are calcium bicarbonate, Ca(HCO$_3$)$_2$, and magnesium bicarbonate, Mg(HCO$_3$)$_2$. Calcium and magnesium combined with carbonate (CO$_3$) also contribute to carbonate hardness. Noncarbonate hardness is a measure of calcium and magnesium salts other than carbonate and bicarbonate salts. These salts are calcium sulfate, calcium chloride, magnesium sulfate (MgSO$_4$), and magnesium chloride (MgCl$_2$). Calcium and magnesium combined with nitrate (NO$_3^-$) may also contribute to noncarbonate hardness, although it is a very rare condition. For carbonate and non-carbonate hardness,

$$\text{total hardness} = \text{carbonate hardness} + \text{noncarbonate hardness}$$

When water is boiled, carbon dioxide is given off. Carbonate salts of calcium and magnesium then settle out of the water to form calcium and magnesium carbonate precipitates. These precipitates form the familiar chalky deposits on teapots. Because it can be removed by heating, carbonate hardness is sometimes called *temporary hardness*. Because noncarbonate hardness cannot be removed or precipitated by prolonged boiling, it is sometimes called *permanent hardness*.

Objections to Hard Water

Scale Formation

Hard water forms scale, usually calcium carbonate, which causes a variety of problems. Left to dry on the surface of glassware and plumbing fixtures, including shower doors, faucets, and sink tops, hard water leaves unsightly white scale known as *water spots*. Scale that forms on the inside of water pipes will eventually reduce the flow capacity or possibly block it entirely. Scale that forms within appliances and water meters causes wear on moving parts.

When hard water is heated, scale forms much faster. In particular, when the magnesium hardness is more than about 40 mg/L (as CaCO$_3$), magnesium hydroxide scale will deposit in hot water heaters operated at normal temperatures of 140–150°F (60–66°C). A coating of only 0.04 in. (1 mm) of scale on the heating surfaces of a hot water heater creates an insulation effect that will increase heating costs by about 10 percent.

Effect on Soap

The historical objection to hardness has been because of its effect on soap. Hardness ions form precipitates with soap, causing unsightly "curd," such as the familiar bathtub ring, as well as reduced efficiency in washing and laundering. To counteract these problems, synthetic detergents have been developed and are now used almost exclusively for washing clothes and dishes. These detergents have additives known as *sequestering agents* that "tie up" the hardness ions so that they cannot form the troublesome precipitates. Although modern detergents counteract many of the problems of hard water, many customers prefer softer water. These customers can install individual softening units or use water from another source, such as a cistern, for washing.

Aesthetic Concerns About Soft Water

Although various problems are caused by hard water, very soft water (near zero hardness) is also not desirable. It can leave a soap-scum feeling on the skin, and it is very corrosive to the water system and plumbing fixtures. For this reason, water systems that provide softening also limit the softening action or blend hard and softened water to provide moderately soft water to the system.

Although moderately soft water is usually preferable for consumer use, it still has a number of disadvantages. There may still be substantial corrosion of pipes and household appliances, which will shorten their service life. In addition, it may be determined that corrosion of lead and copper pipes and fittings will keep the system from meeting the requirements of the Lead and Copper Rule. The problems and corrective steps for reducing corrosion are discussed in Chapter 15.

Removal of Other Contaminants

Although chemical precipitation is normally selected as a treatment method because of its efficiency in softening, it is also useful for the removal of other contaminants. It is particularly effective at removing iron and manganese, heavy metals, radionuclides, dissolved organics, and viruses.

The Decision to Install Softening

The decision to add softening treatment to an existing or new water system depends on an analysis of the various considerations already discussed, including any other water problems that should or must be corrected. An example would be a water system that has a raw-water source that is relatively hard and also exceeds the maximum contaminant level (MCL) for radium. In this case, there may not be enough demand for softening to justify installing the necessary equipment, but softening can be provided at little additional cost in conjunction with the mandated radium removal.

If treatment for softening alone is the only consideration, the public must demand and support it because of the resulting increase in water rates. The cost of a new installation and the continuing added operating costs must be compared with the cost savings and advantages to customers. These benefits include prolonged life of plumbing equipment, reduced costs for washing soap and detergent, and improved aesthetic qualities of the water, which are often hard to quantify.

When water from a public system has been relatively hard over a period of years and central softening treatment is not provided, many homeowners and businesses install their own softeners. Some systems estimate that as many as 80 or 90 percent of their customers have installed softeners. Those systems would obviously find it difficult to justify installing central treatment for the sole purpose of softening the water. A special dilemma arises when one of these systems is required to install treatment (for instance, for radium removal) that will incidentally also accomplish softening. This creates the difficult public relations problem of informing customers that their softeners will no longer be necessary.

Softening Processes

This section discusses the processes that use precipitation, the use of coagulants in softening, and the chemical reactions involved in the lime–soda ash process.

Processes Using Precipitation

Several different softening processes involving precipitation can be used for potable water treatment.

Lime Softening

When the raw water contains little or no noncarbonate hardness, it can normally be softened through the use of lime alone.

Lime–Soda Ash Softening

Both lime and soda ash are necessary when there is a nominal amount of magnesium hardness in the water. When the lime and soda ash are added, the minerals form nearly insoluble precipitates, which are then removed by the conventional processes of flocculation, sedimentation, and filtration. Because the precipitates are very slightly soluble, some hardness remains in the water, amounting to about 50–85 mg/L as $CaCO_3$. This works out to be an advantage because completely soft water is undesirable. Treatment is typically performed through the single-stage process shown in Figure 16-2A. This is the process predominantly used in the United States.

Excess-Lime Treatment

It is usually desirable to reduce the magnesium hardness of water when it exceeds about 40 mg/L. To reduce the magnesium hardness, more lime must be added to the water than is used in the conventional lime–soda ash process. The extra lime will raise the pH above 10.6 so that magnesium hydroxide will precipitate out of the water.

When this treatment process is used, soda ash is added to remove noncarbonate hardness, and recarbonation must be used to reduce the pH of the water before it enters the distribution system. Excess-lime treatment can be performed in either a single-stage or double-stage process. The double-stage process (Figure 16-2B) allows greater removal of magnesium hardness and more control over the quality of the treated water.

Split Treatment

Split treatment is a modification of the excess-lime process and is used to reduce the amount of chemicals required. As shown in Figure 16-2C, only a portion of the water is treated with excess lime. A smaller remaining portion bypasses the treatment process, and the two are recombined. The amount of water bypassing lime treatment depends on the quality of the raw water and the desired quality of the finished water. The carbon dioxide and bicarbonate alkalinity in the untreated portion of water help stabilize the treated portion of water, which minimizes or eliminates the need for adding carbon dioxide for recarbonation. Systems that must meet requirements of the Surface Water Treatment Rule would probably not be able to use this process because it requires that part of the water bypass coagulation treatment.

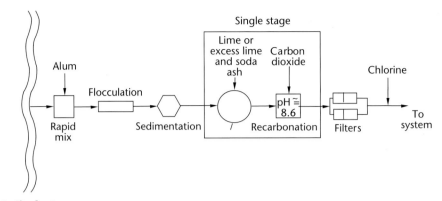

A. Single-stage process

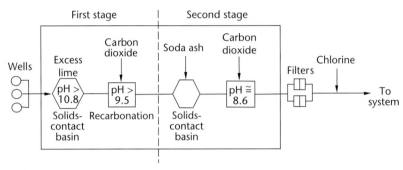

B. Double-stage process

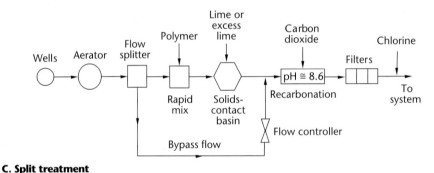

C. Split treatment

Figure 16-2 Types of lime–soda ash softening processes

Caustic-Soda Treatment

Caustic soda (sodium hydroxide, NaOH) can be used in place of lime and soda ash for softening and will remove both carbonate and noncarbonate hardness. The process is usually more expensive than lime or lime and soda ash treatment, and it also increases the total dissolved solids in the treated water. Some advantages are that it produces less sludge, and the chemical is much easier to store, feed, and handle than lime.

WATCH THE VIDEO
Lime Softening (www.awwa.org/wsovideoclips)

Study Questions

1. Which are the two principal chemicals that cause water hardness?
   a. Aluminum and iron
   b. Aluminum and calcium
   c. Iron and manganese
   d. Calcium and magnesium

2. Recarbonation is
   a. adding CO_2 to the water.
   b. adding bicarbonate to the water.
   c. adding acid to precipitate the excess lime.
   d. adding caustic soda.

3. Any material that forms a precipitate with the sodium salt of fatty acids (i.e., soap) can be referred to as
   a. rust.
   b. sulfate.
   c. hardness.
   d. residue.

4. Total hardness is the sum of calcium, magnesium, and
   a. iron.
   b. the primary anions.
   c. all multivalent cations.
   d. nitrate.

5. Which of the following can be used in place of lime and soda ash for softening and will remove both carbonate and noncarbonate hardness?
   a. Magnesium hydroxide
   b. Iron sulfate
   c. Magnesium sulfate
   d. Sodium hydroxide

6. When raw water contains little or no noncarbonate hardness, it can normally be softened through the use of
   a. lime alone.
   b. equal parts lime and soda ash.
   c. soda ash alone.
   d. caustic soda.

7. What comprises carbonate and noncarbonate hardness?

8. How is water hardness expressed?

9. Why is caustic-soda softening not a popular process even though it is effective?

10. What are the principal cations that cause water hardness?

Chapter 17

Introduction to Specialized Treatment Processes

Adsorption

Essentially all natural water contains varying amounts of carbon-containing substances that are dissolved from soil and vegetation. These substances are usually referred to as *natural organic matter*.

In addition, there are thousands of synthetic organic substances, and new ones are invented every day. These substances are generally termed *synthetic organic chemicals (SOCs)*. They include a wide range of pesticides, industrial chemicals, oils, and other manufactured chemicals. Well over 1,000 SOCs have been identified in drinking water at one location or another. Organic chemicals can also appear at an objectionable level in finished water as a result of reactions that take place in the water treatment process. The term most commonly used in referring to organic compounds from all of the different sources is organics.

The organics of interest in water are the following:

- Organic compounds that cause taste, odor, and color problems.
- SOCs that must be limited in drinking water because of concern about adverse health effects. Some are regulated by established maximum contaminant levels (MCLs), and many more have suggested limitations reported in health advisories.
- Organic precursors, principally humic and fulvic acids, that react with disinfectants to produce disinfection by-products (DBPs).
- DBPs that have been formed in the treatment process, such as trihalomethanes (THMs).

Additional information on organic substances may be found in Chapter 1.

Process Description

The adsorption process is used in the water works industry primarily for the removal of organic substances, so it is important to understand where the organics originate and why they are objectionable.

Organic Substance Occurrence and Concerns

Organics in Surface Water   Essentially all surface water contains some natural organic material. Many water systems that use surface sources have bothersome tastes, odors, or color in the source water at some time or another. Organic substances in the source water are also precursors for the development of THMs and other DBPs.

In addition, low levels of SOCs have been identified at times in most surface sources. They are usually so diluted and their presence so variable that they

> **organic compound**
> A chemical substance of animal or vegetable origin, having carbon in its molecular structure.

have not yet been regulated. Some water systems, however, have installed special organics removal systems because the overall level of organics is consistently quite high.

Organics in Groundwater Water from deeper wells usually contains relatively low levels of organics, but water from shallow wells, on occasion, has relatively high levels of humic substances drawn from the surrounding aquifer. In these cases, the water systems face the same operating problems as surface systems.

In addition, tests of groundwater sources in recent years have revealed that an alarmingly high percentage of wells are contaminated by detectable amounts of SOCs. Thousands of manufactured chemicals (such as pesticides and industrial solvents) have, over the years, been leaked, spilled, and disposed of near wells and have filtered down into the aquifer. In many cases, the chemicals have been identified as toxic or carcinogenic to humans at relatively low concentrations.

The concentrations detected in most contaminated wells amount to only a trace. In a great number of locations, however, the concentration is high enough that use of the water has been discontinued, or special treatment has been provided for SOC removal when no other water source was available.

Organic Chemical Removal

Removal at the Source The best place to control organics in drinking water is at the source. To control the organics level of raw water, surface water systems might locate the raw-water intake at a more favorable site, restrict certain human activities in the watershed, or control algae growth. Groundwater systems might establish restrictions on land use in the recharge zone or construct barriers to prevent contaminants from flowing toward a well in the aquifer (see Chapter 5).

Removal by Other Treatment Processes When organic chemicals cannot adequately be controlled at the source, they can often be removed by standard treatment processes. For instance, many taste- and odor-causing substances are sufficiently oxidized by chlorine to make the water quality acceptable. When chlorine is ineffective, permanganate, chlorine dioxide, or ozone may work better. In addition, aeration and the coagulation, sedimentation, and filtration processes work well for reducing the level of many organic substances.

Removal by Adsorption At times the conventional treatment processes are not effective enough to remove organics. In such instances, adsorption might be used instead of other treatment methods because it can be implemented quickly. It can also be more cost-effective than other treatments because of the size or location of the treatment site.

The Principle of Adsorption

Adsorption works on the principle of adhesion. In the case of water treatment, organic contaminants are attracted to the adsorbing material. They adhere to its surface by a combination of complex physical forces and chemical action.

For adsorption to be effective, the adsorbent must provide an extremely large surface area on which the contaminant chemicals can adhere. If the process is to be economical to build and operate, the total surface area of adsorbent required must be contained in a tank of reasonable size.

Porous adsorbing materials help achieve these objectives. Activated carbon is an excellent adsorbent because it has a vast network of pores of varying size to accept both large and small contaminant molecules. These pores give activated carbon a very large surface area. Just 1 lb (0.45 kg) of activated carbon has a total

adsorption
The water treatment process used primarily to remove organic contaminants from water. Adsorption involves the adhesion of the contaminants to an adsorbent, such as activated carbon.

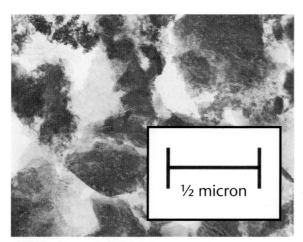

Figure 17-1 Details of the fine structure of activated carbon

Courtesy of Calgon Carbon Corp.

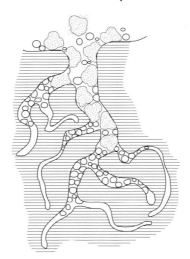

Figure 17-2 Carbon structure after activation showing small and large adsorbed chemical molecules

surface area of about 150 acres (60 ha). This amount of activated carbon can, for example, trap and hold over 0.55 lb (0.25 kg) of carbon tetrachloride.

Figure 17-1 is a photograph taken through an electron microscope showing the large number of pores in a grain of activated carbon. These pores are created during the manufacturing process by exposing the carbon to very high heat in the presence of steam. This process is known as *activating* the carbon. Activation oxidizes all particles on the surface of the carbon, leaving the surface free to attract and hold organic substances. Figure 17-2 shows the structure of the carbon after activation and indicates that different sizes of chemical molecules can be adsorbed within the pores.

Once the surface of the pores is covered by adsorbed material, the carbon loses its ability to adsorb. The spent carbon can then be reactivated by essentially the same process as the original activation, or it can be discarded and replaced with fresh carbon.

Aeration

Aeration is a gas transfer process used in water treatment to dissolve air into water. It is also used to remove volatile organics from water. The removal of a gas from water is a process called **air stripping** or *desorption*. Aeration is also used to reduce the concentration of taste- and odor-causing chemicals, to remove carbon dioxide from water in the cold lime–soda softening process following certain reverse osmosis systems, to remove volatile organics, and to remove radon gas. When aeration is used, it is often the first process at a treatment plant.

Process Description

A common example of aeration occurs naturally in a stream as water tumbles over rocks. Turbulence brings air and water into contact, and the air dissolves into the water.

How Aeration Removes or Modifies Constituents

Aeration is generally considered ineffective for the removal of most inorganic substances. In the few instances where it might be a usable technology, other treatment methods are more cost-effective or convenient.

aeration

The process of bringing water and air into close contact to remove or modify constituents in the water.

air stripping

A means of dissolving air into water (aeration) wherein water is distributed over the packing at the top of a tank and air is forced in at the bottom using a blower. Also called desorption.

The efficiency of the aeration process is governed by the amount of surface contact that can be achieved between air and water. The greater the surface area that is created, the greater the oxygen transfer that can be achieved. Contact is controlled primarily by the size of the water drops or air bubbles that provide the contact area. For example, the cubic foot of water shown in Figure 17-3A has 6 ft² of surface area. When the same volume is divided into eight equal pieces, 0.5 ft² each, as shown in Figure 17-3B, the exposed area is increased to 12 ft². If division of the cube is continued until each exposed face is 1/100 in., the surface area is increased to 7,200 ft².

Constituents Affected by Aeration

Aeration is commonly used in water treatment to absorb oxygen into water and for removal of the following substances:

- Carbon dioxide
- Hydrogen sulfide
- Methane
- Volatile organic chemicals
- Radon
- Iron and manganese (oxidation facilitates their removal)
- Tastes and odors

Carbon Dioxide   Carbon dioxide (CO_2) is very soluble in water. Up to 1,700 mg/L can be dissolved in water at 68°F (20°C). Deep-well water usually contains less than 50 mg/L, but shallow wells may have 50–300 mg/L. Surface water is usually low in CO_2, in the range of 0 to 5 mg/L. The exception is water drawn from a deep location in a lake that may have higher levels as a result of the respiration of microscopic animals and the lack of plant growth near the bottom.

When the CO_2 level in a water supply is above about 5 to 15 mg/L, it can cause the following operating problems:

- The acidity of the water is increased, making the water corrosive.
- The high CO_2 level tends to keep iron in solution, making iron removal more difficult.
- If lime softening is used, the CO_2 reacts with the lime, increasing the cost of softening because of the additional lime that must be used.

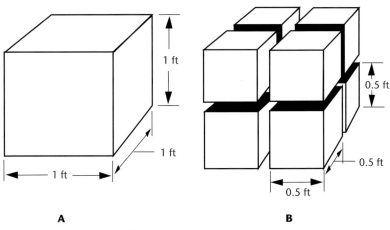

A   **B**

Figure 17-3 Increased surface area

Almost any type of aerator is able to remove CO_2. At normal temperatures, aeration can usually reduce the level to as little as 4.5 mg/L. Equilibrium between the CO_2 in the air and in the water prevents further removal.

Hydrogen Sulfide Hydrogen sulfide (H_2S) occurs mainly in groundwater supplies and is the cause of the rotten-egg odor occasionally noticed in some well water. Even at concentrations as low as 0.05 mg/L, H_2S in drinking water will alter the taste of coffee, tea, ice cubes, and many foods. The gas is corrosive to piping, tanks, water heaters, and other plumbing. Another objection by customers is that silverware washed in water containing H_2S may turn black.

In addition, H_2S is a poisonous gas that can be dangerous if released in a treatment plant. Breathing concentrations as low as 0.1 percent by volume in air for less than 30 minutes can be fatal.

H_2S is very unstable and is easily removed from water by almost any method of aeration. However, care must be taken that there is sufficient air movement in the vicinity of the aerator so that the gas is carried away. This will both facilitate the aeration process and prevent the inhalation danger to treatment plant personnel.

Methane Methane (CH_4) is commonly called "swamp gas." It is often found in groundwater supplies located near natural gas deposits. The gas alone is colorless, odorless, tasteless, and lighter than air, but when mixed with water, methane causes the water to taste like garlic. Methane is highly flammable and explosive when mixed with an appropriate proportion of air. It must be removed from water so that it does not accumulate in customers' homes, where it could cause an explosion.

Methane is only slightly soluble in water, so it is easily removed by aeration. Extreme care must be taken to thoroughly dissipate the gas that is removed.

Volatile Organic Chemicals "Manufactured" chemicals that have been found as contaminants in many groundwater supplies in recent years are called volatile organic chemicals (VOCs). The predominant VOCs found are listed in Table 17-1. VOCs regulated by the US Environmental Protection Agency (USEPA) are classified as known or suspected carcinogens, or as causing other adverse health effects.

When a well is found to be contaminated by VOCs in excess of the MCLs, and long-term removal must be used, aeration is usually found to be the most cost-effective method. Although VOCs can be removed by aeration, they are

Table 17-1 Volatile organic chemicals removable by air stripping

Benzene	Ethylene dibromide (EDB)
Carbon tetrachloride	Hexachlorocyclopentadiene
Di(2-ethylhexyl) adipate	Monochlorobenzene
Dibromochloropropane (DBCP)	Styrene
p-Dichlorobenzene	Tetrachloroethylene
o-Dichlorobenzene	Toluene
1,2-Dichloroethane	1,2,4-Trichlorobenzene
1,1-Dichloroethylene	1,1,1-Trichloroethane
cis-1,2-Dichloroethylene	1,1,2-Trichloroethane
trans-1,2-Dichloroethylene	Trichloroethylene
Dichloromethane (methylene chloride)	Vinyl chloride
1,2-Dichloropropane	Xylenes (total)
Ethylbenzene	

hydrogen sulfide (H_2S)

A toxic gas produced by the anaerobic decomposition of organic matter and by sulfate-reducing bacteria. Hydrogen sulfide has a very noticeable rotten-egg odor.

methane (CH_4)

A colorless, odorless, flammable gas formed by the anaerobic decomposition of organic matter. When dissolved in water, methane causes a garlic-like taste. Also called swamp gas.

volatile organic chemical (VOC)

A manufactured, synthetic chemical generally used as an industrial solvent. VOCs are classified as known or suspected carcinogens or as causing other adverse health effects. They are of particular concern to the water supply industry because they have widely been found as contaminants in groundwater sources.

significantly less volatile than CO_2 and H_2S, so more sophisticated packed tower aeration equipment is required to achieve acceptable removal.

Radon The radioactive gas, radon, is a natural decay product of uranium and a by-product when uranium is used in industry. The colorless, odorless gas is also found naturally in soil and rocks and can be found in groundwater sources of drinking water (rather than surface waters, such as rivers, lakes, and streams). Radon is a naturally occurring radioactive breakdown product of uranium that can dissolve and accumulate in groundwater. However, the primary source of human exposure to radon is inhalation of indoor air in homes. Radon can enter indoor air from soil under foundations. Most of the risk from radon in drinking water (nearly 90 percent) comes from breathing radon released to indoor air from household water uses. Radon is the second most common cause of lung cancer in the United States, after smoking.

Radon is readily released into the air when radon-contaminated water is agitated (e.g., in showers, washing machines, and dishwashers). Radon is particularly dangerous when released into a closed space and subsequently inhaled.

USEPA estimates that a concentration of 10,000 picocuries per liter (pCi/L) in water will emit about 1 pCi/L into the air. On October 19, 1999, USEPA proposed two options to states and water systems for reducing public health risks from radon in both drinking water and indoor air, a unique multimedia framework authorized and outlined in the 1996 amendments to the Safe Drinking Water Act (SDWA).

Under the first option, states can choose to develop enhanced state programs addressing radon in indoor air in conjunction with individual water systems meeting a drinking water standard of 4,000 pCi/L of water. USEPA is encouraging states to adopt this more cost-effective approach, which would address radon in indoor air while requiring individual water systems to reduce the higher levels of radon in drinking water. If a state does not elect this option, individual water systems in that state would be required to either reduce radon in their system's drinking water to 300 pCi/L or to develop individual indoor air radon programs and reduce levels in drinking water to 4,000 pCi/L. Water systems already at or below the 300 pCi/L standard would not be required to treat their water for radon.

Radon is removed from water by a number of processes, including reverse osmosis, ion exchange, granular activated carbon, and packed tower and diffused aeration. The most effective process for removal of radon from groundwater, when considering cost and footprint, is packed tower aeration. Lowry and Brandown (1987) report a liquid loading rate of 30 gpm/ft^2 and an air–water ratio of 15:1. Other processes are effective at point of use or point of entry where flow rates are low.

Design considerations when selecting a treatment process are air quality concerns from the exhaust gas and disposal of the residue. Activated carbon absorbers may be required.

Iron and Manganese Both iron and manganese are found in the dissolved form in many groundwater sources. They can also occasionally be a problem in surface water that is drawn from a stratified reservoir. The method typically used for removal of iron and manganese is to oxidize them to form a precipitate. This precipitate can then be removed by sedimentation and filtration. The processes are described in Chapter 12.

Manganese is not oxidized very well by aeration, but iron generally responds very well to just about any type of aeration process.

Tastes and Odors Volatile materials that cause tastes and odors are easily oxidized and generally can be removed by aeration. This includes a large percentage of the materials that cause tastes and odors in groundwater. Some materials, such as oils produced by some algae and some industrial chemicals, cause tastes and odors that cannot be removed adequately by aeration. These materials may respond to a chemical oxidant or may have to be removed by granular activated carbon.

Dissolved Oxygen   Dissolved oxygen (DO) is introduced into water by the process of aeration. A certain amount of DO in drinking water is beneficial in that it increases palatability by removing the "flat" taste. However, too much DO can cause the water to be corrosive.

Aeration of water may either add or release DO. For example, water from the bottom of a lake is usually low in DO, so aeration will increase the level. Conversely, water from a source with a large algae concentration is often supersaturated with DO because of the oxygen given off by the algae, so aeration will usually reduce the DO level.

The amount of oxygen that can remain dissolved in water depends on the water's temperature. The colder the water, the higher the possible concentration of DO. The saturation levels for DO in water at various temperatures are given in Table 17-2.

Table 17-2 Oxygen saturation (or equilibrium) levels in water

Temperature, °C	Saturation Concentration, mg/L	Temperature, °C	Saturation Concentration, mg/L
0	14.621	26	8.113
1	14.216	27	7.968
2	13.829	28	7.827
3	13.460	29	7.691
4	13.107	30	7.559
5	12.770	31	7.430
6	12.447	32	7.305
7	12.139	33	7.183
8	11.843	34	7.065
9	11.559	35	6.950
10	11.288	36	6.837
11	11.027	37	6.727
12	10.777	38	6.620
13	10.537	39	6.515
14	10.306	40	6.412
15	10.084	41	6.312
16	9.870	42	6.213
17	9.665	43	6.116
18	9.467	44	6.021
19	9.276	45	5.927
20	9.092	46	5.835
21	8.915	47	5.744
22	8.743	48	5.654
23	8.578	49	5.565
24	8.418	50	5.477
25	8.263		

Note: Values given for atmospheric pressure (101.3 kPa).

Adapted from *Standard Methods for the Examination of Water and Wastewater.* 15th ed. 1981.

Membrane Processes

The current regulatory environment in the municipal water industry, in particular, the Interim Enhanced Surface Water Treatment Rule (IESWTR), requires that the water industry remove or inactivate specific protozoa, viruses, and bacteria, and provide a minimum 3-log removal of *Cryptosporidium*. Some of these requirements can be met by chemical disinfection, but chemical dosing can result in higher concentrations of DBPs. Additionally, some protozoa and unwanted hardness or salinity, and heavy metals can be more readily removed with membrane processes.

The effect of the IESWTR and SDWA has been to lead the water treatment industry to nonconventional treatment methods, such as membranes. The trend in the United States is to develop technologies that reduce disinfectant demand and by-product formation, while at the same time improve disinfection requirements in the water treatment plant and the distribution system.

The USEPA regulation for arsenic in drinking water (MCL: 10 micrograms per liter [µg/L]) has increased the use of membrane processes for this contaminant. Arsenic is found in water in two forms—arsenite (AS III) and arsenate (AS IV). Since there is a difference in molecular weights of these two forms of arsenic, the removal efficiencies for each will differ with the pore size of the membrane chosen. Water systems have shown excellent removal of arsenic, however, and the advantage to small systems is important.

A large arsenal of membrane materials and platforms is available to treat most source waters and provide a long service life. For example, membrane materials such as polyvinylidene fluoride (PVDF) provide resistance to most oxidants and allow the integration of membranes with conventional disinfectant technologies to provide multiple-barrier treatment. Microfiltration (MF) and ultrafiltration (UF) systems combined with conventional coagulation offer innovative ways to reduce organics in potable water.

Membranes are used in municipal water treatment today for the separation of select microbiological pathogens, particulate matter, organic and inorganic species, and water softening.

Membrane systems

- provide precision barriers to contaminants,
- allow for rapid modular capacity expansions, and
- allow for treatment of lower-quality source water.

Compared to conventional treatment, membrane systems

- provide more consistent water quality,
- require less chemicals, and
- require smaller equipment footprint.

Types of Membrane Processes

In the simplest membrane processes, water is forced through a porous membrane under pressure while suspended solids (particulates), larger molecules, or ions are held back or rejected.

The two general classes of membrane processes, based on the driving force used to make the process work, are pressure-driven processes and electric-driven processes.

Pressure-Driven Processes

Pressure-driven membrane filtration is a process that uses a semipermeable (porous) membrane to separate particulate matter from soluble components in the carrier fluid, such as water. MF or UF membranes act much like a very fine sieve to retain particulate matter, while water and its soluble components pass through the membrane as filtrate or filtered water. The retained solids are concentrated in a reject or waste stream that is discharged from the membrane system. The pore size of the membrane controls the fraction of the particulate matter that is removed.

MF membranes currently enhance and, in some cases, substitute for conventional municipal water treatment processes. They enable a municipality to meet more stringent regulations. High-quality drinking water, with turbidity concentrations less than 0.05 ntu, can be attained by MF membranes, also resulting in treated water that exceeds SWTR log removal requirements for *Cryptosporidium* and *Giardia*. MF is also often used as effective pretreatment for spiral-wound nanofiltration (NF) and reverse osmosis (RO) membrane systems.

A pleated MF membrane is used today to provide a *Cryptosporidium* barrier for very high-quality groundwaters under the influence of surface water. This MF technology was also developed to serve as a *Cryptosporidium* guard filter for conventional water plants treating surface waters.

The following are the four general membrane processes that operate by applying pressure to the raw water:

- Microfiltration
- Ultrafiltration
- Nanofiltration
- Reverse osmosis

Figure 17-4 compares the sizes of substances that can be separated from water by these membrane processes. Pressure-driven membranes are defined and classified according to their nominal pore size or nominal molecular weight cutoff (MWCO). Nominal pore size refers to the smallest pore size in the membrane matrix. MWCO refers to the smallest molecule retained by the membrane, most often expressed in daltons (D). Table 17-3 summarizes contaminant removal by membrane type.

Table 17-4 provides a summary of the operating characteristics of the three primary membrane platforms in use today. Table 17-5 lists the most popular membrane materials in use today, their resistance to oxidants, and susceptibility

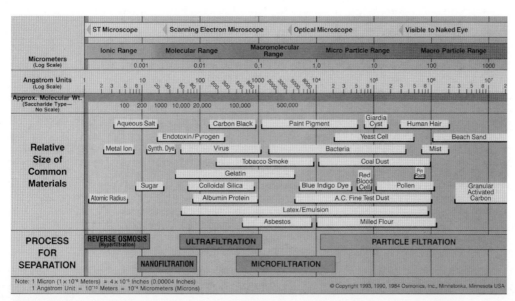

Figure 17-4 Comparison of sizes of particles removed by membrane processes
Courtesy of GE Osmonics, Minnetonka, Minnesota.

Table 17-3 Membrane removal of typical drinking water contaminants

Contaminant	MF	UF	NF	RO
Suspended solids	Yes	Yes	Yes	Yes
Dissolved solids	No	No	Some	Yes
Bacteria and cysts	Yes	Yes	Yes	Yes
Viruses	No	Yes	Yes	Yes
Dissolved organic matter	No*	No*	Yes	Yes
Iron and manganese	Yes, if oxidized		Yes†	Yes†
Hardness	No	No	Yes	Yes

*Could remove some with appropriate pretreatment.

†High levels will foul these membranes.

Table 17-4 Membrane platform characteristics

	Hollow Fiber	Spiral Wound	Pleated
Flux maintenance	Yes	Not generally	Yes
Chemical cleaning	Clean in place	Clean in place	Clean in place
Operating pressures	5–40 psi	20–100 psi	1–100 psi
Membrane life	3–10 years	8 years	3–10 years
Prefilter requirements	50–500 microns	5-micron cartridge to 0.1-micron microfilter	50–500 microns
Operating mode	Dead-end/ crossflow	Crossflow	Dead-end/ crossflow

Table 17-5 Characteristics of commercially available membranes

Membrane	Oxidant Resistance	Biodegradability	MF/UF	NF/RO
PP	Poor	No	Yes	
PE	Moderate	No	Yes	
PES	Good	No	Yes	
PVDF	Very good	No	Yes	Yes
Teflon	High	No	Yes	
CA	Moderate	Yes	Yes	Yes
Polyamide	Poor	No		Yes

PP = Polypropylene; PE = Polyethylene; PES = Polyethersulfone; PVDF = Polyvinylidene fluoride; Teflon = Polytetrafluoroethylene; CA = Cellulose acetate

to attack from microorganisms. Table 17-6 provides information on membrane area, typical expected fluxes, and recoveries for MF, UF, NF, and RO. A discussion of membrane terminology follows.

Microfiltration Microfiltration (MF) is a size-exclusion, pressure-driven membrane process that operates at ambient temperature. It is usually considered an intermediate between UF and multimedia granular filtration with pore sizes ranging from 0.03 to 1.2 microns. It is an effective barrier for particles, bacteria, and protozoan cysts. Operating pressures range from 5 to 30 psi (34 to 207 kPa).

Table 17-6 Design criteria for membrane processes

Type of Membrane	Element Construction	Membrane Area per Element	Typical Flux	Maximum Flux	Recovery per Stage
MF/UF	Hollow fiber	Up to 1,000 ft²	30–50 gfd	100 gfd	98%
NF/RO	Spiral wrap	Up to 500 ft²	10–15 gfd	25 gfd	80%

Ultrafiltration Ultrafiltration (UF) is a size-exclusion, pressure-driven membrane process that retains particulate, bacteria, protozoa, viruses, and organic molecules greater than their MWCO. Operating pressures range from 10 to 50 psi (69 to 345 kPa). Most UF systems used for water treatment range from 80,000 to 100,000 MWCO.

Nanofiltration Nanofiltration (NF) membrane systems retain dissolved organic compounds in the range of 200 to 400 D, essentially all multivalent cations and anions, and a fraction of the monovalent species. NF membranes are often used to soften water. They effectively remove DBP precursors, such as humic acid. Operating pressures range from 50 to 150 psi (345 to 1,034 kPa).

Reverse Osmosis Reverse osmosis (RO) membrane systems remove essentially all organic and inorganic constituents. Operating pressures range from 300 to 600 psi (2,068 to 4,137 kPa).

Compliance with the SDWA requires 3-log reduction of *Cryptosporidium* and *Giardia* and 4-log removal of viruses. *Cryptosporidium* and *Giardia* range in size from 3 to 15 microns. Viruses range in size from 0.02 to 0.08 microns. Although all membrane types are capable of meeting the SDWA, RO and NF membrane systems are more expensive because their high power requirements and low flux cannot compete with MF, UF, and conventional technologies.

Electric-Driven Processes

There are two membrane processes that purify a water stream by using an electric current to move ions across a membrane: electrodialysis and electrodialysis reversal. These types of systems are primarily used to treat brackish water for potable use.

Electrodialysis Electrodialysis (ED) is a process in which ions are transferred through a membrane as a result of a direct electric current applied to the solution. The current carries ions through a membrane from the less concentrated solution to the more concentrated one.

Electrodialysis Reversal Electrodialysis reversal (EDR) is a process similar to ED, except that the polarity of the direct current is periodically reversed. The reversal in polarity reverses the flow of ions between demineralizing compartments, which provides automatic flushing of scale-forming materials from the membrane surface. As a result, EDR can often be used with little or no pretreatment of feedwater to prevent fouling. Although innovative, ED and EDR have been used at only a few locations for drinking water treatment.

 WATCH THE VIDEO
Membranes (www.awwa.org/wsovideoclips)

reverse osmosis (RO)
A pressure-driven process in which almost-pure water is passed through a semipermeable membrane. Water is forced through the membrane and most ions (salts) are left behind. The process is principally used for desalination of sea water.

electrodialysis
A process in which ions are transferred through a membrane as a result of a direct electric current applied to the solution.

Ion Exchange

The **ion exchange** process is most often used in municipal water treatment to remove unwanted ions, such as arsenate, nitrate, and hardness (calcium and magnesium). Some utilities are using ion exchange processes to remove fulvates and humates in source water. Still others are using ion exchange to remove fluorides and anionic complexes of uranium. Ion exchange is a common alternative to cold process lime–soda ash softening.

Ion exchange units are equipped with synthetic resins, which are capable of stripping away the contaminant ions and exchanging them for more desirable ions. Many of these processes are reversible and allow the resins to be regenerated. The waste material from these units should be disposed of, which sometimes creates a challenge because of the concentrated contaminant levels in the waste. Resins provide long-term use, and with good care, they will serve the utility for periods that help amortize the costs. Some loss and breakdown of the media is expected, and poor operating conditions can hasten the loss. Operators typically refer to the number of "bed volumes" that can be treated before the bed is exhausted and needs to be regenerated. Bed volumes in the range of 300 to as many as 300,000 are seen in practice at utilities.

In the case of activated alumina beds, the material is in the form of alumina granules that are partially dissolved while in use. Activated alumina is used for fluoride and/or arsenate removal, especially in water high in total dissolved solids. It also is useful in removing humic substances in source water, and therefore is used to aid in compliance of DBP rules. The activated alumina process is sensitive to pH; anion removal is best at pH levels lower than 8.2.

A recent development in ion exchange processes that remove total organic carbon (TOC) in source water has been named *MIEX*, a registered trademark owned by Orica Watercare International of Australia. MIEX stands for *magnetic ion exchange resin*. Its use differs from other ion exchange processes in that it is fed as slurry into a mixing stage with the source water instead of remaining still in a bed. The material is about 10 times smaller than standard ion exchange beads; thus it can be mixed and held in suspension. The resin is comprised of magnetically enhanced polymeric beads. The suspension of these small beads creates relatively large surface areas. The magnetized particles settle rapidly in downstream stages where mixing is not taking place, and the TOC attached to the beads is removed.

Producers of exchange resins are able to engineer a wide variety of functioning chemical matrices onto resins and can also control exchange capacity and porosity. For these reasons, the ability to remove all sorts of source water contaminants exists. Other factors, such as expense, resin fouling from source water conditions, and brine/contaminant disposal, tend to determine the feasibility of ion exchange use at any given utility.

Ion Exchange Softening

When ion exchange units are used to soften water, they use a resin that releases the nonhardness-causing ion attached to it in favor of the hardness-causing ions present in the raw water. The resin holds the unwanted ion temporarily and releases it when a regenerant solution is used to restore the resin to its original form. The process of regeneration allows the resin to be reused.

The regeneration process using sodium chloride, or salt, as the regenerant involves the following chemical reactions:

$$CaX + 2NaCl \longrightarrow CaCl_2 + Na_2X$$

$$MgX + 2NaCl \longrightarrow MgCl_2 + Na_2X$$

ion exchange

A process used to remove hardness from water that depends on special materials known as resins. The resins trade nonhardness-causing ions (usually sodium) for the hardness-causing ions, calcium and magnesium. The process removes practically all the hardness from water.

The ion exchange softening process does not alter the pH or alkalinity of the water. However, the stability of the water is altered by the removal of calcium and by an increase in the total dissolved solids (TDS). For each 1 mg/L of calcium removed and replaced with sodium, the TDS increases 0.15 mg/L. For each 1 mg/L of magnesium removed and replaced with sodium, the TDS increases by 0.88 mg/L.

The measurements commonly used to express water hardness in the ion exchange softening process are different from those in the lime–soda ash process. Hardness in the lime–soda ash process is commonly expressed in terms of milligrams per liter as calcium carbonate ($CaCO_3$). In the ion exchange process, hardness is expressed in grains per gallon, simply referred to as *grains*. Currently, both grains/gallon and mg/L as $CaCO_3$ are used. The following conversion factors show the relationship between mg/L and grains:

1 grain = 17.12 mg/L

1 grain = 0.142 lb per 1,000 gal

7,000 grains = 1 lb per gal

Early ion exchangers were natural silica compounds called *zeolites*. Today, synthetic organic exchange materials are available with improved properties and expanded uses.

The ion exchange process requires the following basic components:

- Ion exchange materials (resins)
- Ion exchange units
- Salt storage tanks

Ion Exchange Resins

The majority of commercially available ion exchange resins are made by the copolymerization of the organic polymers, styrene and divinylbenzene (DVB). Styrene provides the basic matrix of the resin. DVB is used to cross-link the resin. Cross-linking provides insolubility and toughness to the resin. The degree of cross-linking determines the internal pore structure, which in turn affects the movement of ions into and out of the resin.

Figure 17-5 shows that a synthetic resin has a "whiffle ball," skeleton-like structure. It is insoluble in water, with electrically charged exchange sites holding ions of opposite charge at the exchange sites.

Synthetic resins are available in bead form and range in size from 20 mesh (0.84 mm in diameter) to 325 mesh (0.044 mm in diameter). Most ion exchange applications in water use resins in the 20- to 50-mesh size range. Figure 17-6 shows typical resin beads.

Each ion exchange resin has its own order of exchange preference. A bumping order based on valence exists. In general, trivalent is preferred over divalent, which is preferred over monovalent. Aluminum ions are preferred over calcium, and calcium is preferred over sodium. A bumping order, based on atomic number, exists for ions with the same valence; as such, sodium is preferred over hydrogen. This means that an ion exchanger can be used in either the sodium or calcium cycle to remove aluminum ions.

Cation Exchangers Cations are positively charged ions, such as calcium and magnesium, that migrate toward the cathode. Cation exchange resins are used to exchange unwanted positively charged cations with cation species, such as sodium or hydrogen.

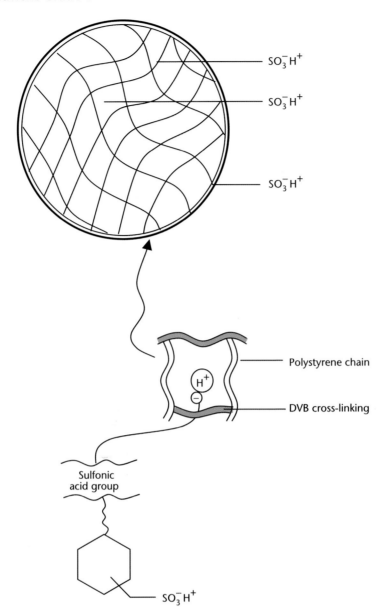

SO$_3^-$H$^+$

SO$_3^-$H$^+$

SO$_3^-$H$^+$

Polystyrene chain

H$^+$

DVB cross-linking

Sulfonic
acid group

SO$_3^-$H$^+$

Figure 17-5 Cation
exchange resin structure
Courtesy of Pall Corp.

Figure 17-6 Beads of
polystyrene resin
Courtesy of US Filter/Permutit.

Cation exchangers are available with different properties. The most common cation exchangers are called *strong-acid resins*.

Strong-acid cation exchangers exchange one cation for another and operate over the entire pH range. Their operating capacity (i.e., the practical usable portion or ion exchange capacity of an ion exchange resin bed) is less than stoichiometric. Strong-acid cation resins must be regenerated more frequently than weak-acid resins. Most strong-acid resins used in water treatment applications contain sulfonic acid functional groups (see Figure 17-5). These resins differ mainly in their DVB content or structure. Water softening applications (i.e., removal of calcium and magnesium ions) typically use strong-acid resins.

Weak-acid cation exchangers are not highly dissociated. They operate only above pH 4. The functional group is the organic compound carboxylic acid. Weak-acid cation exchangers remove more cations per unit volume than strong-acid resins and generate almost stoichiometrically. They are sometimes used in conjunction with a strong-acid polishing resin. This combination allows for economic operation in terms of regenerant requirements but also produces a treated water of quality comparable to the use of just a strong-acid resin.

Anion Exchangers   Anions are negatively charged ions, such as nitrate and sulfate, that migrate toward the anode. Anion exchange resins are used to exchange unwanted anions with anion species, such as chloride or hydroxide. If cations are exchanged for hydrogen and the anions exchanged for hydroxide, the result is HOH, or demineralized water.

Anion exchangers were developed almost exclusively as synthetic resins. Organic exchangers were among the earliest ion exchange resins produced. The first patents issued for anion exchangers were for resins having weak-base amino groups. Later, resins with strong-base quaternary ammonium groups were prepared.

Strong-base anion exchangers operate over the entire pH range, but their capacity is less than stoichiometric. Like strong-acid resin cation exchangers, they must be regenerated more frequently than weak-base resins, which exhibit much higher capacities and regenerate almost stoichiometrically. A problem with strong-base resins is that they tend to irreversibly sorb humic acid substances, losing capacity. Activated carbon or a weak-base organic trap is typically used to prevent resin fouling.

Weak-base anion exchange resins behave much like their weak-acid counterparts. They do not remove anions above a pH of 6. They regenerate with a nearly stoichiometric amount of base (with the regeneration efficiency possibly exceeding 90 percent) and are resistant to organic fouling. They do not remove carbon dioxide or silica, and they have capacities about twice as great as that of strong-base exchangers. They are useful following strong-acid exchangers to save the cost of regenerant chemicals. They act as organic "traps" to protect strong-base exchangers and to remove color. Weak-base resins have a higher capacity for the removal of chlorides, sulfates, and nitrates. For waters containing organic contaminants (humic and fulvic acids), macroreticular weakly basic anion resins are preferred.

Ion Exchange Units

The vessels used in ion exchange systems (Figure 17-7) resemble those used in pressure filters. A major difference is that the interior of the tanks is coated with a special lining to protect them from the corrosion caused by the brines (high salt concentration) used in regeneration.

Figure 17-7 Ion exchange pressure tanks

Courtesy of Ionics, Inc.

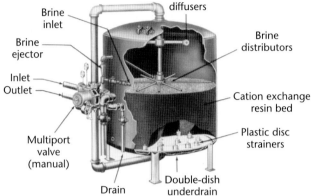

Figure 17-8 Vertical-downflow ion exchange unit

Courtesy of US Filter/Permutit.

Figure 17-8 is a cutaway view of a vertical-downflow ion exchange unit designed with the following components:

- Hard-water inlet
- Soft-water outlet
- Wash-water inlet and collector
- Brine inlet and distribution system
- Brine and rinse-water outlet
- Rate-of-flow controllers
- Sampling taps
- Underdrain system, which also serves to distribute backwash water
- Graded gravel to support the ion exchange resins

Both upflow and downflow ion exchange units are available. Units designed for the water to flow downward are more commonly used because they can be operated at higher flow rates during the softening cycle. All units are equipped with automatic controls.

The size of the ion exchange unit and the volume of resin required are determined by the concentration of ions to be removed; for example, unit size may depend on the hardness of the raw water and the desired length of time between regenerations. The minimum recommended depth is 24 in. (0.6 m). The resin is supported either by an underdrain system or by 15–18 in. (0.40–0.5 m) of graded gravel.

In downflow units, a regenerant distribution system is used to direct the flow of regenerant downward and evenly through the unit during regeneration so that all resin comes into contact with it. The rinse water can be distributed through the same system.

Regenerant Storage Tanks (Softening)

Sodium chloride or potassium chloride are the most common salts used in the water softening process to form brine, which is used to regenerate the resin. The amount of salt used in creating the brine ranges from 0.25 to 0.45 lb (0.11 to

0.20 kg) for every 1,000 grains of hardness removed (7,000 grains = 1 lb, 1 grain/gal = 17.1 mg/L).

The salt is normally stored in tanks large enough to hold brine for a 24-hour period of operation or for three regenerations, whichever is greater. Salt brines are corrosive to salt attacks and wear away concrete and steel and stainless steel. Tanks are coated with a salt-resistant material.

The salt used for resin regeneration must meet standards for purity. Rock salt or pellet-type salt is the best for preparing the brine. Road salt is not suitable because it often contains impurities. Block salt is sometimes used for home softeners, but it is not suitable for larger installations because its small surface area does not allow it to dissolve fast enough. Fine-grained salt, such as table salt, is not suitable because it packs tightly and does not dissolve easily.

Salt storage tanks are covered to prevent dirt and foreign material from entering. The access holes in the cover should have raised lips so that any dirty water on the cover does not flow into the hole and contaminate the salt.

To fill a salt storage tank and prepare the brine, water is added to the tank and the tank is filled with rock salt. More water is then added to submerge the salt so that it will dissolve. The water fill line must allow for an air gap above the top of the tank to prevent the possibility of brine siphoning back into the water supply. An excess of undissolved salt should be kept in the tank to ensure that a concentrated solution is achieved.

Because brine is heavier than water, the highest concentration of brine will be in the lower part of the storage tank. The brine used for regeneration is therefore usually pumped from the bottom of the tank.

Other Disinfectants

Ozone

Ozone was first used as a disinfectant in the Netherlands in 1893. A few years later, a permanent installation for a continuous ozonator was built in Nice, France. Until the outbreak of *Cryptosporidium* in 1993 in Milwaukee, Wisconsin, only a handful of US water treatment plants used ozone. Since 1993, many utilities have resorted to its use.

Ozone (O_3) must be generated on-site, because it is an unstable gas (Figure 17-9). The formula for the ozone reaction is

$$O_2 + energy \longrightarrow O + O$$

$$O + O_2 \longrightarrow O_3$$

The elemental, or nascent, oxygen produced in the first reaction is provided by an electrical discharge with large amounts of voltage. The air or oxygen that is used must be dry and refrigerated, and it must be particle-free. The yield of ozone can be up to 14 percent by volume.

Ozone is very unstable in water, and maintaining a **residual** is difficult. High-alkalinity waters allow for a more stable ozone residual, which is very reactive with natural organic material in the source water. When the residual reacts with the organic contaminants, it oxidizes them to a lower-molecular-weight species, including a variety of organic acids. Because these acids may contribute to biofouling of the distribution system, they are usually controlled using biologically active filtration. Ozone may also react with waters containing bromide and thus produce bromate, bromoform, and other DBPs.

residual

An excess of chemical left in the water after treatment. The presence of disinfectant residuals indicates that an adequate amount of disinfectant has been added at the treatment stage to ensure completion of all reactions with some disinfectant remaining.

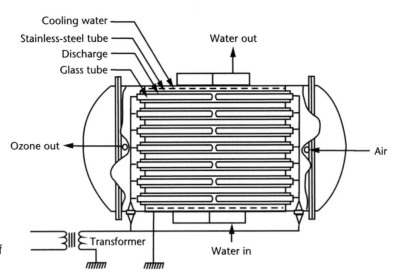

Figure 17-9 Schematic of an ozone generator

It is difficult to understand or study how ozone attacks and kills pathogens because it is difficult to measure low concentrations of dissolved ozone.

Ozone off-gas collection systems are necessary because ozone is toxic. It must be kept within Occupational Safety and Health Administration limits in the plant and surrounding areas and may be regulated as a discharge gas in some cases. The dissolution of ozone in water produces such a corrosive product that stainless-steel tanks and fluorocarbon gaskets are a must; basins used are made of concrete and caulked with an inert material.

Chlorine Dioxide

Chlorine dioxide is a greenish yellow gas at room temperature and is odorous like chlorine. Because it is unstable at high concentrations, it is never shipped in bulk but rather generated on-site. Gaseous chlorine dioxide is generated from solutions of sodium chlorite that have been reacted with chlorine solutions at low pH levels. In solution, the chlorine dioxide remains in its molecular form, ClO_2. The gas formation is shown in the following two reactions:

$$\text{Using chlorine: } 2NaClO_2 + Cl_2(g) \longrightarrow 2ClO_2(g) + 2Na^+ + 2Cl^-$$

$$\text{Using hypochlorous acid: } 2NaClO_2 + HOCl \longrightarrow 2ClO_2(g) + 2Na^+ + Cl^- + OH^-$$

Excess chlorine is often used in the generation step to drive the reaction to completion and to avoid the presence of unreacted chlorite. Chlorine dioxide can be dissolved in water and is stable in the absence of light and elevated temperatures. At higher pH and at higher temperatures, chlorine dioxide can revert to chlorite and chlorate, which are undesirable in drinking water. Chlorine dioxide was developed to aid in taste-and-odor control but is also used to destroy iron and manganese. Its use as a primary disinfectant for water supplies has gained popularity because it produces less DBPs than chlorine and is effective against *Cryptosporidium*.

Taste-and-odor problems may occur at residuals greater than 0.5 mg/L. Because it introduces chlorite to the water, which can cause certain types of anemia, its use is limited to a USEPA maximum residual disinfectant level (MRDL) of 0.8 mg/L.

Plant Waste Treatment Process Description

The majority of wastes generated in conventional or softening water treatment plants come from two sources: the naturally occurring contaminants in the source water and the treatment chemicals used in the process to purify the water. In plants that use a relatively clean source, the chemicals will make the largest contribution to solids production. Plants that rely on sources subject to large runoff events or are otherwise low in quality may produce residuals comprised mostly of the naturally occurring contaminants. Full knowledge of the quantity and quality of the solids is important for compliance efforts.

Wastes from ion exchange plants typically are the brines produced in the regeneration process, which will include the ions removed in the exchange. Wastes from membrane plants are composed of the concentrate that is discarded and the backwash and cleaning agents used to remove foulants.

When the water treatment plant needs to dispose of its wastes, it will use manual or mechanical methods to remove the accumulated floc, sludge, or residuals for collection into some sort of holding area or basins for future disposal. Ideally, the handling facilities are designed large enough so that upstream unit processes can be operated without interruption, and disposal of wastes can take place in an orderly fashion with planned frequency and scheduling.

Residual Facilities and Operations

Residuals are comprised of all of the unwanted material that has been removed from the water and all of the compounds that are created by the addition of treatment chemicals (floc, lime solids, etc.). Alum sludge is the most common form of residual material produced in water plant sedimentation basins, but ferric sludge also is common. Both of these wastes come from the filter backwash process or the sedimentation basins at low concentrations by weight. Disposal of this low concentration of sludge is inefficient, and so water plant operators must use techniques that dewater and concentrate it.

Dewatering is the process of removing water from the thin sludge, allowing the solid material to remain (thickening) for ultimate disposal. Dewatering of alum and ferric sludges is difficult because the water is chemically bound to the aluminum and ferric hydroxide floc. These flocs are gelatinous, and thus difficult to handle. As a rule of thumb, the thicker the sludge, the less space it takes up, and so the less storage facilities the plant will need. Additionally, the thicker the sludge, the less expensive it is to dispose. Wastewater plants and landfills usually charge by volume of material they receive (there may be other surcharges for strength of solids, or for special considerations due to the nature of the sludge). Disposal of thin sludge, therefore, forces the water plant operator to pay for disposal of a larger proportion of water than may be necessary.

In many water treatment plants, sludge from processes is pumped to a gravity thickener designed to dewater the waste to a specific concentration before disposal. The thickener is a gravity system that allows the solids to settle to the bottom and provides for removal of the clear supernatant at the top of the unit. Supernatant from the thickener is either returned to the process or is sent to waste. The thickener also serves as an equalization tank; it allows for continuous or intermittent wasting of solids that might otherwise burden the receiving sewers or treatment facility.

Further treatment of the sludge after thickening can take place in the plant or at the site of disposal. Water treatment plants often treat thickened sludge with polymers or lime and may subject the sludge to flotation or belt press thickening to obtain the desired concentration. When sand drying beds, lagoons, and freeze-thawing beds are employed, the process is referred to as *nonmechanical dewatering*. Mechanical dewatering of sludge is usually accomplished by use of vacuum filtration, belt presses, and centrifuges. All of the processes are effective, but costly. Each water treatment plant needs to determine the most cost-effective procedure for its situation, taking into account all of the economic factors at its disposal. Local regulations will also be a factor.

Spent filter backwash water (SFBW) from conventional water treatment plants is sometimes recycled. This waste will benefit from simple settling in static tanks or from settling in dynamic sedimentation basins if the overflow rate is kept low, especially if the stream is treated with a polymer. Equalization basins can allow for better operational control of the SFBW sedimentation process by allowing the downstream sedimentation basins to operate at a controlled flow. Controlled flow through sedimentation basins allows operators greater control over polymer dosage and allows the operator to reintroduce the SFBW to the head of the plant at a desirable percentage of the total source water flow.

Study Questions

1. Which process is used to concentrate sludge?
   a. Sand bed
   b. Solar lagoon
   c. Thickener
   d. Centrifuge

2. Powdered activated carbon is usually added to the treatment process
   a. before the normal coagulation–flocculation step.
   b. before the sedimentation basin.
   c. after the sedimentation basin.
   d. in the filters.

3. In the ion-exchange softening process, once the resin can no longer soften water, it must be
   a. renewed.
   b. recatalyzed.
   c. regenerated.
   d. recharged.

4. The best place to control organics in drinking water is
   a. in the treatment plant.
   b. at the point of use.
   c. at the source.
   d. in the aqueduct.

5. Methane is only slightly soluble in water, so it is easily removed by
   a. air stripping.
   b. desorption.
   c. adsorption.
   d. aeration.

6. Ozone is _____, and maintaining a residual is difficult.
   a. very unstable in water
   b. extremely dense
   c. unlikely to react with other elements found in water
   d. nontoxic

7. What regulated substances can be removed by aeration?

8. Which membrane process is most commonly call a "softening" membrane?

9. Why is ultraviolet disinfection most suitable for groundwater?

10. What is the term for the gas transfer process used in water treatment to dissolve air into water?

11. What is the process in which ions are transferred through a membrane as a result of a direct electric current applied to the solution?

Chapter 18
Introduction to Electrical Systems

Electricity and Magnetism

For purposes of explanation, electricity is often classified as either static or dynamic. Both forms of electricity are composed of large numbers of electrons, and both forms interact with magnetism. The study of the interaction of electricity and magnetism is called **electromagnetics**.

Static Electricity

Static electricity refers to a state in which electrons have accumulated but are not flowing from one position to another. Static electricity is often referred to as electricity at rest. Once given the opportunity, it is ready to flow. An example of this phenomenon is often experienced when one walks across a dry carpet and then touches a doorknob; a spark at the fingertips is likely noticed and a shock is usually felt. Static electricity is often caused by friction between two bodies, as by rotating machinery—conveyor belts and the like—moving through dry air. Another common example of static electricity is the natural buildup of static electricity between clouds and the earth that results in an electrical discharge—a lightning bolt. In this case, the friction occurs between the air molecules. Static electricity is prevented from building up by properly bonding equipment to ground or earth.

Dynamic Electricity

Dynamic electricity is electricity in motion. Motion can be of two types—one in which the electrical current flows continuously in one direction (direct current), and a second in which the electrical current reverses its direction of flow in a periodic manner (alternating current).

Direct Current

Current that flows continuously in one direction is referred to as **direct current (DC)**. In this case, the voltage remains at a fixed polarity, or direction, across the path through which the current is flowing. Direct current is developed by batteries and can also be developed by rotating-type DC generators.

Alternating Current

Electrical current that reverses its direction in a periodic manner—rising from zero to maximum strength, returning to zero, and then going through similar variations of strength in the opposite direction—is referred to as **alternating current (AC)**. In this case, the voltage across the circuit varies in potential force in a

electromagnetics
The study of the combined effects of electricity and magnetism.

static electricity
A state in which electrons have accumulated but are not flowing from one position to another. Static electricity is often referred to as electricity at rest.

direct current (DC)
Current that flows continuously in one direction.

alternating current (AC)
Electrical current that reverses its direction in a periodic manner.

periodic manner similar to the variations in current. Alternating current is generated by rotating-type AC generators.

Induced Current

A change in current in one electrical circuit will induce a voltage in a nearby conductor. If the conductor is configured in such a way that a closed path is formed, the induced voltage causes an induced current to flow. This phenomenon is the basis for explaining the property of a transformer. Since changes of current are a requirement for a transformer to operate, it is obvious that DC circuits cannot use transformers, whereas AC circuits are adaptable to the use of transformers. The function of a transformer is of great value because it allows the voltage of the induced current to be increased or diminished.

Electromagnetics

The behavior of electricity is determined by two types of forces: electrical and magnetic. A familiar example of the electrical force is the static force that attracts dust to phonograph records in dry climates. The magnetic force holds a horseshoe magnet to a piece of iron and aligns a compass with magnetic north. Wherever there are electrons in motion, both forces are created. These electromagnetic forces act on the electrons themselves and on the matter through which they move. Under certain conditions, the motion of electrons sends electromagnetic waves of energy over great distances. Figure 18-1 shows an electrical current being produced when a coil of wire is moved through a magnetic field.

Electromagnetic energy is responsible for the transmission of a source of power. Because of electromagnetic energy, power can be transmitted across the air gap between the stator and rotor of a motor. Radio waves are electromagnetic. Radar is electromagnetic. So is light, which, unlike most forms of electromagnetic waves, can be seen. The doorbell is an electromagnetic device; so is the solenoid valve on your dishwasher. In fact, much of the electrical equipment with which you are familiar is electromagnetic; your clock motor, the alternator on your car, and the electric typewriter use electromagnetics.

You will find it worthwhile to make your own list of equipment and appliances that are all-electric and that are electromagnetic. You will be surprised at how much you already know about this subject.

In fact, because electricity is such a part of everyday life, even persons who have not studied electricity know more about it today than did early scientific observers. Electricity is often taken for granted, but it can be dangerous and should be respected. Every operator should become familiar with safety rules and practices pertaining to electricity.

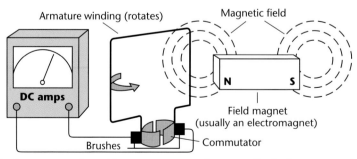

Figure 18-1 Current produced in a generator when a coil of wire moves through a magnetic field

Electrical Measurements and Equipment

The following paragraphs introduce the basic terminology used to describe electricity and electrical equipment. To help illustrate the new concepts, the behavior of electricity is compared to the behavior of water (Figure 18-2).

Molecule of liquid ↔ electron of electricity. The smallest unit of liquid is a molecule, whereas the smallest unit of electricity is an electron.

Flow rate (gpm) ↔ current (A). The rate at which water flows through a pipe is expressed as gallons per minute (gpm) or liters per minute (L/min). It could be expressed as molecules per minute, but the numbers involved would be inconveniently large. Similarly, the rate at which electricity flows through a conductor (called current) could be expressed as electrons per second, but the numbers involved would be too large to be practical. Therefore, the unit of electrical current commonly used is the ampere (A), which represents a flow rate of about 6,240,000,000,000,000,000 electrons per second (also termed 1 coulomb per second). The flow rate of liquid expressed in gallons per minute is, therefore, analogous to the flow rate (current) of electricity expressed in amperes.

Pressure (psi) ↔ potential (V). Liquid flow requires a certain head or pressure. The liquid will tend to flow from the high pressure to the low pressure. Electrical potential is similar to head or pressure. Electrical current will always tend to flow from high potential to low potential. Electrical potential is expressed in terms of volts (V). Whereas liquid pressure is generally expressed in terms of pounds per square inch with reference to atmospheric pressure, electrical potential is generally expressed in terms of voltage with respect to ground or earth, with the general assumption that ground or earth is at zero potential.

Pressure drop ↔ voltage drop. The flow of liquid through a pipe is accompanied by a pressure drop as a result of the friction of the pipe. This pressure drop is often referred to as friction head loss. Similarly, the flow of electricity through a wire is accompanied by a voltage drop as a result of the resistance of the wire.

Friction ↔ resistance. The flow of water through a pipe is limited by the amount of friction in the pipe. Similarly, the flow of electricity through a wire is limited by resistance.

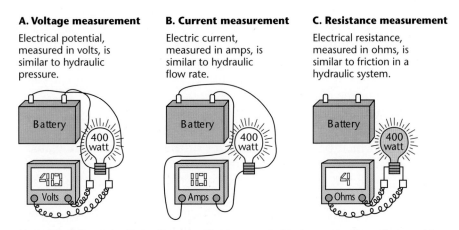

A. Voltage measurement

Electrical potential, measured in volts, is similar to hydraulic pressure.

B. Current measurement

Electric current, measured in amps, is similar to hydraulic flow rate.

C. Resistance measurement

Electrical resistance, measured in ohms, is similar to friction in a hydraulic system.

NOTE: Ohm's law states that voltage drop E across an electrical component equals current I flowing through the component multiplied by resistance R of the component: $E = IR$.

Figure 18-2 Representation of Ohm's law

Pump ↔ *generator.* A pump uses the energy of its prime mover, perhaps a gasoline engine, to move water; the pump creates pressure and flow. Similarly, a generator, powered by a prime mover such as a gasoline engine or a water turbine, causes electricity to flow through the conductor; the generator creates voltage and current.

Turbine ↔ *motor.* A water-driven turbine, like those found in hydroelectric power stations, takes energy from flowing water and uses it to turn the output shaft. An electric motor uses the energy of an electrical current to turn the motor shaft.

Turbine-driven pump ↔ *motor-driven generator.* A turbine running off a high-pressure, low–flow-rate stream of water (or hydraulic fluid) can be used to drive a pump to move water at low pressure, but at a high flow rate. (Such an arrangement might be useful for dewatering, for example, although it is not common.) Similarly, a motor operating from a high-voltage, low-current source can be used to run a generator having a low-voltage, high-current output. Note that both the water system and the electrical system could be reversed, taking a source with a low pressure (voltage) and high flow rate (current) and creating an output with a high pressure (voltage) and low flow rate (current). The motor-driven generator (also called a dynamotor) is sometimes used to convert DC battery power to a higher-voltage, lower-current AC power.

Turbine-driven pump ↔ *AC transformer.* For most electrical applications, the motor-driven generator is replaced with a transformer, which does exactly the same thing—it transforms low-voltage, high-current electricity into high-voltage, low-current electricity; or, it can transform high-voltage, low-current into low-voltage, high-current electricity. The transformer will work only with alternating current. It is a very simple device that uses the electromagnetic properties of electricity.

Reservoir ↔ *storage battery.* Liquids can be stored in tanks and reservoirs, whereas direct-current electricity can be stored in batteries and capacitors.

Flooding ↔ *short circuits.* The washout of a dam or the break of a water main can cause various degrees of flooding and damage, depending on the pressure and, more important, on the quantity of water that is released. Similarly, an electrical fault current, referred to as a short circuit, can cause excessive damage, depending on the voltage and, more important, on the quantity of electrical energy that is released. This latter item, the quantity of electrical energy that might be released, is referred to as the short-circuit capability of the power system. It is important to recognize that the short-circuit capability determines the physical size and ruggedness of the electrical switching equipment required at each particular plant. In other words, for nearly identical plants, the electrical equipment may be quite different in size because of the different short-circuit capabilities of the power system at the plant site.

Instantaneous transmission of pressure ↔ *electricity.* When we let water into a pipe that is already filled, the water that we let into the pipe at one end is not the same as that which promptly rushes out of the other end. The water we let in pushes the water already in the pipe out ahead of it. The pressure, however, is transmitted from end to end almost instantaneously. The action of electricity is much the same. The electrical current in a wire travels from end to end at high speeds, very close to that of light. However, individual electrons within the wire move relatively slowly and over short distances. When a light switch is turned on, the power starts the electrons on their way.

The purpose of this chapter is to introduce the key elements of electricity. To ensure that an electrical system is operating correctly, the operator must be able to measure and assess the presence of these elements and understand their significance.

WATCH THE VIDEO
Instrumentation (www.awwa.org/wsovideoclips)

Treatment Plant Instrumentation and Control Basics

Electrical instrumentation and control systems are vital to the efficient operation of water treatment plants. Meters, recorders, alarms, and automatic control systems are installed in a water plant primarily for the following reasons:

- To provide information for the operation of equipment
- To meet state and federal requirements
- To improve the efficiency of operation
- To provide historical records
- To provide more precise control of equipment
- To improve the safety of working conditions
- To reduce the workload on operators

The most basic instrumentation is that which is required for the operation of plant equipment. Instruments such as turbidimeters and the loss-of-head gauges on filters are absolutely necessary for plant operation.

State regulations typically require data on plant pumpage, chemical quantities used, and details of equipment and process information (such as the plant effluent chlorine residual required by the Surface Water Treatment Rule [SWTR]). Even the smallest treatment systems must provide a number of flowmeters and analyzing tools in order to meet these requirements.

Many instruments are available to improve the efficiency of treatment plant operations. The reliability, simplicity of operation, and cost of many types of instruments have improved over the past 20 years to where the instruments are now affordable for even small systems. Continuous turbidity monitors are common in treatment plants. Particle counters have become commonplace in treatment plants and have proven to provide much more resolution as to the effluent quality of filters. Streaming current detectors and other instruments designed to assist in the efficient use of coagulants are installed in many treatment plants.

All water systems should maintain good records of plant operations. Historical data and trending allows the operator to improve plant performance by linking events that show on trends with operational events or practices.

In addition to documenting a system's operation, in the event the system is questioned by the public or authorities, historical records are important to engineers who design plant improvements. Recorder charts from flowmeters, pressure indicators, and automatic analysis instruments provide important records for these purposes.

A great deal of instrumentation is available to replace manual control or visual inspection. Automatic control is typically used to relieve the operator of some duties to make time available for other work, or because it is more accurate or will eliminate the chance of human error. For example, a chlorinator might be automated so that a uniform residual is maintained regardless of chlorine demand or pumping rate. Not only is this approach more accurate than manual control, but it also eliminates the possibility of an incorrect feed caused by human error.

For these reasons, automation continues to be used in water treatment plants every day. As a result, there is a greater number of meters and control systems that the operator must understand and use properly. A balance between good experience and up-to-the-minute automation is the best set of tools that a water treatment plant staff can achieve.

There is a tendency for engineers to design state-of-the-art controlling devices into water plants in an effort to "free up" time for other tasks, or to allow for minimal or remote staffing of facilities. While it is quite possible to design and build just about any nonhuman controlling and monitoring device, the operators of water treatment plants still play a significant role in the decisions made to retrofit or build new automated processes. As automation of processes has evolved, so too have the incidences of treatment mishap because operators were not present to observe pending problems. Even as of now, designers have not created a foolproof system for water treatment plants that completely outperforms an experienced human. Within reason, the operator also must learn to maintain and repair this new equipment. Many analyzers, for instance, require regular cleaning, replacement of elements, and recalibration. Most electronic equipment cannot be repaired locally, but sometimes key elements can simply be replaced or returned to the factory.

Study Questions

1. Which basic electrical unit is used to measure a material's opposition to the flow of electricity?
   a. Ampere
   b. Ohm
   c. Volts
   d. Resistance or impedance

2. Which device consists of a pair of metallic plates that are separated by an insulating material called a dielectric?
   a. Storage battery
   b. Voltage regulator
   c. Rectifier
   d. Capacitor

3. Which of the following is *not* a reason that meters, recorders, alarms, and automatic control systems are installed in a water plant?
   a. To provide information for the operation of equipment
   b. To reduce the need for written documentation
   c. To improve the efficiency of operation
   d. To improve the safety of working conditions

4. The flow rate of liquid expressed in _____ is analogous to the flow rate of electricity expressed in amperes.
   a. gallons per day
   b. liters per minute
   c. megaliters per day
   d. gallons per minute

5. What are some of the concerns about automatic control of treatment plant processes?

6. What is SCADA and how is it useful?

7. Give an example of feed-forward control.

8. Friction reduces the flow of water through a pipe like _____ reduces the flow of electricity through a wire.

9. Electricity is often classified as either static or what?

10. Static electricity is often referred to as what?

11. What type of electrical current flows continuously in one direction?

Chapter 19

Pumps

Types of Pumps

Two basic categories of pumps are used in water supply operations: velocity pumps and positive-displacement pumps. Velocity pumps, which include centrifugal and vertical turbine pumps, are used for most distribution system applications. Positive-displacement pumps are most commonly used in water treatment plants for chemical metering.

Velocity Pumps

Velocity pumps use a spinning **impeller**, or propeller, to accelerate water to high velocity within the pump casing. The high-velocity, low-pressure water leaving the impeller can then be converted to high-pressure, low-velocity water if the casing is shaped so that water moves through an area of increasing cross section. This increasing cross-sectional area may be achieved in two ways:

1. The volute (expanding spiral) casing shape, as in the common centrifugal pump (Figure 19-1A), may be used.
2. Specially shaped diffuser vanes or channels may be used, such as those built into the bowls of vertical turbine pumps (Figure 19-1B).

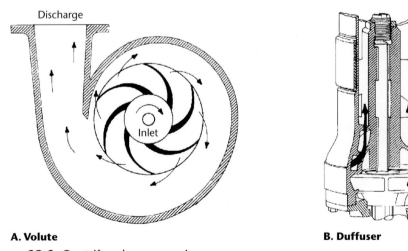

A. Volute **B. Duffuser**

Figure 19-1 Centrifugal pump casings

This material is used with permission of John Wiley & Sons, Inc., from *Centrifugal Pump Design*, John Tuzson, ©2000 by John Wiley & Sons, Inc.

velocity pump

The general class of pumps that use a rapidly turning impeller to impart kinetic energy or velocity to fluids. The pump casing then converts this velocity head, in part, to pressure head. Also called kinetic pump.

impeller

The rotating set of vanes that forces water through a pump.

Velocity Pump Design Characteristics

Two designs of velocity pumps are widely used in water systems: centrifugal pumps (volute pumps) and turbine pumps. A feature distinguishing velocity pumps from positive-displacement pumps is that velocity pumps will continue to operate undamaged, at least for a short period, when the discharge is blocked. When this happens, a head builds up that is typically greater than the pressure generated during pumping, and water recirculates within the pump impeller and casing. (*Head* refers to pressure measured in terms of the height of water, in meters or feet.) This flow condition is referred to as slip.

Depending on the casing shape, impeller design, and direction of flow within the pump, velocity pumps can be manufactured with a variety of operating characteristics.

Radial-Flow Designs   In the radial-flow (or centrifugal) pump, shown in Figure 19-1, water is thrown outward from the center of the impeller into the volute or diffusers that convert the velocity to pressure. The type of centrifugal pump commonly used in water supply practice is a radial-flow, volute-case type. A cutaway of a typical single-stage pump is shown in Figure 19-2. Centrifugal pumps of this type generally develop very high heads and have correspondingly low-flow capacities.

In general, any centrifugal pump can be designed with a multistage configuration. Each stage requires an additional impeller and casing chamber in order to develop increased pressure, which adds to the pressure developed in the preceding stage.

Although the pressure increases with each stage, the flow capacity of the pump does not increase beyond that of the first stage. There is no theoretical limit to the number of stages that are possible. However, mechanical considerations such as casing strength, packing leakage, and input power requirements do impose practical limitations.

Axial-Flow Designs   The axial-flow pump, shown in Figure 19-3, is often referred to as a propeller pump. It has neither a volute nor diffuser vanes. A propeller-shaped impeller adds head by the lifting action of the vanes on the water. As a result, the water moves parallel to the axis of the pump rather than being

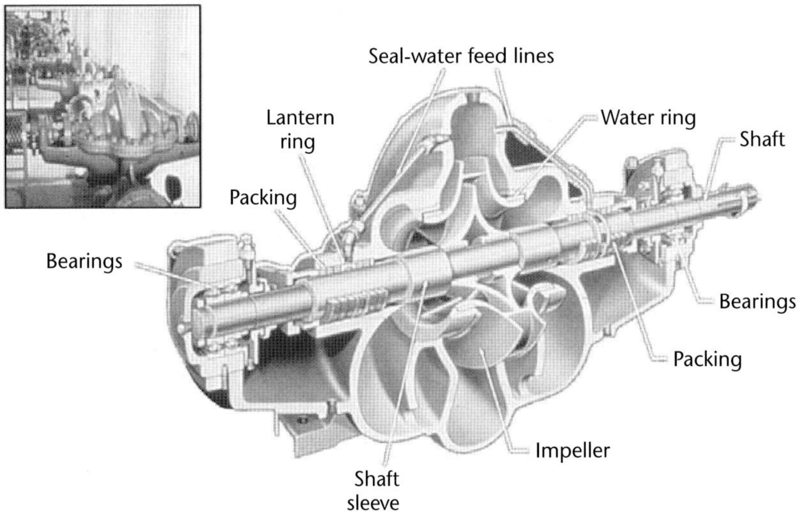

head (pressure)
(1) A measure of the energy possessed by water at a given location in the water system, expressed in feet (or meters). (2) A measure of the pressure (force) exerted by water, expressed in feet (or meters).

slip
(1) In a pump, the percentage of water taken into the suction end that is not discharged because of clearances in the moving unit. (2) In a motor, the difference between the speed of the rotating magnetic field produced by the stator and the speed of the rotor.

Figure 19-2 Cutaway of a single-stage pump

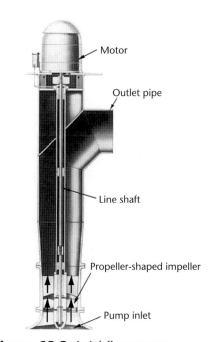

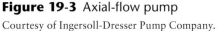

Figure 19-3 Axial-flow pump
Courtesy of Ingersoll-Dresser Pump Company.

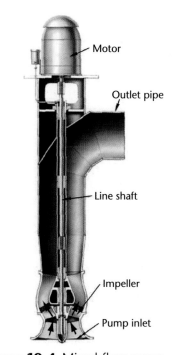

Figure 19-4 Mixed-flow pump
Courtesy of Ingersoll-Dresser Pump Company.

thrown outward as with a radial-flow pump. Axial-flow pumps handle very high volume but add limited head. Pumps of this design must have the impeller submerged at all times because they are not self-priming.

Mixed-Flow Designs The mixed-flow pump, illustrated in Figure 19-4, is a compromise in features between radial-flow and axial-flow pumps. The impeller is shaped so that centrifugal force will impart some radial component to the flow. This type of pump is useful for moving water that contains solids, as in raw-water intakes.

Centrifugal Pumps

The volute-casing type of centrifugal pump, shown in Figure 19-5, is used in most water utility installations. A wide range of flows and pressures can be

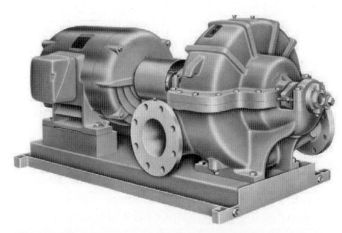

Figure 19-5 Volute-casing type of centrifugal pump

centrifugal pump
A pump consisting of an impeller on a rotating shaft enclosed by a casing that has suction and discharge connections. The spinning impeller throws water outward at high velocity, and the casing shape converts this high velocity to a high pressure.

achieved by varying the width, shape, and size of the impeller, as well as by varying the clearance between the impeller and casing. The pumps can develop a head up to 250 ft (76 m) per stage and efficiencies up to 75 or 85 percent.

Initial cost is relatively low for a given pump size, and relatively little maintenance is required. However, periodic checks are advised to monitor impeller wear and packing condition.

Advantages and disadvantages vary with the type of centrifugal pump used. Advantages include the following:

- Wide range of capacities (Available capacities range from a few gpm to 50,000 gpm [190,000 L/min]. Heads of 5–700 ft [1.5–210 m] are generally available.)
- Uniform flow at constant speed and head
- Simple construction
- Small amounts of suspended matter in the water, which helps prevent jamming of the pump
- Low to moderate initial cost for a given size
- Ability to adapt to several drive types—motor, engine, or turbine
- Moderate to high efficiency at optimal operation
- No need for internal lubrication
- Little space required for a given capacity
- Relatively low noise level
- Ability to operate against a closed discharge valve for short periods without damage

Disadvantages include the following:

- An efficiency that is at best limited to a narrow range of discharge flows and heads
- Flow capacity that is greatly dependent on discharge pressure
- Generally no self-priming ability
- Potential for running backward if stopped with the discharge valve open
- Potential for impeller to be damaged by abrasive matter in water or become clogged by large quantities of particulate matter

Vertical Turbine Pumps

Vertical turbine pumps have an impeller rotating in a channel of constant cross-sectional area, which imparts mixed or radial flow to the water. As liquid leaves the impeller (Figure 19-6), velocity head is converted to pressure head by diffuser guide vanes. The guide vanes form channels that direct the flow either into the discharge or through diffuser bowls into succeeding stage inlets.

Turbine pumps are manufactured in a wide range of sizes and designs, combining efficiency with high speeds to create the highest heads obtainable from velocity pumps. The clearance between the diffuser and the impeller is usually very small, limiting or preventing internal backflow and improving efficiency. Efficiencies in the range of 90–95 percent are possible for large units. However, the closely fitting impeller prohibits pumping of any solid sediment, such as sand, fine grit, or silt. Turbine pumps have a higher initial cost and are more expensive to maintain than centrifugal volute pumps of the same capacity.

vertical turbine pump
A centrifugal pump, commonly of the multistage diffuser type, in which the pump shaft is mounted vertically.

Figure 19-6 Turbine impeller
Courtesy of Ingersoll-Dresser Pump Company.

The major advantages of turbine pumps include the following:

- Uniform flow at constant speed and head
- Simple construction
- Individual stages capable of being connected in series, thereby offering multiple head capacities for a single pump model
- Adaptability to several drive types—motor, engine, or turbine
- Moderate to high efficiency under the proper head conditions
- Little space occupied for a given capacity
- Low noise level

The main disadvantages include the following:

- High initial cost
- High repair costs
- The need to lubricate support bearings located within the casing
- Inability to pump water containing any suspended matter
- An efficiency that is at best limited to a very narrow range of discharge flow and head conditions

Deep-Well Pumps   For deep-well service, a shaft-type vertical turbine pump requires a lengthy pipe column housing, a drive unit, a driveshaft, and multiple pump stages. In this type of pump, a drive unit is located at the surface, with the lower shaft, impeller, and diffuser bowls submerged (Figure 19-7). This type of pump requires careful installation to ensure proper alignment of all shafting and impeller stages throughout its length. Deep-well turbines have been installed in wells with lifts of over 2,000 ft (610 m).

Submersible Pumps   Multistage mixed-flow centrifugal pumps or turbine pumps with an integral or close-connected motor may be designed for operation while completely submerged, in which case they are termed submersible pumps. As shown in Figure 19-8, the entire pump and motor unit is placed below the water level in a well.

Booster Pumps   Vertical turbine pumps are often used for in-line booster service to increase pressure in a distribution system. The unit is actually a turbine pump that has the motor and pumps mounted close together and is installed in a sump.

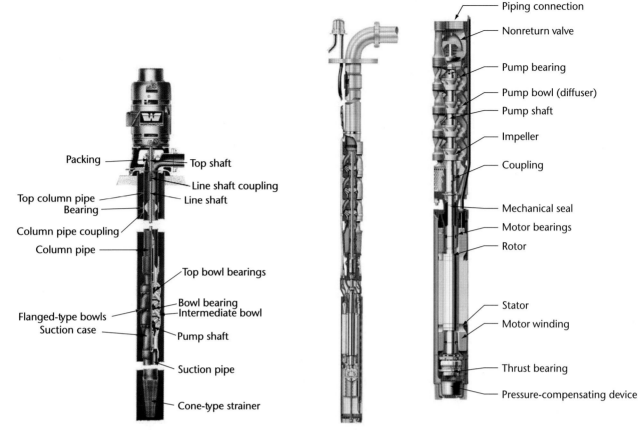

Figure 19-7 Deep-well pump

Courtesy of Ingersoll-Dresser Pump Company.

Figure 19-8 Vertical turbine pump driven by a submersible motor (left) and a cross-sectional view of a submersible pump (right)

Images provided courtesy of Flowserve Corporation.

As shown in Figure 19-9, this type of unit is commonly called a "can" pump. The sump receives fluid and maintains an adequate level above the turbine pump suction.

Centrifugal–Jet Pump Combination

Figure 19-10 illustrates a centrifugal–jet pump combination at the ground surface that generates high-velocity water that is directed down the well to an ejector. Jet pumps are widely used for small, private wells because of their low initial cost and low maintenance. They are rarely used for public water systems because of their relatively low efficiency.

Positive-Displacement Pumps

Early water systems used reciprocating positive-displacement pumps powered by steam engines to obtain the pressure needed to supply water to customers. These pumps have essentially all been replaced with centrifugal pumps, which are much more efficient. The only types of positive-displacement pumps used in current water systems are some types of portable pumps used to dewater excavations, as well as chemical feed pumps.

Reciprocating Pumps

As illustrated in Figure 19-11, reciprocating pumps have a piston that moves back and forth in a cylinder. The liquid is admitted and discharged through check valves. Flow from reciprocating pumps generally pulsates, but this can be

reciprocating pump

A type of positive-displacement pump consisting of a closed cylinder containing a piston or plunger to draw liquid into the cylinder through an inlet valve and force it out through an outlet valve. When the piston acts on the liquid in one end of the cylinder, the pump is termed single-action; when the piston acts in both ends, the pump is termed double-action.

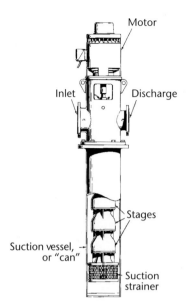

Figure 19-9 Turbine booster pump

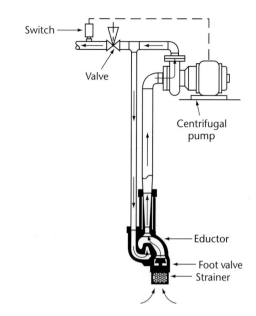

Figure 19-10 Centrifugal–jet pump combination

Reproduced with permission of McGraw-Hill Companies from *Pump Handbook* by Karassik et al., 2001. Published by McGraw-Hill.

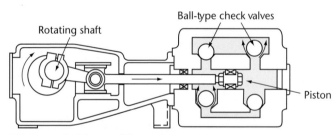

Figure 19-11 Double-acting reciprocating pump

Courtesy of the Hydraulic Institute.

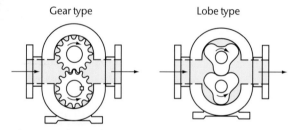

Figure 19-12 Rotary pumps

Courtesy of the Hydraulic Institute.

minimized by the use of multiple cylinders or pulsation dampeners. Reciprocating pumps are particularly suited for applications where very high pressures are required or where abrasive or viscous liquids must be pumped.

Rotary Pumps

Rotary pumps use closely meshed gears, vanes, or lobes rotating within a close-fitting chamber. The two most common types, which use gears or lobes, are shown in Figure 19-12.

Mechanical Details of Centrifugal Pumps

Size and construction may vary greatly from one volute-type centrifugal pump to another, depending on the operating head and discharge conditions for which the pumps are designed. However, the basic operating principle is the same. Water enters the impeller eye from the pump suction inlet. There it is picked up by curved vanes, which change the flow direction from axial to radial. Both pressure and velocity increase as the water is impelled outward and discharged into the pump casing. The major components of a typical volute-type centrifugal pump are described in the following paragraphs.

rotary pump

A type of positive-displacement pump consisting of elements resembling gears that rotate in a close-fitting pump case. The rotation of these elements alternately draws in and discharges the water being pumped. Such pumps act with neither suction nor discharge valves, operate at almost any speed, and do not depend on centrifugal forces to lift the water.

Casing

Water leaving the pump impeller travels at high velocity in both radial and circular directions. To minimize energy losses due to turbulence and friction, the casing is designed to convert the velocity energy to additional pressure energy as smoothly as possible. In most water utility pumps, the casing is cast in the form of a smooth volute, or spiral, around the impeller. Casings are usually made of cast iron, but ductile iron, bronze, and steel are usually available on special order.

Single-Suction Pumps

Single-suction pumps are designed with the water inlet opening at one end of the pump and the discharge opening placed at right angles on one side of the casing. Single-suction pumps, also called end-suction pumps, are used in smaller water systems that do not have a high volume requirement. These pumps are capable of delivering up to 200 psi (1,400 kPa) pressure if necessary, but for most applications they are usually sized to produce 100 psi (700 kPa) or less.

The impeller on some single-suction pump units is mounted on the shaft of the motor that drives the pump, with the motor bearings supporting the impeller (Figure 19-13A). This arrangement is called the close-coupled design. Single-suction pumps are also available with the impeller mounted on a separate shaft, which is connected to the motor with a coupling (Figure 19-13B). In this design, known as the frame-mounted design, the impeller shaft is supported by bearings placed in a separate housing, independent of the pump housing.

The casing for a single-suction pump is manufactured in two or three sections or pieces. All housings are made with a removable inlet-side plate or cover, held in place by a row of bolts located near the outer edge of the volute. Removing the side plate provides access to the impeller. The pump does not have to be removed from its base for the side plate to be removed. However, all suction piping must be removed to provide sufficient access.

Some manufacturers cast the volute and the back of the pump as a single unit. Other manufacturers cast them as two separate pieces, which are connected by a row of bolts, similar to the inlet side plate. In units with separate backs, the impeller and drive unit can be removed from the pump without having to disturb any piping connections.

Double-Suction Pumps

Water enters the impeller of a **double-suction pump** from two sides and discharges outward from the middle of the pump. Although water enters the impeller from each side, it enters the housing at one location (usually on the opposite side of the discharge opening). Internal passages in the pump guide the water to the impeller suction and control the discharge water flow.

single-suction pump
A centrifugal pump in which the water enters from only one side of the impeller. Also called end-suction pump.

double-suction pump
A centrifugal pump in which the water enters from both sides of the impeller. Also called a split-case pump.

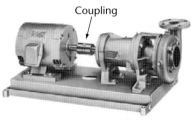

A. Close-coupled pump   **B. Frame-mounted pump**

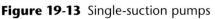

Figure 19-13 Single-suction pumps

The double-suction pump is easily identified because of its casing shape (Figure 19-14). The motor is connected to the pump through a coupling, and the pump shaft is supported by ball or roller bearings mounted external to the pump casing.

The double-suction pump is usually referred to as a horizontal split-case pump. The term horizontal does not indicate the position of the pump. It refers to the fact that the housing is split into two halves (top and bottom) along the center line of the pump shaft, which is normally set in the horizontal position. However, some horizontal split-case pumps are designed to be mounted with the driveshaft in a vertical position, with the drive motor placed on top. Double-suction pumps can pump over 10,000 gpm (38,000 L/min), with heads up to 350 ft (100 m). They are widely used in large systems.

Removing the bolts that hold the two halves of the double-suction casing together makes it possible to remove the casing's top half. Most manufacturers place two dowel pins in the bottom half of the casing to ensure proper alignment between the halves when they are reassembled. It is important that the machined surfaces not be damaged when the halves are separated.

Impeller

Most pump impellers for water utility use are made of bronze, although a number of manufacturers offer cast iron or stainless steel as alternative materials. The overall impeller diameter, width, inlet area, vane curvature, and operating speed affect impeller performance and are modified by the manufacturer to attain the required operating characteristics. Impellers for single-suction pumps may be of the open, semiopen, or closed design, as shown in Figure 19-15. Most single-suction pumps in the water industry use impellers of the closed design, although a few have semiopen impellers. Double-suction pumps use only closed-design impellers.

Wear Rings

In all centrifugal pumps, a flow restriction must exist between the impeller discharge and suction areas to prevent excessive circulation of water between the two. This restriction is made using wear rings. In some pumps, only one wear ring is used, mounted in the case. In others, two wear rings are used, one mounted in the case and the other on the impeller. The wear rings are identified in Figure 19-16.

The rotating impeller wear ring (or the impeller itself) and the stationary case wear ring (or the case itself) are machined so that the running clearance between the two effectively restricts leakage from the impeller discharge to the pump suction. The clearance is usually 0.010–0.020 in. (0.25–0.50 mm). Rings are normally machined from bronze or cast iron, but stainless-steel rings are available. The machined surfaces will eventually wear to the point that leakage

Figure 19-14 Double-suction pump casing shape

Courtesy of Ingersoll-Dresser Pump Company.

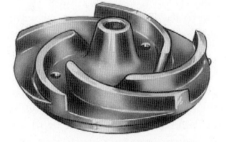

Semiopen

Figure 19-15 Types of impellers

Courtesy of Goulds Pumps, ITT Industries.

Closed

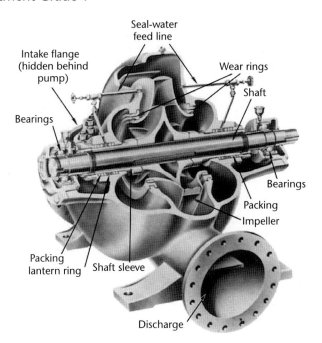

Seal-water
feed line

Intake flange
(hidden behind
pump)

Wear rings

Shaft

Bearings

Bearings

Packing

Impeller

Packing
lantern ring

Shaft sleeve

Discharge

Figure 19-16 Double-suction pump

Courtesy of Ingersoll-Dresser Pump Company.

occurs, decreasing pump efficiency. At this point, the rings need to be replaced or the wearing surfaces of the case and impeller need to be remachined.

Shaft

The impeller is rotated by a pump shaft, usually machined of steel or stainless steel. The impeller can be secured to the shaft on double-suction pumps using a key and a very tight fit (also called a shrink fit). Because of the tight fit, an arbor press or gear puller is required to remove an impeller from the shaft.

In end-suction pumps, the impeller is mounted on the end of the shaft and held in place by a key nut. The end of the shaft may be machined straight or with a slight taper. However, removing the impeller usually will not require a press. Several other methods are also used for mounting impellers.

Shaft Sleeves

Most manufacturers provide pump shafts with replaceable sleeves for the packing rings to bear against. If sleeves are not used, the continual rubbing of the packing can eventually wear out the shaft, which would require replacement. A shaft could be ruined almost immediately if the packing gland were too tight. Where shaft sleeves are used, operators can repair a damaged surface by replacing the sleeve, a procedure considerably less costly than replacing the entire shaft. The sleeves are usually made of bronze alloy, which is much more resistant than steel to the corrosive effects of water. Stainless-steel sleeves are usually available for use where the water contains abrasive elements.

Packing Rings

To prevent leakage at the point where the shaft protrudes through the case, either packing rings or mechanical seals are used to seal the space between the shaft and the case. Packing consists of one or more (usually no more than six) separate rings of graphite-impregnated cotton, flax, or synthetic materials placed on the shaft or shaft sleeves (Figure 19-17). Asbestos material, once common for packing, is no longer used on potable water systems. The section of the case in which the packing is mounted is called the stuffing box. The adjustable packing gland maintains

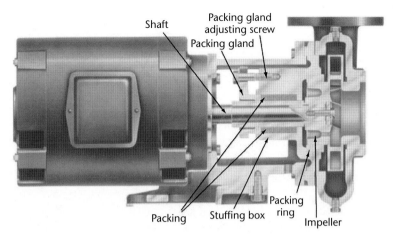

Figure 19-17 Pump packing locations

Courtesy of Aurora Pump.

the packing under slight pressure against the shaft, stopping air from leaking in or water from leaking out.

To reduce the friction of the packing rings against the pump shaft, the packing material is impregnated with graphite or polytetrafluoroethylene to provide a small measure of lubrication. It is important that packing be installed and adjusted properly.

Lantern Rings

When a pump operates under suction lift, the impeller inlet is actually operating in a vacuum. Air will enter the water stream along the shaft if the packing does not provide an effective seal. It may be impossible to tighten the packing sufficiently to prevent air from entering without causing excessive heat and wear on the packing and shaft or shaft sleeve. To solve this problem, a lantern ring (Figure 19-18) is placed in the stuffing box. Pump discharge water is fed into the ring and flows out through a series of holes leading to the shaft side of the packing. From there, water flows both toward the pump suction and away from the packing gland. This water acts as a seal, preventing air from entering the water stream. It also provides lubrication for the packing.

Mechanical Seals

If the pump must operate under a high suction head (60 psig [400 kPa (gauge)] or more), the suction pressure itself will compress the packing rings, regardless of operator intervention. Packing will then require frequent replacement. Most

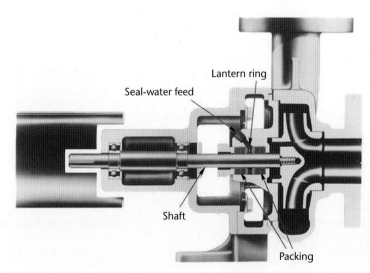

Figure 19-18 Lantern ring placed in the stuffing box

Courtesy of Aurora Pump.

manufacturers recommend using a mechanical seal under these conditions, and many manufacturers use mechanical seals for low-suction-head conditions as well. The mechanical seal (Figure 19-19) is provided by two machined and polished surfaces; one is attached to and rotates with the shaft; the other is attached to the case. Contact between the seal surfaces is maintained by spring pressure.

The mechanical seal is designed so that it can be hydraulically balanced. The result is that the wearing force between the machined surfaces does not vary regardless of the suction head. Most seals have an operating life of 5,000 to 20,000 hours. In addition, there is little or no leakage from a mechanical seal; a leaky mechanical seal indicates problems that should be investigated and repaired. A major advantage of mechanical seals is that there is no wear or chance of damage to shaft sleeves.

A major disadvantage of mechanical seals is that they are more difficult to replace than packing rings. Replacing the mechanical seal often requires removing the shaft and impeller from the case. Another disadvantage is that failure of a mechanical seal is usually sudden and accompanied by excessive leakage. Packing rings, by contrast, normally wear gradually, and the wear can usually be detected long before leakage becomes a problem. Mechanical seals are also more expensive than packing.

Bearings

Most modern pumps are equipped with ball-type radial and thrust bearings. These bearings are available with either grease or oil lubrication and provide good service in most water utility applications. They are reasonably easy to maintain when manufacturer's recommendations are followed, and new parts are readily available if replacement is required. Ball bearings will usually start to get noisy when they begin to fail, enabling operators to plan a shutdown for replacement.

Couplings

Frame-mounted pumps have separate shafts connected by a coupling. The primary function of couplings is to transmit the rotary motion of the motor to the pump shaft. Couplings are also designed to allow slight misalignment between the pump and motor and to absorb the startup shock when the pump motor is switched on. Although the coupling is designed to accept a little misalignment, the more accurately the two shafts are aligned, the longer the coupling life will be and the more efficiently the unit will operate (Figure 19-20).

Various coupling designs are supplied by pump manufacturers. Couplings may be installed dry or lubricated. Most couplings are of the lubricated style and

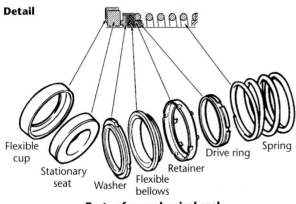

Parts of a mechanical seal

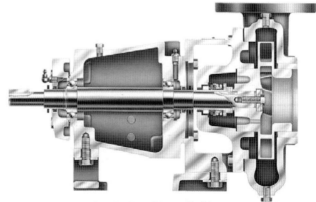

Mechanical seal installed in a pump

Figure 19-19 Mechanical seal parts and placement

Courtesy of Aurora Pump.

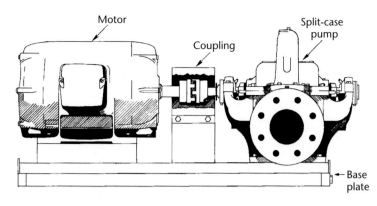

Figure 19-20 Alignment of motor and pump at coupling

require periodic maintenance, usually lubrication at 6-month or annual intervals. Dry couplings using rubber or elastomeric membranes do not require any maintenance, except for periodic visual inspection to make sure they are not cracking or wearing out. The rubber or elastomer used for the membrane must be carefully selected for the pump, because the corrosive chemicals used in water treatment plants could affect the life and operation of the coupling.

 WATCH THE VIDEOS
Pumps and Pump Parts (www.awwa.org/wsovideoclips)

Study Questions

1. The main purpose of mechanical seals is to
   a. keep lubrication in and dirt and other foreign materials out.
   b. control water leakage from the stuffing box.
   c. keep contamination from entering or leaving.
   d. save on costs, as they last longer than packing.

2. The purpose of packing is to
   a. keep oil or graphite on the shaft.
   b. control water leakage along the pump's shaft.
   c. prevent water leakage from the pump shaft.
   d. help prevent shaft from warping.

3. Which part of a pump houses the packing or mechanical seal?
   a. The shroud
   b. The stuffing box
   c. The volute
   d. The casing head

4. Which of the following is the only type of pump that can be operated against a closed valve?
   a. Vertical turbine pump
   b. Centrifugal pump
   c. Axial-flow pump
   d. Mixed-flow pump

5. To prevent leakage at the point where the shaft protrudes through the case, _____ are used to seal the space between the shaft and the case.
   a. lantern rings
   b. packing rings
   c. shaft sleeves
   d. mechanical seals

6. Which type of pump is useful for moving water that contains solids, as in raw-water intakes?

7. Which type of pump has an impeller rotating in a channel of constant cross-sectional area, which imparts mixed or radial flow to the water?

8. Which type of pump is widely used for small, private wells because of its low initial cost and low maintenance, but is rarely used for public water systems because of its relatively low efficiency?

9. Which type of pump is designed such that the entire pump and motor unit can be placed below the water level in a well?

Chapter 20
Treatment Plant Safety

The discussion of plant safety presented in this chapter is not intended to be a comprehensive guide on the subject. It is the responsibility of utility personnel to follow safety regulations and to be properly trained to perform their duties safely. The information provided in this chapter should be adequate for most operator certification test examinations.

Safety and safe working conditions are the responsibility of each individual associated with a water utility. The degree of responsibility varies among upper management, supervisors, and operations personnel, but all play a role and all are responsible for their individual actions. Safety regulations guide those actions, but the creation of policies, procedures, and methods to meet safety requirements is the result of a collaborative effort within the water utility.

Utility managers are responsible for ensuring safe working conditions, maintaining the physical condition of their facilities, and supporting policies that encourage the safe performance of work duties. Supervisors at all levels directly control all work conditions and are responsible for the activities of the personnel they supervise. Each supervisor, foreman, crew chief, or lead staffer is responsible for ensuring that all work is done in compliance with safety practices, utility policies, and regulations.

Employees have a particular responsibility when it comes to safety. That responsibility is to correctly use the safety equipment provided and follow all safety policies and procedures. All employees must be aware of the safety requirements and help guard against unsafe acts and conditions.

Safety Regulations

The primary reason for developing and maintaining safe working conditions and practices is to eliminate injuries. Beyond the personal cost to an injured employee are the costs to the utility from lost time, medical expenses, and possible legal judgments. Other considerations include damage to equipment and property and resulting repair costs, and the potential need to hire and train new employees to perform the work duties of the injured employee.

Occupational Safety and Health Administration Act

Another reason for developing safety policies and procedures is the federal Occupational Safety and Health Administration (OSHA) Act (Public Law 91-596). Passed in 1971, the act established OSHA and compiled numerous safety and health standards that are applicable to every industry. Specific standards have been developed for most work activities and chemical substances that an employee may be exposed to in the course of his or her employment. These are minimum standards that must be followed; their requirements are itemized in the Code of Federal Regulations (CFR) (29 CFR, 1910 and 1926). The act provides for monetary penalties, which are escalated depending on the seriousness of the safety violation, and the potential for incarceration if OSHA safety standards are violated.

If a specific requirement does not exist, OSHA relies on the general duty clause, which requires each employer to provide employment, and a place of employment, that is free of recognized hazards that are likely to cause death or serious physical harm. The general duty clause also requires employees to comply with safety practices and procedures. In addition to OSHA, many states and cities have their own safety requirements. In most cases, these standards mirror the OSHA standards; however, in some cases, state or local requirements are more stringent and carry additional penalties for failing to comply.

Confined Space Rules

A common hazard encountered in the water industry is confined spaces. Examples of confined spaces in the water and wastewater industry include access holes for valves, meters, and air vents; chemical storage tanks or hoppers; wet wells; digesters; sedimentation basins; filters; and reservoirs.

One of the most sobering statistics related to confined space safety is one relating to the death rate for those entering confined spaces. Although the death rate relating to confined spaces continues to decrease, the percentage of those who die while attempting a confined-space rescue remains roughly the same. Each year about two-thirds of those who die in confined spaces are would-be rescuers. The cause of death is usually asphyxiation or the result of an atmospheric hazard that could not be seen.

Requirements

Under OSHA regulations, there are two basic types of confined spaces—permit-required and nonpermit-required. For a location to be classified as a confined space, the following three criteria must be met: the space must have limited means of entry and exit, the space must not be designed for continuous human occupancy, and the space must be of a size and configuration that allow humans to enter the space to perform work. If all three criteria are met, it is necessary to assess the space and determine if the space is also permit-required. A permit-required confined space meets one or more of the following criteria:

- The space contains, or has the potential to contain, a hazardous atmosphere.
- The material within the space has the potential to engulf the entrant.
- The internal configuration is such that it could trap the entrant (i.e., downward-sloping and converging floors).
- The space contains any other recognized serious health or safety hazard.

If the only hazard is atmospheric and the hazard can be controlled with ventilation, the space may be reclassified as nonpermit-required. Figure 20-1 is a decision tree that can be used to identify the need for permitting a confined space.

A written program is required when it is necessary to enter permit-required confined spaces. This program must contain a mechanism for identifying and controlling the hazard, have a written entry permit, provide for the identification and labeling of confined spaces, and provide employee training, among other requirements. A key component of this program is the requirement that before an

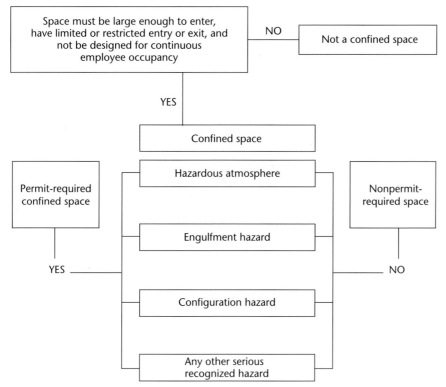

Figure 20-1 Confined space decision tree
Source: Melinda Raimann, Cleveland, Ohio, Division of Water

employee enters a permit-required confined space, the internal atmosphere of the space be tested with a calibrated, direct-reading instrument capable of measuring oxygen content, presence of flammable gases and vapors, and potentially toxic air contaminants. In addition to these preentry tests, the atmosphere must be retested while work is being performed inside the space to ensure that acceptable conditions are being maintained. More details regarding the required program can be found in 29 CFR 1910.146.

An employer is required to provide its employees with the specialized equipment that is required for confined space entry. This equipment includes the following:

- Testing and monitoring equipment
- Ventilation equipment (to eliminate or control atmospheric hazards)
- Communications equipment, as necessary
- Personal protective equipment (PPE)
- Lighting equipment, as necessary
- Barriers and shields to prevent unauthorized entry, as necessary
- Ladders for safe entry and exit
- Fall-prevention equipment required because of the difference in elevation
- Rescue and emergency equipment, including harnesses and hoists, self-contained breathing apparatus (SCBA), stretchers or backboards, and supplies

Personnel

There are three classes of employees, as they relate to confined spaces: the entry supervisor, the authorized entrant, and the authorized attendant.

The *entry supervisor* is responsible for knowing the conditions within the confined space, verifying that all equipment and procedures are in place prior to entry, verifying the availability of rescue services and the means of summoning them, terminating entries and canceling permits, and determining that acceptable conditions as specified in the permit continue for the duration of the entry.

The *authorized entrant* is responsible for knowing what hazards are to be faced, recognizing the signs and symptoms of exposure and understanding the potential consequences, knowing how to use any needed equipment, communicating with the attendant as necessary, alerting the attendant when a warning symptom or other hazardous condition exists, and quickly exiting when ordered or alerted.

Authorized attendants are responsible for being aware of the confined space hazards and the behavioral effects of exposure; maintaining a count and the identity of the authorized entrants; preventing unauthorized entry; remaining outside the space until relieved; communicating with the entrants and monitoring activities inside and outside of the permit space; and ordering exit, summoning rescuers, and performing nonentry rescue as required.

 WATCH THE VIDEO
Confined Spaces (www.awwa.org/wsovideoclips)

General Plant Safety

Right to Know and MSDS

In order to follow safety practices and procedures that will protect an employee and fellow workers, an employee must be aware of the hazards to which he or she is exposed. A primary method of doing this is through a right-to-know program developed by the employer. The main premise of a right-to-know program is that employees have the right to be advised of the hazards associated with the chemicals and materials that they work with or that exist nearby in the course of their daily job activities.

Chemicals, as defined under the Hazard Communications standard (29 CFR 1910.1200), include those used for water treatment, lab procedures, cleaning, and maintenance applications. A **material safety data sheet (MSDS)** lists a chemical's identity, composition, and type or types; the hazard(s) associated with its use (is it flammable, an oxidizer, poisonous?); how it enters the body; the effects of exposure; health effect (short term, long term); the permissible exposure limit; how to handle spills or releases; and other related information. An MSDS for every chemical that is used in a water treatment plant should be kept in an organized fashion in a location that is readily accessible to all employees.

Employees are to be trained on the hazards of the chemicals they use or are exposed to and in the methods used to protect themselves from those hazards.

Risk Management and Emergency Response

The US Environmental Protection Agency (USEPA) issued the Risk Management Rule on July 20, 1996, in an effort to protect public health and safety. OSHA had previously released the Process Safety Rule in February 1992 (29 CFR 1910.119), which focused on employee health and safety but did not address the safety of

material safety data sheet (MSDS)

A product description listing a chemical's identity, composition, and type or types; the hazard(s) associated with its use (is it flammable, an oxidizer, poisonous?); how it enters the body; the effects of exposure; health effect (short term, long term); the permissible exposure limit; how to handle spills or releases; and other related information.

nonemployees. According to the Risk Management Rule, employers must not store or use chemicals in quantities greater than the threshold quantity, which is defined by USEPA (e.g., more than 1,500 lb [680 kg] of chlorine), and must develop release scenarios, conduct hazard assessments, determine means and methods to limit public exposure should a spill or release occur, and provide the public with information about their plan.

Emergency response at a water treatment facility generally means responding to a chemical release. This response is governed under the Risk Management Rule and under OSHA (29 CFR 1910.1). A number of decisions must be made regarding emergency response, the first of which is to determine who will respond in the event of a chemical release. If the utility elects to have its employees respond to chemical releases, the utility is required to comply with the requirements of OSHA's Hazardous Waste Operations and Emergency Response (HAZWOPER) regulations.

Compliance requires the employer to provide specialized chemical response suits and respirators, medical exams to determine the fitness of the employees designated as responders, spill-containment materials, and annual training. Initial training is usually 24 to 40 hours in duration, depending on the responsibilities the response team is expected to assume; an annual 8-hour refresher course is also required. Even if a utility chooses to have others act as the designated emergency response team, the HAZWOPER regulations, as they relate to awareness-level training for those who may be exposed during a chemical release, are to be followed. This awareness-level training is an 8-hour course with an annual refresher that focuses on the hazards of the chemicals used and evacuation procedures, routes, and staging areas to be used.

A key component of any emergency response plan is for the responder to be aware of the hazards of the chemicals that may be released and to understand the precautions that must be taken to ensure the safety and well-being of all designated responders. This information is usually provided on the specific MSDS or as part of the facility's risk management or hazard communications program.

Standard practice for emergency response is to follow the incident response system first developed by fire and safety forces and designate someone in charge of the emergency site. Red (hot), yellow (decontamination), and green (clean) zones should be designated, and strict controls are used to ensure that no unauthorized or unprotected entrant enters the chemical-release area. A spill or release area should never be entered alone; one standby person, fully suited in the appropriate level of PPE, should be assigned to each entrant into the hot zone.

First Aid

Water treatment plants often provide first-aid stations for their employees. These stations are stocked with emergency supplies that are used when operators sustain minor injuries on the job. The stations (Figure 20-2) may include oxygen, bandages and antiseptics, fire blankets, and eyewash solutions. SCBA equipment may also be stored here if the location is near the chlorine area. Be sure to document use of all supplies immediately after use.

Chlorine Safety

Chlorine safety is a subset of chemical safety at many water treatment plants. Chlorine is a toxic chemical and is an irritant to the eyes, skin, mucous membranes, and respiratory system. Effects of exposure generally are evident first in

Figure 20-2 First-aid and safety station

Source: Conneaut, Ohio, Water Department

the respiratory system and then in the eyes. The impact of exposure to chlorine is dependent on both concentration and time. The very young, the elderly, and people with respiratory problems are most susceptible to chlorine's effects. As the duration of exposure or the concentration increases, the affected individual may become apprehensive and restless, with coughing accompanied by throat irritation, sneezing, and excess salivation. At higher levels, vomiting associated with labored breathing can occur. In extreme cases, difficulty in breathing can progress to the point of death through suffocation. An exposed person with a preexisting medical or cardiovascular condition can have an exaggerated response.

Anyone exhibiting these symptoms should see a qualified health-care provider immediately, as his or her condition will deteriorate over the next few hours. The physiological effects from exposure to various levels of gaseous chlorine are presented in Table 20-1.

To protect employees who work with or around chlorine, the employer must ensure that chorine equipment is kept in safe working order, regular maintenance is performed on all chlorine equipment and the equipment used to handle it such as overhead cranes, and employees have the proper tools and PPE.

Chlorine cylinders of 150 lb (68 kg) are equipped with fusible plugs that will melt at temperatures between 157°F and 162°F (69–72°C) and release the contents of the cylinder (Figure 20-3). Consequently, cylinders must be stored in a temperature-controlled area. Labels identifying the contents of any cylinder or tank car should be legible and prominently displayed. Placards with Department of Transportation (DOT) codes identifying the contents and their hazards are to be posted on the exterior of chlorine rooms so that emergency response teams can identify and address the hazards they will be exposed to in the event of a release. All cylinders should be secured and protected from accidental contact by moving equipment or vehicles.

WATCH THE VIDEO
Chlorine Safety (www.awwa.org/wsovideoclips)

Table 20-1 Physiological effects of chlorine exposure

Exposure Level, ppm	Effects
0.02–0.2	Odor threshold (varies by individual)
<0.5	No known acute or chronic effect
0.5	ACGIH (American Conference of Governmental Industrial Hygienists Inc.) 8-hour time-weighted average
1.0	OSHA ceiling level
1–10	Irritation of the eyes and mucous membranes of the upper respiratory tract. Severity of symptoms depends on concentrations and length of exposure.
3	ERPG-2 (Emergency Response Planning Guidelines as values developed by the American Industrial Hygiene Association) is the maximum airborne concentration below which it is believed that nearly all individuals could be exposed for up to 1 hour without experiencing or developing irreversible or other serious health effects that could impair an individual's ability to take protective action.
10	Immediately dangerous to life and health (per the National Institute of Occupational Safety and Health)
20	ERPG-3 is the maximum airborne concentration below which it is believed that nearly all individuals could be exposed for up to 1 hour without experiencing or developing life-threatening health effects.

Source: The Chlorine Institute.

Figure 20-3 Safely stored 150-lb (68-kg) chlorine cylinders. Caps are on and the chain is set.

Source: Conneaut, Ohio, Water Department

Personal Protective Equipment (PPE)

OSHA requirements governing PPE are found in 29 CFR 1910 subpart I (see appendix E in the CFR), which also references various American National Standards Institute guidelines. As a general rule, PPE is to be considered as a last resort. The elimination of the hazard through engineering changes is the optimal solution, followed by administrative changes. If these methods do not eliminate or minimize the hazard to the appropriate level, PPE is to be used. The PPE must be appropriate for the hazard it is being provided to protect the employee against. This can be determined only through a hazard assessment and equipment evaluation. In general, PPE is provided by the employer, unless it is used voluntarily or by an employee outside the work environment. In addition to providing the equipment, the employer is responsible for ensuring that it is maintained in a sanitary and reliable condition.

PPE can be provided for nearly every portion of the body. Occupational foot protection, or safety shoes, should be used when there is the potential for injury to the foot from falling, rolling, or piercing objects or when extreme thermal conditions exist. Different types of shoes or devices provide different types of foot protection. There are steel toe caps, both internal and external to the shoe; metatarsal guards; steel shanks; and various combinations of these devices. They are commonly worn in machine shops and during construction activities.

Another common piece of PPE is the hard hat, which is required when there is the potential for injury to the head from impact or falling objects. In a water treatment plant, hard hats are usually worn when an overhead crane is in use or during construction projects. They may be required if there are low vertical clearances and an employee has to crouch or duck to travel through the area, such as in a pipe gallery or subbasement location. There are also specific types of hard hats designed to provide protection from high-voltage shocks and burns.

Treatment plants typically have high-noise areas, usually on pump floors or in machine shops. If the employer is unable to lower the noise levels or limit employee exposure, hearing protection must be provided. Hearing protection comes in various forms, from earplugs to muffs, and offers varying degrees of protection. Noise-level sampling is required to determine what level of noise reduction is needed, which will be marked on the protective devices as a noise reduction reading. As a general rule of thumb, if an employee must raise his or her voice to be heard in the area in question, hearing protection is probably required. Exposures to noise levels above an 8-hour time-weighted average of 85 dB_A (decibels measured on the A scale) require a hearing-conservation program, which includes monitoring. Specific requirements are found in 29 CFR 1910, subpart G.

Eye and face protection may also be required when handling chemicals or doing work that produces flying debris. Impact-resistant eye and face protection (glasses, goggles, face shields) are required if flying debris is likely to be present. Chemical splash–resistant and/or vapor-resistant equipment is required for chemical handling, as specified on the chemical MSDS. Body protection, such as aprons or coats, may also be required for handling chemicals. Again, refer to the MSDS for the appropriate type and composition of protective device to be selected. The employer is responsible for providing the equipment and ensuring that it is maintained. The employee is responsible for using it as required.

Self-Contained Breathing Apparatus

self-contained breathing apparatus (SCBA)

A type of respirator that supplies safe, grade D (or better) breathing air to the wearer.

Self-contained breathing apparatus (SCBA) are a type of respirator that supplies safe, grade D (or better) breathing air to the wearer. These units are commonly used in the water and wastewater industries for emergency response or for employee protection when maintenance activities can reasonably be expected to result in the release of a hazardous material. They are also required in oxygen-deficient atmospheres or where the existing atmosphere is immediately dangerous to life and health. The other type of respirator that supplies breathing air is an airline respirator. These devices are not commonly used for emergency response because the length of the airline supplying the breathing air is only 300 ft (91 m). This type of respirator will not be discussed in this section.

The major components of an SCBA include an air tank, a harness for wearing the tank on the back, a pressure regulator, hoses, a face mask, and a low-air alarm; all components require routine inspection and maintenance. Refer to the manufacturers' literature for specific maintenance intervals. DOT also has testing, labeling, and maintenance requirements for air cylinders. OSHA inspection requirements mandate inspection during routine cleaning if respirators are worn routinely and at least monthly and after each use when used for emergency purposes.

OSHA requires employees to be medically fit to wear an SCBA. Wearing an SCBA puts additional strain on the human body; therefore, it is important to ensure that there are no underlying medical conditions that would limit an employee's ability to use the device. An employee must be medically evaluated before using an SCBA and on a periodic basis thereafter. Annual medical exams are no longer required, but annual review of an employee's fitness by a medical provider should be performed.

In addition to medical surveillance, OSHA requires fit testing of tight-fitting respirators. The two types of fit testing are qualitative and quantitative. Qualitative fit testing involves determining whether or not the employee can detect the odor of a test medium. Irritant smoke and banana oil are commonly used for this type of test. *Qualitative* fit testing is subject to the impression of the wearer and may not always yield an accurate result. *Quantitative* fit testing involves using a probed face mask identical in brand and size to the one assigned to the employee. The testing device measures the particles in the air outside the mask and the particles inside the mask and compares the levels to determine an acceptable fit. A number of manufacturers produce these testing devices. If an appropriate fit cannot be obtained with the assigned mask, another brand or size of respirator face mask may be needed to provide the required level of protection. Specific requirements regarding fit testing can be found in 29 CFR 1910.1050 (see appendix E in the CFR).

 WATCH THE VIDEO
Personal Protective Equipment (www.awwa.org/wsovideoclips)

Lab Safety

General safety rules for laboratory workers or those who use chemical reagents in their duties can be found in the latest addition of *Standard Methods for the Examination of Water and Wastewater*. All water treatment plant employees should be familiar with the general rules. The previous discussion on PPE applies to laboratory workers in particular.

 WATCH THE VIDEO
Laboratory Safety (www.awwa.org/wsovideoclips)

Study Questions

1. Which of the following is the most important thing to consider in automatic startup after a power failure?
   a. Operator safety
   b. Power surges that could trip a breaker
   c. Importance to process
   d. Importance to water quality

2. Which part of the human body is the most vulnerable to allowing microorganisms to enter it?
   a. Stomach area, where most of the organs are located
   b. Heart
   c. Eyes
   d. Throat and neck area

3. Safety and safe working conditions are the responsibility of _____ associated with a water utility.
   a. each individual
   b. the supervisor
   c. senior operators
   d. safety committees

4. Which of the following is *not* a class of employee designated to work in confined spaces?
   a. Authorized attendant
   b. Authorized entrant
   c. Entry supervisor
   d. Hazard technician

5. A(n) _____ for every chemical that is used in a water treatment plant should be kept in an organized fashion in a location that is readily accessible to all employees.
   a. log sheet
   b. material safety data sheet
   c. right-to-know-sheet
   d. hazard disclaimer

6. After respiratory problems, effects of exposure to chlorine generally manifest as
   a. rapid heart rate.
   b. extreme weakness.
   c. shaking of the hands.
   d. irritation to the eyes.

7. Where should SDS information be kept?

8. What is SCBA?

9. What is classified as a confined space?

10. What item of personal protective equipment is a type of respirator that supplies safe, grade D (or better) breathing air to the wearer?

Chapter 21
Administration, Records, and Reporting Procedures

Records of plant operations and maintenance activities provide a basis for predictive decision making and proof of compliance. Records also help operators to efficiently use chemicals (minimize waste) and equipment.

Process Records

In addition to the records that are required by the local regulatory agency, a water treatment plant should maintain records of activities as they relate to each process or discipline. The following sections describe the types of records operators should keep when performing their duties.

Coagulation and Flocculation

Maintain records of past performances for coagulants, including dosages, turbidities (sedimentation basin and filtration), particle counts, filterability indices, and zeta potentials as well as the temperatures, pH values, and color values at which the coagulants performed. For softening plants, record which softening chemicals are used. Also record detention times and overflow rates in basins used for softening as well as residual quantities produced. Keep equipment records such as hours run for each mixer and flocculator, basin-cleaning activities, maintenance performed on motors and gears, and electrical use records.

Sedimentation

Calculate and record surface overflow rate, weir overflow rate, turbidity performance of each basin, and quantity of sludge removed from each basin (with a calculation for percent solids).

Maintain records of any operations and maintenance activities for each unit, including blowdown, cleaning, raking, and so on. Safety records for confined space entry may be necessary.

The Partnership for Safe Water suggests that the turbidity performance (and particle count, if available) in each sedimentation basin be recorded periodically (daily, every 4 hours, or hourly). Record the settled water turbidity as a combined flow, but realize that it cannot characterize the performance of an individual basin.

Filtration

For each filter, record the rate of flow, in million gallons per day or gallons per minute; head loss; length of run and unit filter run volume (UFRV); turbidity (in accordance with the Interim Enhanced Surface Water Treatment Rule [IESWTR]); particle counts; and dosage of any filter aid used (Table 21-1). At each backwash,

Table 21-1 A sample filter record

Time	Rate of Flow, mgd or gpm	Head Loss, ft	Hours in Service	Total Volume Filtered (cumulative)	UFRV, gal/ft²	Turbidity, ntu and particle counts	Backwash Start	Length of Backwash, minutes and amount used (gal)	Surface Wash, amounts and minutes	Filter Aid Applied? Dosage?	Filter to Waste? ntu at Startup
0000											
0200											
0400											
0600											
0800											
1000											
1200											
1400											
1600											
1800											
2000											
2200											

record the amount of backwash water and surface wash water used, the length of the backwash, any observations during backwash, and time of filter-to-waste if used. Record the percentage of water treated that the backwash water represents (make note of amounts greater than 4 percent). All information can be included on one form.

On a quarterly basis, record bed expansion measurements, condition and depth of media, and an evaluation of the bed surface. On a yearly basis, record the results of solids retention analysis before and after backwash and the results of sieve analysis of the media. Record the addition of any media to the bed, including amounts and types. Keep a record of underdrain inspections and any work that was done on any appurtenances.

Record results of any testing required for filter-exceptions reporting under the IESWTR (this is regulated). Many states have required forms for plant operators to submit for filter performance. Consult the state regulatory agency for specific requirements.

Chlorination or Disinfection

Maintain records of the type of disinfectant used, including ordering information (phone number, address, and shipment amounts and container types), as well as information on costs and current dosage rates. Also results of bacteriological testing should be recorded for each process that uses a disinfectant, the water temperature and pH, and any unusual conditions that may occur. Keep records of safety training.

Precipitative Softening

Record the amount of softening chemicals used and the results of jar testing and lab analyses that justify these amounts. Record the results of analysis for alkalinity, pH, hardness, and related parameters for each shift, preferably every two hours for raw water and for all steps in the process. Keep a record of the chemical feeder setting and record the amount of water treated. Put everything on one form and maintain it daily.

Record the amounts of sludge produced. If a solids contact unit is used, record the sludge blanket depth and results of settling tests. Keep records of the amounts and rates of solids returned to the process, if applicable.

Ion Exchange

Record the hardness, alkalinity, magnesium, calcium, and pH of the source and treated waters. Record the total amount of water treated and the amount of water treated by each softening unit, including bypass water. Also, keep a record of the amount of salt used for regeneration and the length of each cycle between regenerations. Record the amount of backwash water used and the amount of waste sent to sewer or other disposal places.

Aeration

Keep process records of raw water and finished water quality to determine if processing is accomplishing its goals. Also, record the daily quantity of water treated, the details of safety and maintenance procedures, and changes in other treatment processes that may be affected by aeration. Document the process operating conditions including the air-to-water ratio to calculate performance and cost information.

Adsorption

Records kept regarding activated carbon differ depending on the type of carbon used.

- Powdered activated carbon (PAC): Record the types of tastes and odors being experienced, the threshold odor number (TON), and the dates of taste-and-odor occurrences. Keep a record of the coagulant and PAC dosage predicted from jar tests as well as the actual dosage used.
- Granular activated carbon (GAC): Record the number of filter hours; UFRV; any losses of GAC from the filter, measured monthly; dates of installation; and periodic TON from each filter. Also record when backwashing was performed and the amount of backwash water used as well as the raw-to-finished organic content removal.

Iron and Manganese Removal

If using ion exchange, the previously referenced records can be used. In addition, record raw and finished iron and manganese levels and results of distribution systems analyses performed. If permanganate is used, record amounts and dosages, including those predicted by jar testing.

If a sequestrant is used to control iron and manganese, record the amount and type used and the data from distribution system flushing efforts.

Fluoridation

Keep a daily record of the amount of fluoride in the finished water and the raw water, if necessary (a weekly raw water analysis may be sufficient if the regulator allows). Also, keep a daily record of the chemical dosages used and record the chemical feed rate each hour of each shift. Compute and record the daily fluoride chemical feed and compare it to the lab analysis as a double-check. Record safety classes and lectures that were provided to operators.

Corrosion Control

Maintain records of corrosion chemical dosages and any data available as to their performance, such as coupon testing results, Corrator® readings, temperatures, flushing activities, and lead and copper compliance results (i.e., 90th percentile levels and maximum levels). If phosphates are used, keep strict records of dosages and amounts of total and dissolved phosphate in the system. Flush mains regularly, especially dead-end mains; sample for phosphates at 5-, 10-, and 15-minute intervals into the flush; and record results. Record the main flushing velocities, in feet per second. Track any customer complaints that may relate to use of corrosion chemicals.

Water Main Flushing

Main flushing records are best kept in a searchable database. Record main location and size; size of flushing pipe or hydrant; flow rate at flush; gallons used for flushing; velocity, in feet per second; chlorine residual; amount of phosphate used, if any; and results of biological testing, such as heterotrophic plate count quantity or quantity of coliform. Query the database by main size and show gallons used and time needed, along with any chemical and biological data, to generate monthly reports. In this way, a profile will emerge that shows the amount of water necessary to flush each size main, the time it takes, and the results obtained.

powdered activated carbon (PAC)
Activated carbon in a fine powder form. It is added to water in a slurry form primarily for removing those organic compounds causing tastes and odors.

granular activated carbon (GAC)
Activated carbon in a granular form, which is used in a bed, much like a conventional filter, to adsorb organic substances from water.

Reporting

Reporting requirements are generally a function of the compliance reports that local and federal regulators require. In general, compliance testing results must be reported no later than 10 days after the end of the month in which they were accumulated. It is good practice for water treatment plant staff to provide reports to upper management. Even if the administration does not require these reports, they should be generated and kept on file for future reference.

Like a diary, a written report is an excellent reminder of events that took place and the methods used to handle these events. Internal memos of safety issues, personnel and disciplinary actions, purchases, and maintenance events can actually help protect staff from allegations of nonfeasance. Reports should be written as soon as possible after an event takes place so that details can be easily recalled. Do not write reports or internal memos in anger; take time to cool down before recalling an event.

Most compliance reports must conform to a specific format. This enables the regulator to assemble large amounts of data from many utilities in an orderly fashion. Internal or outsourced reports, other than compliance reports to regulators, should include the following:

- Times and dates of the audit and any description of incidents or accomplishments
- Financial or inventory considerations
- Personnel involved
- Conclusions drawn, with supporting data and references
- List of report recipients, with acknowledgment of receipt, if appropriate
- An executive summary if the report is lengthy and involved

The report should be filed in a logical order (e.g., file reports under general categories such as research, safety, finance, and so on) so that the report can be easily retrieved in the future. As time permits, reread all reports to gauge progress in reaching goals and to learn from past mistakes.

Reporting Treatment Incidents

There are specific requirements for the time and method of reporting a regulatory violation. These are described in the drinking water regulations for the applicable regulatory agency. However, there are times when it is not clear if there has been a violation or when there is a water quality incident that may affect consumers. The water plant personnel should have a predetermined plan of action to deal with these situations.

The notification and action plan for incident reporting should include plant management, utility management, other utility officials, and regulatory agencies. The utility should have discussions with the regulatory agency representatives prior to any incident to establish an understanding of how they will handle this type of communication. The agency may have technical resources to assist the plant personnel with a response. Also, the agency may be helpful when dealing with mass communication media regarding the incident.

Plant Performance Reports

Periodic (monthly, quarterly, and annual) plant performance reports should be prepared and should be examined to detect trends and identify opportunities for improvement. The operating reports previously described are the basis for these performance reports. Performance reports summarize the operating results and usually include various charts and calculated performance measures. These summary reports do not need to be lengthy and, indeed, can be added to the operating reports if desired. The purpose of the performance reports is to examine the plant results over longer time periods to see if there are trends that need to be investigated. All plant operating personnel should review these reports to provide feedback and to participate in efforts to meet plant operating goals.

Public Relations

It is important for a water utility to maintain public confidence. Satisfied customers will pay their bills, are less likely to complain if they are temporarily inconvenienced during system maintenance and construction, and are more likely to be supportive of rate increases and bond issues. Operations personnel are often engaged with customers when they are investigating a complaint. Not only is this an opportunity to solve a problem and gain customer confidence, but also important information can be obtained on the system's condition.

Dealing With the Media

On occasion, distribution system employees may be approached by reporters from the local media asking about the work they are doing. Although one must be courteous, the general rule in talking to reporters is, *Don't unless you absolutely have to!* There are many opportunities for being misquoted, and it is quite embarrassing for the utility to see the wrong information in print.

The best policy is to give a very brief explanation and offer no more information than is requested. Beyond that, the workers should say they are not qualified to go into more detail. Large municipalities and water utilities maintain a public relations department whose job is to deal with the media, so reporters should be referred there for additional details. If such a department does not exist, the reporter should be referred to the utility manager, city manager, or mayor.

 WATCH THE VIDEO
Media Relations (www.awwa.org/wsovideoclips)

Customer Complaint Response

Responding to customer complaints is an important element in assessing system performance. Information from customers about water quality, reliability of service, and security can be helpful when these topics are of concern. A professional interaction with customers is often the most effective method to convey a positive view of the utility and gain customer satisfaction. Also, customer complaint reporting procedures may be required by some state or local agencies.

The objectives of a customer complaint response program are to (1) address the customer's concerns, (2) gather information that can be used to identify system problems, and (3) catalog data that can be used to assess long-term system performance goals. System operators need specific training to achieve these objectives.

Study Questions

1. How often should operators record bed expansion measurements, condition and depth of media, and an evaluation of the bed surface?
   a. Quarterly
   b. Yearly
   c. Daily
   d. As determined by water condition

2. Keep process records of raw water and finished water quality to determine
   a. the condition of equipment.
   b. the need for continued sampling.
   c. if processing is accomplishing its goals.
   d. operator proficiency.

3. Generally speaking, keep a _____ record of the amount of fluoride in the finished water and the raw water.
   a. daily
   b. biweekly
   c. hourly
   d. weekly

4. Main flushing records are best kept
   a. in whatever location is most convenient for each operator.
   b. in a secure location that can be accessed only by authorized personnel.
   c. in a daily log folder.
   d. in a searchable database.

5. The general rule in talking to reporters is,
   a. "Give only yes or no answers."
   b. "Don't unless you absolutely have to."
   c. "Leave them wanting more."
   d. "Never give a straight answer."

6. Acute MCL violations must be reported to the public within what amount of time?

7. Why are filter operation records important?

8. Why are plant chemical usage records important?

Study Question Answers

Chapter 1 Answers

1. **b.** Coliform group bacteria
2. **d.** inorganic compounds.
3. **c.** coliform bacteria.
4. **a.** turbidity.
5. **d.** Calcium and magnesium
6. **c.** Viruses cannot survive in the environment for any length of time outside of a human's or an animal's body.
7. **b.** Coliform bacteria
8. Atom
9. A radical is a group of elements that bond together and act like single atoms or ions in forming compounds.
10. Milligrams per liter (mg/L) and grains per gallon (gpg)

Chapter 2 Answers

1. **b.** 15,800 gpm

$$(35.1 \text{ cfs})(60 \text{ sec/min})(7.48 \text{ gal/ft}^3) = 15{,}752.88 \text{ gpm},$$
which rounds to **15,800 gpm**

2. **b.** 12 cfs

$$\frac{(7.7 \text{ mgd})(1{,}000{,}000 \text{ gal})(1 \text{ ft}^3)(1 \text{ day})(1 \text{ min})}{(1 \text{ mil gal})(7.48 \text{ gal})(1440 \text{ min})(60 \text{ sec})} = 11.91 \text{ cfs, which rounds to } \textbf{12 cfs}$$

3. **a.** 104 mil gal

$$[(318 \text{ acre-ft})(43{,}560 \text{ ft}^3/\text{acre-ft})(7.48 \text{ gal/ft}^3)] \div 1{,}000{,}000 =$$
103.61, which rounds to **104 mil gal**

4. **c.** 2.2% soda ash slurry

Know: 1 gal of water = 8.34 lb

$$\text{Percent soda ash} = \frac{(8.25 \text{ lb})(100\%)}{8.25 \text{ lb} + 45 \text{ gal } (8.34 \text{ lb/gal})} = \frac{(8.25 \text{ lb})(100\%)}{8.25 \text{ lb} + 375.3 \text{ lb}}$$

$$\frac{(8.25 \text{ lb})(100\%)}{383.55 \text{ lb}} = 2.15\%, \text{ which rounds to } \textbf{2.2\% soda ash slurry}$$

5. **d.** 133,000 ft²

Equation: Area = πr², where π = 3.14

First find the radius: Radius = Diameter ÷ 2 = 411 ÷ 2 = 205.5 ft

Area of tank, ft² = (3.14)(205.5 ft)(205.5 ft) = 132,602.985 ft², round to **133,000 ft²**

6. **c.** rounding.

7. **a.** know the values for all but one of the terms of the equation to be used.

8. Scientific notation allows people to express any number as a term multiplied by a power of 10.

9. A proportionate change will occur in some other condition.

10. Linear measurement defines the distance along a line; it is the measurement between two points.

Chapter 3 Answers

1. **c.** Disinfectants and Disinfection By-products Rule

2. **a.** running annual average

3. **c.** Fire department hydrants

4. **d.** is higher than the technically feasible level.

5. 10 mg/L, 1 mg/L, 4.0 mg/L, 0.080 mg/L, 0.060 mg/L, 0.010 mg/L

6. 1.3 mg/L, 0.015 mg/L, action levels

7. MCL goal is zero for *E. coli*. Total coliform positive samples require three repeat samples tested for *E. coli*. A positive *E. coli* repeat sample triggers a violation notice and further actions to eliminate the contamination.

8. Disinfection effectiveness is based on the concentration of the disinfectant and the time it is in contact with the water. Higher dosages may require less contact time.

9. This is an assessment of the water supply system and its capability to produce safe water.

10. A supply of piped water for human consumption that has at least 15 service connections, or serves 25 or more persons 60 or more days each year

Chapter 4 Answers

1. **c.** transpiration.

2. **c.** condensation.

3. **a.** confined aquifer.

4. **d.** advection.

5. **d.** aquifer.

6. **a.** palatable.

7. The multiple-barrier approach to water treatment

8. Advection

9. Snowmelt

10. Downhill toward the lowest point

Chapter 5 Answers

1. **c.** oxidant to reduce iron bacteria.
2. **b.** Calcium hypochlorite
3. **c.** Plugging of the well screen
4. **d.** Pump test to confirm capacity
5. **a.** Hydrogen sulfide
6. **c.** 12–24 hours; 50 mg/L
7. **b.** because faster and easier methods have been developed.
8. Hard water, high iron content, potential for radon, hydrogen sulfide from anaerobic conditions
9. A concrete area placed around the casing of some wells to support pumping equipment and to help prevent surface water from contaminating the well water
10. Static water level
11. Well yield
12. Radial wells

Chapter 6 Answers

1. **b.** relatively flat
2. **d.** ephemeral streams.
3. **a.** with locally available materials to the extent possible.
4. **b.** Emergent plants
5. Increased nutrients, ideal temperature, plentiful sunlight, specific algae types
6. Rapid changes in water quality from natural and human activity
7. Copper sulfate, potassium permanganate
8. Taste and odor in the water, iron and manganese
9. Zebra mussels, rooted aquatic vegetation
10. Infiltration gallery

Chapter 7 Answers

1. **c.** Clogging
2. **b.** 60- to 80-degree
3. **d.** Wide
4. **b.** Presedimentation
5. 1/2 to 1 inches
6. Screening
7. Date of inspection, amount of material removed from screens (in cubic feet or cubic meters), notations regarding unusual or unexpected types of debris or water conditions
8. A very fine screen used primarily to remove algae, other aquatic organisms, and small debris that can clog treatment plant filters

Chapter 8 Answers

1. **b.** 15–45 minutes.
2. **c.** 5.8–7.5.
3. **a.** Colloidal particles are so small that gravity has little effect on them.
4. **c.** Zeta potential
5. **a.** electrons
6. **c.** suspended solids.
7. **b.** tapered flocculation.
8. An attraction that exists between all particles in nature and tends to pull any two particles together
9. It will increase the rate of coagulation, reduce the coagulant dosage needed, and widen the pH range for effective coagulation.
10. They cost much less than a conventional rapid-mixing installation, they provide good instantaneous mixing with little short-circuiting, and they allow for adjustment to provide the correct amount of mixing energy.

Chapter 9 Answers

1. **d.** Effluent launder
2. **d.** At least twice per day
3. **d.** to draw off the liquid from a vessel of any size without stirring up bottom sediment.
4. **b.** Once a year
5. **b.** To remove pathogens
6. **d.** Sedimentation
7. Settling zone
8. Sludge zone
9. An angle greater than 50–60 degrees
10. Sludge

Chapter 10 Answers

1. **c.** it is becoming more efficient in particle removal.
2. **c.** 100 mg/L Cl_2.
3. **a.** Minor
4. **a.** 1–2 ntu.
5. **d.** conventional treatment.
6. The Interim Enhanced Surface Water Treatment Rule
7. Sedimentation
8. Package treatment plants
9. Low operating costs, low construction costs, low maintenance costs

Chapter 11 Answers

1. **c.** the concentration of chlorine and the contact time.
2. **c.** *Cryptosporidiosis*

3. **c.** 157–162°F (69–72°C)

4. **a.** every time.

5. **d.** diffuser

6. Disinfection

7. Bromine

8. Breakpoint

9. Turbidity

Chapter 12 Answers

1. **c.** 100 mg/L Cl_2.

2. **d.** Polyphosphates and chlorine

3. **d.** Right after the water leaves the well

4. **d.** Potassium permanganate

5. **b.** Discolored laundry and changed taste of water, coffee, tea, and other beverages

6. **a.** turbid yellow to black

7. **b.** provides a food source for bacterial growth.

8. Manganese greensand filters

9. Volume of water used in a backwash

10. A process in which polyphosphates or sodium silicates are added before the water is exposed to air or disinfectants

Chapter 13 Answers

1. **b.** 4 mg/L

2. **d.** is odorless.

3. **c.** Every day

4. **a.** 20–30%

5. **c.** Crystalline sodium fluoride

6. **a.** proper tooth and bone formation.

7. **b.** dry feed system.

8. Proper tooth and bone formation

9. Sodium fluorosilicate

10. Simple to operate and less expensive to purchase

Chapter 14 Answers

1. **a.** Bacteriological

2. **c.** based on population.

3. **b.** Coliform group bacteria

4. **d.** grab sample

5. **c.** USEPA

6. **a.** must reject the samples.

7. Every day

8. Raw-water supply, treatment plant, and distribution system

Chapter 15 Answers

1. **b.** stabilization.
2. **d.** Calcium carbonate
3. **d.** tuberculation.
4. **c.** tubercles.
5. **b.** To reduce the need for quality sampling
6. **a.** Corrosion
7. Adjustment of pH and alkalinity, calcium carbonate coating, corrosion inhibitors and sequestering agents
8. Protect the public health, improve water quality, extent the life of pipelines and plumbing, meet federal and state regulations
9. Hydrogen sulfide
10. They will be corrosive.

Chapter 16 Answers

1. **d.** Calcium and magnesium
2. **a.** adding CO2 to the water.
3. **c.** hardness.
4. **c.** all multivalent cations.
5. **d.** Sodium hydroxide
6. **a.** lime alone.
7. Carbonate hardness is mostly attributed to calcium and magnesium bicarbonate and carbonate. Noncarbonate is attributed to calcium and magnesium compounds of chloride and sulfate and sometimes nitrate.
8. mg/L as calcium carbonate ($CaCO_3$)
9. It is more expensive than lime or lime and soda ash treatment, and it increases the total dissolved solids in the treated water.
10. Calcium and magnesium

Chapter 17 Answers

1. **c.** Thickener
2. **a.** before the normal coagulation–flocculation step.
3. **c.** regenerated.
4. **c.** at the source.
5. **d.** aeration.
6. **a.** very unstable in water
7. Radon, volatile organic chemicals
8. Nanofiltration (Reverse osmosis can also soften water.)
9. It does not provide a lasting residual.
10. Aeration
11. Electrodialysis

Chapter 18 Answers

1. **b.** Ohm
2. **d.** Capacitor
3. **b.** To reduce the need for written documentation
4. **d.** gallons per minute
5. Automated process sequences like filter backwashing may reduce opportunities for operators to observe and detect system malfunctions. Operators must, therefore, introduce periodic observation into their daily routine.
6. Supervisory control and data acquisition computer control systems gather and display operational data for operator review. Process changes can be automatic, semiautomatic, or manual. Data can be displayed in digital form or using trend graphs.
7. Chemical feed is controlled proportional to the plant flow.
8. resistance
9. Dynamic
10. Electricity at rest
11. Direct current

Chapter 19 Answers

1. **b.** control water leakage from the stuffing box.
2. **b.** control water leakage along the pump's shaft.
3. **b.** The stuffing box
4. **b.** Centrifugal pump
5. **b.** Packing rings
6. Mixed-flow pump
7. Vertical turbine pump
8. Jet pump
9. Submersible pump

Chapter 20 Answers

1. **a.** Operator safety
2. **c.** Eyes
3. **a.** each individual
4. **d.** Hazard technician
5. **b.** material safety data sheet
6. **d.** irritation to the eyes.
7. In a location readily accessible to all employees
8. SCBA stands for self-contained breathing apparatus. It is used for chlorine leak repairs.
9. A confined space has limited entry and exit, is not designed for continuous human occupancy, and is large enough for humans to perform work.
10. Self-contained breathing apparatus

Chapter 21 Answers

1. **a.** Quarterly
2. **c.** if processing is accomplishing its goals.
3. **a.** daily
4. **d.** in a searchable database.
5. **b.** "Don't unless you absolutely have to."
6. 24 hours
7. To detect trends in slow developing problems. To make adjustments to optimize performance.
8. To anticipate needs to re-order chemicals to maintain a safe inventory. To detect changes in usage over time.

References

Bloetscher, F. 2009. The Impact of Unsustainable Ground Water, *Groundwater Protection Council Annual Forum (Salt Lake City, Utah)*. New York, NY: McGraw-Hill.

Bloetscher, F., and A. Muniz. 2008. Water Supply in South Florida—The New Limitations. *Sustainable Water Sources Conference Proceedings (Reno, Nev.)*. Denver, CO: American Water Works Association.

Ekins, P. 2003. Identifying Critical Natural Capital—Conclusions about Critical Natural Capital. *Ecological Economics* 44:277–292.

Hutson, S. S., N. L. Barber, J. F. Kenny, K. S. Linsey, D. S. Lumia, and M. A. Maupin. 2004. Estimated Use of Water in the United States in 2000. US Geological Survey Circular 1268, 46 pp. Reston, VA: USGS.

Lowry, J. D., and J. E. Brandown. 1987. Removal of Radon From Ground Water Supplies Using Granular Activated Carbon or Diffused Aeration. *Radon in Ground Water*. Michigan: Lewis Publishers, Inc.

Nace, R. L. 1960. Water Management, Agriculture, and Ground-Water Supplies. US Geological Survey Circular 415, 12 pp. Reston, VA: USGS.

Reilly, T. E., K. F. Dennehy, W. M. Alley, and W. L. Cunningham. 2009. Ground-Water Availability in the United States. USGS Circular 1323. Reston, VA: USGS.

Glossary

acid   Any substance that releases hydrogen ions (H+) when it is mixed into water.

activated silica   A coagulant aid used to form a denser, stronger floc.

adsorption   The water treatment process used primarily to remove organic contaminants from water. Adsorption involves the adhesion of the contaminants to an adsorbent, such as activated carbon.

advection   Water movement with the air currents in the atmosphere.

aeration   The process of bringing water and air into close contact to remove or modify constituents in the water.

air stripping   A means of dissolving air into water (aeration) wherein water is distributed over the packing at the top of a tank and air is forced in at the bottom using a blower. Also called *desorption*.

alkalinity   A measurement of water's capacity to neutralize an acid. Compare *pH*.

alternating current (AC)   Electrical current that reverses its direction in a periodic manner.

anion   A negative ion.

aquifer   A porous, water-bearing geologic formation. Generally restricted to materials capable of yielding an appreciable supply of water.

arithmetic mean   A measurement of average value, calculated by summing all terms and dividing by the number of terms.

atom   The smallest particle of an element that still retains the characteristics of that element.

atomic number   The number of protons in the nucleus of an atom.

atomic weight   The sum of the number of protons and the number of neutrons in the nucleus of an atom.

average   A method to group the information so that trends in the information may be determined.

bacteria   A one-celled microscopic organism that has no chlorophyll. Usually has a spherical, rodlike, or curved shapes. Usually regarded as plants.

bar screen   A series of straight steel bars, welded at their ends to horizontal steel beams, forming a grid. Bar screens are placed on intakes or in waterways to remove large debris.

$C \times T$ value   The product of the residual disinfectant concentration C, in milligrams per liter, and the corresponding disinfectant contact time T, in minutes. Minimum $C \times T$ values are specified by the Surface Water Treatment Rule as a means of ensuring adequate kill or inactivation of pathogenic microorganisms in water.

carbon dioxide (CO_2)   A common gas in the atmosphere that is very soluble in water. High concentrations in water can cause the water to be corrosive. Carbon dioxide is added to water after the lime-softening process to lower the pH in order to reduce calcium carbonate scale formation. This process is known as recarbonation.

cation   A positive ion.

centrifugal pump   A pump consisting of an impeller on a rotating shaft enclosed by a casing that has suction and discharge connections. The spinning impeller throws water outward at high velocity, and the casing shape converts this high velocity to a high pressure.

chain of custody   A written record of the sample's history of SDWA compliance, from the time of collection to the time of analysis and subsequent disposal.

channel flow   Water runoff that eventually flows into small channels that feed into larger channels that carry rivers and streams.

chemical equation   A shorthand way, using chemical formulas, of writing the reaction that takes place when chemicals are brought together. The left side of the equation indicates the chemicals brought together (the reactants); the arrow indicates in which direction the reaction occurs; and the right side of the equation indicates the results (the products) of the chemical reaction.

chemical formula   Using the chemical symbols for each element, a shorthand way of writing what elements are present in a molecule and how many atoms of each element are present in each of the molecules. Also called a *chemical formula*.

chemical symbol   The standard abbreviation, either one or two letters, for an element (e.g., H for hydrogen, Cl for chlorine).

chlorinator   Any device that is used to add chlorine to water.

chlorine cylinder   A container that holds 150 lb (68 kg) of chlorine and has a total filled weight of 250–285 lb (110–130 kg).

chlorine evaporator   A heating device used to convert liquid chlorine to chlorine gas.

coagulation   The water treatment process that causes very small suspended particles to attract one another and form larger particles. This is accomplished by the addition of a chemical, called a coagulant, that neutralizes the electrostatic charges on the particles that cause them to repel each other.

coliform bacteria   A group of bacteria predominantly inhabiting the intestines of humans or animals but also occasionally found elsewhere. Presence of the bacteria in water is used as an indication of fecal contamination (contamination by human or animal wastes).

colloidal solid   Finely divided solid that will not settle out of water for very long periods of time unless the coagulation–flocculation process is used.

composite sample   A series of individual or grab samples taken at different times from the same sampling point and mixed together.

compound   Two or more elements bonded together by a chemical reaction.

concentration   In chemistry, a measurement of how much solute is contained in a given amount of solution. Concentrations are commonly measured in milligrams per liter (mg/L).

concentration cell corrosion   A form of localized corrosion that can form deep pits and tubercles.

condensation   Water vapor in the air that forms tiny droplets.

cone of depression   The cone-shaped depression in the groundwater level around a well during pumping.

contaminant   Anything found in water other than water itself.

conventional treatment   A term that describes the treatment process used by most US surface water systems, consisting of the steps of coagulation, flocculation, sedimentation, and filtration.

corrosion   The gradual deterioration or destruction of a substance or material by chemical action. The action proceeds inward from the surface.

cyclone degritter   A centrifugal sand-and-grit removal device.

destratification   Use of a method to prevent a lake or reservoir from becoming stratified. Typically consists of releasing diffused compressed air at a low point on the lake bottom.

diatomaceous earth filter   A pressure filter using a medium made from diatoms. The water is forced through the diatomaceous earth by pumping.

diffuser   (1) A section of a perforated pipe or porous plates used to inject a gas, such as carbon dioxide or air, under pressure into water. (2) A type of pump.

direct current (DC)   Current that flows continuously in one direction.

direct filtration   A filtration method that includes coagulation, flocculation, and filtration but excludes sedimentation. Only applicable to raw water relatively low in turbidity because all suspended matter must be trapped by the filters.

disinfection   The water treatment process that kills disease-causing organisms in water, usually by the addition of chlorine.

disinfection by-product (DBP)   A new chemical compound formed by the reaction of disinfectants with organic compounds in water. At high concentrations, many DBPs are considered a danger to human health.

dissolved oxygen (DO)   The oxygen dissolved in water, wastewater, or other liquid, usually expressed in milligrams per liter, parts per million, or percent of saturation.

dissolved solid   Any material that is dissolved in water and can be recovered by evaporating the water after filtering the suspended material.

double-suction pump   A centrifugal pump in which the water enters from both sides of the impeller. Also called a *split-case pump*.

drainage basin   An area from which surface runoff is carried away by a single drainage system. Also called *catchment area, watershed,* or *watershed drainage area*.

drawdown   The difference between the static water level and the pumping water level in a well.

effluent   Water flowing from a basin.

electrodialysis   A process in which ions are transferred through a membrane as a result of a direct electric current applied to the solution.

electromagnetics   The study of the combined effects of electricity and magnetism.

electron   One of the three elementary particles of an atom (along with protons and neutrons). An electron is a tiny, negatively charged particle that orbits around the nucleus of an atom. The number of electrons in the outermost shell is one of the most important characteristics of an atom in determining how chemically active an element will be and with what other elements or compounds it will react.

epilimnion   The upper, warmer layer of water in a stratified lake.

***Escherichia coli* (E. coli)**   A bacterium of the coliform group used as a substitute for fecal coliforms in the regulations of the Total Coliform Rule.

evaporation   Water that moves off land and water surfaces and into the atmosphere.

filter (laboratory)   A porous layer of paper, glass fiber, or cellulose acetate used to remove particulate matter from water samples and other chemical solutions.

filter media   Granular material through which material is collected and stored when water passes through it.

filtration The water treatment process involving the removal of suspended matter by passing the water through a porous medium, such as sand.

floc Collections of smaller particles (such as silt, organic matter, and microorganisms) that have come together (agglomerated) into larger, more settleable particles as a result of the coagulation–flocculation process.

flocculation The water treatment process, following coagulation, that uses gentle stirring to bring suspended particles together so that they will form larger, more settleable clumps called floc.

fluoridation The water treatment process in which a chemical is added to the water to increase the concentration of fluoride ions to an optimal level. The purpose of fluoridation is to reduce the incidence of dental cavities in children.

fluoride An ion from the element fluorine. It is a constituent of the earth's crust and consequently is found naturally, to some degree, in all drinking water sources. A small amount of fluoride in the diet is essential for proper tooth and bone formation.

fluorosilicic acid A strongly acidic liquid used to fluoridate drinking water.

fluorosis Staining or pitting of the teeth due to excessive amounts of fluoride in the water.

galvanic corrosion A form of localized corrosion caused by the connection of dissimilar metals in an electrolyte, such as water.

Giardia lamblia A protozoan that can survive in water and that causes human disease.

grab sample A single water sample collected at one time from a single point.

granular activated carbon (GAC) Activated carbon in a granular form, which is used in a bed, much like a conventional filter, to adsorb organic substances from water.

groundwater Subsurface water occupying the saturation zone, from which wells and springs are fed. In a strict sense, the term applies only to water below the water table. Contrast with *surface water*.

haloacetic acids Chemicals formed as a reaction of disinfectants with contaminants in water, consisting of monochloroacetic acid, dichloroacetic acid, trichloroacetic acid, monobromoacetic acid, and dibromoacetic acid.

hardness A characteristic of water, caused primarily by the salts of calcium and magnesium. Hardness causes deposition of scale in boilers, damage in some industrial processes, and sometimes objectionable taste.

head (pressure) (1) A measure of the energy possessed by water at a given location in the water system, expressed in feet (or meters). (2) A measure of the pressure (force) exerted by water, expressed in feet (or meters).

hydrogen sulfide (H2S) A toxic gas produced by the anaerobic decomposition of organic matter and by sulfate-reducing bacteria. Hydrogen sulfide has a very noticeable rotten-egg odor.

hydrologic cycle The water cycle; the movement of water to and from the surface of the earth.

hydrology The science dealing with the properties, distribution, and circulation of water and its constituents in the atmosphere, on the earth's surface, and below the earth's surface.

hypochlorination Chlorination using solutions of calcium hypochlorite or sodium hypochlorite.

hypolimnion The lower layer of water in a stratified lake. The water temperature is near 39.2°F (4°C), at which water attains its maximum density.

impeller   The rotating set of vanes that forces water through a pump.

impoundment   A pond, lake, or reservoir constructed by carving out a basin or building a dam across a stream valley.

infiltration   The process of rain water reaching the ground soaking through the soil.

infiltration gallery   A subsurface structure to receive water filtered through a streambed.

influent   Water flowing into a basin.

injector   The portion of a chlorination system that feeds the chlorine solution into a pipe under pressure.

inorganic compound   A chemical substance of mineral origin not having carbon in its molecular structure.

intake structure   A structure or device placed in a surface water source to permit the withdrawal of water from that source.

interception   The process of rain water landing on vegetation and not reaching the ground.

ion   An atom that is electrically unstable because it has more or fewer electrons than protons. A positive ion is called a cation. A negative ion is called an anion.

ion exchange   A process used to remove hardness from water that depends on special materials known as resins. The resins trade nonhardness-causing ions (usually sodium) for the hardness-causing ions, calcium and magnesium. The process removes practically all the hardness from water.

iron   An abundant element found naturally in the earth. As a result, dissolved iron is found in most water supplies. When the concentration of iron exceeds 0.3 mg/L, it causes red stains on plumbing fixtures and other items in contact with the water. Dissolved iron can also be present in water as a result of corrosion of cast-iron or steel pipes. This is usually the cause of red-water problems.

isotope   An atom of the same element, but containing varying numbers of neutrons in the nucleus. For each element, the most common naturally occurring isotope is called the principal isotope of that element.

launder   A trough that collects the water flowing from a basin (effluent) and transports it to the effluent piping system.

lime–soda ash process   A precipitation process used to remove hardness from water.

manganese   An abundant element found naturally in the earth. Dissolved manganese is found in many water supplies. At concentrations above 0.05 mg/L, it causes black stains on plumbing fixtures, laundry, and other items in contact with the water.

material safety data sheet (MSDS)   A product description listing a chemical's identity, composition, and type or types; the hazard(s) associated with its use (is it flammable, an oxidizer, poisonous?); how it enters the body; the effects of exposure; health effect (short term, long term); the permissible exposure limit; how to handle spills or releases; and other related information.

matter   Anything that occupies space and has weight (mass).

maximum contaminant level (MCL)   The maximum permissible level of a contaminant in water as specified in the regulations of the Safe Drinking Water Act.

maximum contaminant level goal (MCLG)   Nonenforceable health-based goals published along with the promulgation of an MCL. Originally called *recommended maximum contaminant levels (RMCLs)*.

membrane filter   A filter made of cellulose acetate with a uniform small pore size. Used for microbiological examination.

methane (CH4)   A colorless, odorless, flammable gas formed by the anaerobic decomposition of organic matter. When dissolved in water, methane causes a garlic-like taste. Also called *swamp gas*.

microorganism   An organism too small to be seen by the naked eye and visible only with a microscope

microstrainer   A rotating drum lined with a finely woven material, such as stainless steel. Microstrainers are used to remove algae and small debris before they enter the treatment plant.

mixture   Two or more elements, compounds, or both, mixed together with no chemical reaction (bonding) occurring.

MMO–MUG technique   An approved bacteriological procedure for the detection of total coliforms and *E. coli*. The results are qualitative rather than quantitative.

molecular weight   The sum of the atomic weights of all the atoms in the compound. Also called *formula weight*.

molecule   Two or more atoms joined together by a chemical bond.

multiple-tube fermentation (MTF) method   A laboratory method used for coliform testing that uses a nutrient broth placed in culture tubes. Gas production indicates the presence of coliform bacteria.

neutron   An uncharged elementary particle that has a mass approximately equal to that of the proton. Neutrons are present in all known atomic nuclei except the lightest hydrogen nucleus.

nonsettleable solids   Finely divided solids, such as bacteria and fine clay particles, that will stay suspended in water for long periods of time.

nucleus   The center of an atom, made up of positively charged particles called protons and uncharged particles called neutrons. Plural is *nuclei*.

organic compound   A chemical substance of animal or vegetable origin having carbon in its molecular structure.

organic substance (organic)   A chemical substance of animal or vegetable origin, having carbon in its molecular structure.

package treatment plant   A small, prefabricated unit that has been designed and assembled at a factory and then shipped to the installation site.

palatable   Pleasing to the taste.

parasite   An organism that lives within, and may cause harm to, other organisms.

pathogen (pathogenic)   A disease-causing organism.

percent by weight   The proportion, calculated as a percentage, of each element in a compound.

percentage   The fraction of the whole expressed as parts per one hundred.

periodic table   A chart showing all elements arranged according to similarities of chemical properties.

permeability   The characteristic of how easily water will flow through a material.

peroxidation   Source water oxidation with hypochlorite or ozone.

pH   A measurement of how acidic or basic a substance is. The pH scale runs from 0 (most acidic) to 14 (most basic). The center of the range (7) indicates the substance is neutral, neither acidic nor basic.

polyatomic ion   A group of elements chemically bonded together and acting like single atoms or ions in their ability to form other compounds.

polyelectrolyte   High–molecular weight, synthetic organic compound that forms ions when dissolved in water. Also called *polymer*.

porosity   An indication of the volume of space within a given amount of a material.

powdered activated carbon (PAC) Activated carbon in a fine powder form. It is added to water in a slurry form primarily for removing those organic compounds causing tastes and odors.

precipitation Water that falls out of the atmosphere as rain, snow, or ice.

presedimentation A preliminary treatment process used to remove gravel, sand, and other gritty material from the raw water before it enters the main treatment plant. This is usually done without the use of coagulating chemicals.

presence–absence (P–A) test An approved bacteriological procedure for detecting the presence or absence of total coliforms.

proportion The relationship between two numbers in a ratio. When it is the same as that between two other numbers in another ratio, the two ratios are said to be in proportion, or proportionate.

proton One of the three elementary particles of an atom (along with neutrons and electrons). The proton is a positively charged particle located in the nucleus of an atom. The number of protons in the nucleus of an atom determines the atomic number of that element.

protozoa Small single-celled animals including amoebae, ciliates, and flagellates.

public water system (PWS) A supply of piped water for human consumption that has at least 15 service connections, or serves 25 or more persons 60 or more days each year.

quality assurance (QA) A plan for laboratory operation that specifies the measures used to produce data of known precision and bias.

quality control (QC) A laboratory program of continually checking techniques and calibrating instruments to ensure consistency in analytical results.

radial flow Flow that moves across a basin from the center to the outside edges or vice versa.

radial well A very wide, relatively shallow caisson that has horizontally drilled wells with screen points at the bottom. Radial wells are large producers.

radiation absorption dose (rad) A measure of the dose absorbed by the body from radiation (100 ergs of energy in 1 g of tissue).

radioactivity Behavior of a material that has an unstable atomic nucleus, which spontaneously decays or disintegrates, producing radiation.

rapid mixing The process of quickly mixing a chemical solution uniformly through the water.

ratio A relationship between two numbers. A ratio may be expressed using colons (for example, 1:2 or 3:7), or it may be expressed as a fraction (for example, ½ or ³⁄₇).

recharge The addition of water to the groundwater supply from precipitation and by infiltration from surface streams, lakes, reservoirs, and snowmelt.

reciprocating pump A type of positive-displacement pump consisting of a closed cylinder containing a piston or plunger to draw liquid into the cylinder through an inlet valve and force it out through an outlet valve. When the piston acts on the liquid in one end of the cylinder, the pump is termed single-action; when the piston acts in both ends, the pump is termed double-action.

rectilinear flow Uniform flow in a horizontal direction.

red water Rust-colored water resulting from the formation of ferric hydroxide from iron naturally dissolved in the water or from the action of iron bacteria.

representative sample A sample containing all the constituents that are in the water from which it was taken.

residual An excess of chemical left in the water after treatment. The presence of disinfectant residuals indicates that an adequate amount of disinfectant has been added at the treatment stage to ensure completion of all reactions with some disinfectant remaining.

reverse osmosis (RO) A pressure-driven process in which almost-pure water is passed through a semipermeable membrane. Water is forced through the membrane and most ions (salts) are left behind. The process is principally used for desalination of sea water.

roentgen equivalent man (rem) A quantification of radiation in terms of its dose effect on the human body; the number of rads times a quality factor.

roentgen equivalent physical (rep) The quantity of radiation (other than X-rays or other generated radiation) that produces in one gram of human tissue ionization equivalent to the quantity produced in air by one roentgen of radiation or X-rays (equivalent to 83.8 ergs of energy).

rotary pump A type of positive-displacement pump consisting of elements resembling gears that rotate in a close-fitting pump case. The rotation of these elements alternately draws in and discharges the water being pumped. Such pumps act with neither suction nor discharge valves, operate at almost any speed, and do not depend on centrifugal forces to lift the water.

runoff A portion of water that reaches the ground and flows toward nearby bodies of water.

sand trap An enlargement of a conduit carrying raw water that allows the water velocity to slow down so that sand and other grit can settle.

sanitary seal A well feature that prevents contamination from entering the well.

saturation point The point at which a solution can no longer dissolve any more of a particular chemical. Precipitation of the chemical will occur beyond this point.

scaling Metal deposits left in pipelines and plumbing fixtures.

schmutzdecke The layer of solids and biological growth that forms on top of a slow sand filter, allowing the filter to remove turbidity effectively without chemical coagulation.

scientific notation A method by which any number can be expressed as a number between 1 and 9 multiplied by a power of 10.

screening A pretreatment method that uses coarse screens to remove large debris from the water to prevent clogging of pipes or channels to the treatment plant.

sedimentation The water treatment process that involves reducing the velocity of water in basins so that the suspended material can settle out by gravity.

sedimentation basin A basin or tank in which water is retained to allow settleable matter, such as floc, to settle by gravity. Also called a *settling basin*, *settling tank*, or *sedimentation tank*.

self-contained breathing apparatus (SCBA) A type of respirator that supplies safe, grade D (or better) breathing air to the wearer.

settleable solid A denser and heavier suspended solid that will settle unaided to the bottom of a sedimentation basin within 4 hours.

siltation The accumulation of silt (small soil particles between 0.00016 and 0.0024 in. [0.004 and 0.061 mm] in diameter) in an impoundment.

single-suction pump A centrifugal pump in which the water enters from only one side of the impeller. Also called *end-suction pump*.

slip   (1) In a pump, the percentage of water taken into the suction end that is not discharged because of clearances in the moving unit. (2) In a motor, the difference between the speed of the rotating magnetic field produced by the stator and the speed of the rotor.

slow sand filtration   A filtration process that involves passing raw water through a bed of sand at low velocity, resulting in particulate removal by physical and biological mechanisms.

sludge   The accumulated solids separated from water during treatment.

snowmelt   Water that has collected as snow or ice and been released as liquid.

sodium fluoride   A dry chemical used in the fluoridation of drinking water. It is commonly used in saturators.

sodium fluorosilicate   A dry chemical used in the fluoridation of drinking water. It is derived from fluorosilicic acid.

softening   The water treatment process that removes calcium and magnesium, the hardness-causing constituents in water.

solute   The substance dissolved in a solution. Compare with *solvent*.

solution   A liquid containing a dissolved substance. The liquid alone is called the solvent, the dissolved substance is called the solute. Together they are called a solution.

solvent   The liquid used to dissolve a substance. See *solution*.

specific capacity   A well's pumping rate divided by the drawdown.

spring   A location where groundwater emerges on the surface of the ground.

stabilization   The water treatment process intended to reduce the corrosive or scale-forming tendencies of water.

static electricity   A state in which electrons have accumulated but are not flowing from one position to another. Static electricity is often referred to as electricity at rest.

static mixer   A device designed to produce turbulence and mixing of chemicals with water, by means of fixed sloping vanes within the unit, without the need for any application of power.

static water level   The level of the water surface in the well when no water is being taken from the aquifer.

storage   The removal of water from circulation because it is frozen, held in a lake aboveground, or held in an aquifer belowground.

stratification   The separation of water in lakes and reservoirs such that a warm layer of water overlies a colder layer.

subsurface flow   Water movement below the surface that is influenced by gravity and the presence of natural barriers in the rock or soil.

surface water   All water on the surface, as distinguished from *groundwater*.

suspended solid   A solid organic and inorganic particle that is held in suspension by the action of flowing water.

synthetic organic chemical (SOC)   A chemical produced by humans that can contaminate water.

thermocline   The temperature transition zone in a stratified lake, located between the epilimnion and the hypolimnion.

ton container   A reusable, welded tank that holds 2,000 lb (910 kg) of chlorine. Containers weigh about 3,700 lb (1,700 kg) when full and are generally 30 in. (0.76 m) in diameter and 80 in. (2.03 m) long.

Total Coliform Rule (TCR) A regulation that became effective December 31, 1990, doing away with the previous maximum contaminant level relating to the density of organisms and relating only to the presence or absence of the organisms in water.

transpiration The release of water into the air by plants, primarily through their leaves.

tubercle A knob of rust formed on the interior of cast-iron pipes as a result of corrosion.

turbidity A physical characteristic of water making the water appear cloudy. The condition is caused by the presence of suspended matter.

US Environmental Protection Agency (USEPA) A US government agency responsible for implementing federal laws designed to protect the environment. Congress has delegated implementation of the Safe Drinking Water Act to the USEPA.

valence electron An electron in an outermost electron shell. These electrons are one of the most important factors in determining which atoms will combine with other atoms.

velocity pump The general class of pumps that use a rapidly turning impeller to impart kinetic energy or velocity to fluids. The pump casing then converts this velocity head, in part, to pressure head. Also called *kinetic pump*.

vertical turbine pump A centrifugal pump, commonly of the multistage diffuser type, in which the pump shaft is mounted vertically.

virus The smallest and simplest form of life. The many types of viruses reproduce themselves in a manner that causes infectious disease in some larger life forms, such as humans.

volatile organic chemical (VOC) A manufactured, synthetic chemical generally used as an industrial solvent. VOCs are classified as known or suspected carcinogens or as causing other adverse health effects. They are of particular concern to the water supply industry because they have widely been found as contaminants in groundwater sources.

water table The upper surface of the zone of saturation closest to the ground surface.

waterborne disease A disease caused by a waterborne organism or toxic substance.

watershed See *drainage basin*.

weighting agent A material, such as bentonite, added to low-turbidity waters to provide additional particles for good floc formation.

well casing The metal pipe used to line the borehole of a well.

well screen A well feature that prevents rock and soil from entering the well while letting in water.

well slab A concrete area placed around the casing of some wells to support pumping equipment and to help prevent surface water from contaminating the well water.

well yield The rate of water withdrawal that a well can supply over a long period of time.

wire-mesh screen A screen made of a wire fabric attached to a metal frame. The screen is usually equipped with a motor so that it can move continuously through the water and be automatically cleaned with a water spray. It is used to remove finer debris from the water than the bar screen is able to remove.

Index

NOTE: *f* indicates a figure; *t* indicates a table.